REPRESENTATIVE
NARRATIVES

BY

CARROLL LEWIS MAXCY, M.A.

Morris Professor of Rhetoric in Williams College
Author of "The Rhetorical Principles of Narration"

01288

BOSTON   NEW YORK   CHICAGO
HOUGHTON MIFFLIN COMPANY
The Riverside Press Cambridge

The Riverside Press
CAMBRIDGE . MASSACHUSETTS
U . S . A

TO

L. H. M.

"If my slight Muse do please these curious days,
The pain be mine, but thine shall be the praise."

PREFACE

THE compiler of this volume realizes that there would seem to be little excuse for adding to the number of similar collections already in existence; and yet he has brought the following pages together in response to the demands of the classroom. Other compilations are based largely on the historical development of the short-story or upon the various characteristics of the short-story as a distinct literary type. The purpose of this volume is to present types of narrative structure, without regard to the problem of literary evolution. The matter of setting, of characterization, of plot, of dialogue has been the fundamental consideration guiding the choice of specimens.

The introductions to the individual selections are intentionally brief, and indicate merely the principal qualities for which they have been found useful as illustrative types. It is hardly necessary to add that each narrative may serve other purposes than those indicated in the preliminary paragraphs.

In the proper place acknowledgment is made to the various publishing houses that have courteously permitted the use of copyrighted material.

CARROLL LEWIS MAXCY

WILLIAMS COLLEGE
WILLIAMSTOWN, MASSACHUSETTS
March, 1914

CONTENTS

GENERAL

REPRESENTATIVE NARRATIVES

SETTING

LANDOR'S COTTAGE

BY EDGAR ALLAN POE

It is, indeed, only by straining the term "narration" that one is justified in including *Landor's Cottage* among narrative specimens, for description constitutes the great body of the work. Nor can the descriptive portions be termed typical "setting," because they do not present a background against which action is projected for added effectiveness. Yet one may, perhaps, argue that the 'pedestrian' adventure, chronicled in the opening paragraphs, presents a sufficient approximation to the "chronological ordering of the episodes constituting an event" to justify the contention that the selection has in it something of the narrative character.

The picture of Landor's cottage itself, the main theme, presents a noteworthy example of what is known as "expository description" — a phase of descriptive composition so often found in setting. Its purpose is, in the main, to appeal to the understanding rather than to the emotions, to produce in the reader's mind an exact representation of the object described rather than to suggest feelings associated therewith. In *Landor's Cottage* Poe presents a picture of the utmost definiteness, and the student will find it quite possible from the data presented to prepare a very definite map, or ground-plan, of the scene; and, if he has the skill, to sketch the cottage itself or some view selected from the picture.

"Point of view," which is necessary in any artistic undertaking of this character, is also strikingly illustrated in the selection; and the student, as he reads, should observe carefully how this changes as he advances from one part of the composition to another.

During a pedestrian trip last summer, through one or two of the river counties of New York, I found myself, as the day declined, somewhat embarrassed about

the road I was pursuing. The land undulated very remarkably; and my path, for the last hour, had wound
about and about so confusedly, in its effort to keep in the
valleys, that I no longer knew in what direction lay the
sweet village of B——, where I had determined to stop
for the night. The sun had scarcely *shone* — strictly
speaking — during the day, which, nevertheless, had
been unpleasantly warm. A smoky mist, resembling that
of the Indian summer, enveloped all things, and, of
course, added to my uncertainty. Not that I cared
much about the matter. If I did not hit upon the village
before sunset, or even before dark, it was more than
possible that a little Dutch farmhouse, or something of
that kind, would soon make its appearance — although,
in fact, the neighborhood (perhaps on account of being
more picturesque than fertile) was very sparsely inhabited. At all events, with my knapsack for a pillow, and
my hound as a sentry, a bivouac in the open air was just
the thing which would have amused me. I sauntered
on, therefore, quite at ease — Ponto taking charge of
my gun — until at length, just as I had begun to consider whether the numerous little glades, that led hither
and thither, were intended to be paths at all, I was conducted by one of them into an unquestionable carriage
track. There could be no mistaking it. The traces of
light wheels were evident; and although the tall shrub-
beries and overgrown undergrowth met overhead, there
was no obstruction whatever below, even to the passage
of a Virginia mountain wagon — the most aspiring
vehicle, I take it, of its kind. The road, however, except
in being open through the wood — if wood be not too
weighty a name for such an assemblage of light trees —
and except in the particulars of evident wheel-tracks —
bore no resemblance to any road I had before seen. The

tracks of which I speak were but faintly perceptible —
having been impressed upon the firm, yet pleasantly
moist surface of what looked more like green Genoese
velvet than anything else. It was grass, clearly — but
grass such as we seldom see out of England — so short,
so thick, so even, and so vivid in color. Not a single
impediment lay in the wheel-route — not even a chip or
a dead twig. The stones that once obstructed the way
had been carefully *placed* — not thrown — along the
sides of the lane, so as to define its boundaries at bottom
with a kind of half-precise, half-negligent, and wholly
picturesque definition. Clumps of wild flowers grew
everywhere, luxuriantly, in the interspaces.

What to make of all this, of course, I knew not. Here
was *art* undoubtedly — *that* did not surprise me — all
roads, in the ordinary sense, are works of art; nor can I
say that there was much to wonder at in the mere *excess*
of art manifested; all that seemed to have been done,
might have been done *here* — with such natural "capa-
bilities" (as they have it in the books on Landscape
Gardening) — with very little labor and expense. No;
it was not the amount but the *character* of the art which
caused me to take a seat on one of the blossomy stones
and gaze up and down this fairy-like avenue for half
an hour or more in bewildered admiration. One thing
became more and more evident the longer I gazed: an
artist, and one with a most scrupulous eye for form, had
superintended all these arrangements. The greatest
care had been taken to preserve a due medium between
the neat and graceful, on the one hand, and the *pittor-
esque*, in the true sense of the Italian term, on the other.
There were few straight, and no long, uninterrupted
lines. The same effect of curvature or of color appeared
twice, usually, but not oftener, at any one point of view.

Everywhere was variety in uniformity. It was a piece of "composition," in which the most fastidiously critical taste could scarcely have suggested an emendation.

I had turned to the right as I entered this road, and now, arising, I continued in the same direction. The path was so serpentine, that at no moment could I trace its course for more than two or three paces in advance. Its character did not undergo any material change.

Presently the murmur of water fell gently upon my ear — and in a few moments afterward, as I turned with the road somewhat more abruptly than hitherto, I became aware that a building of some kind lay at the foot of a gentle declivity just before me. I could see nothing distinctly on account of the mist which occupied all the little valley below. A gentle breeze, however, now arose, as the sun was about descending; and while I remained standing on the brow of the slope, the fog gradually became dissipated into wreaths, and so floated over the scene.

As it came fully into view — thus *gradually* as I describe it — piece by piece, here a tree, there a glimpse of water, and here again the summit of a chimney, I could scarcely help fancying that the whole was one of the ingenious illusions sometimes exhibited under the name of "vanishing pictures."

By the time, however, that the fog had thoroughly disappeared, the sun had made its way down behind the gentle hills, and thence, as if with a slight *chassez* to the south, had come again fully into sight, glaring with a purplish luster through a chasm that entered the valley from the west. Suddenly, therefore, — and as if by the hand of magic, — this whole valley and everything in it became brilliantly visible.

The first *coup d'œil*, as the sun slid into the position

described, impressed me very much as I have been impressed, when a boy, by the concluding scene of some well-arranged theatrical spectacle or melodrama. Not even the monstrosity of color was wanting: for the sunlight came out through the chasm, tinted all orange and purple; while the vivid green of the grass in the valley was reflected more or less upon all objects from the curtain of vapor that still hung overhead, as if loath to take its total departure from a scene so enchantingly beautiful.

The little vale into which I thus peered down from under the fog-canopy could not have been more than four hundred yards long; while in breadth it varied from fifty to one hundred and fifty, or perhaps two hundred. It was most narrow at its northern extremity, opening out as it tended southwardly, but with no very precise regularity. The widest portion was within eighty yards of the southern extreme. The slopes which encompassed the vale could not fairly be called hills, unless at their northern face. Here a precipitous ledge of granite arose to a height of some ninety feet; and, as I have mentioned, the valley at this point was not more than fifty feet wide; but as the visitor proceeded southwardly from this cliff, he found, on his right hand and on his left, declivities at once less high, less precipitous, and less rocky. All, in a word, sloped and softened to the south; and yet the whole vale was engirdled by eminences, more or less high, except at two points. One of these I have already spoken of. It lay considerably to the north of west, and was where the setting sun made its way, as I have before described, into the amphitheater, through a cleanly cut natural cleft in the granite embankment; this fissure might have been ten yards wide at its widest point, so far as the eye could trace it. It seemed to lead

up, up, like a natural causeway, into the recesses of
unexplored mountains and forests. The other opening
was directly at the southern end of the vale. Here, generally, the slopes were nothing more than gentle inclinations, extending from east to west about one hundred
and fifty yards. In the middle of this extent was a depression, level with the ordinary floor of the valley. As
regards vegetation, as well as in respect to everything
else, the scene *softened and sloped* to the south. To the
north — on the craggy precipice — a few paces from the
verge — upsprang the magnificent trunks of numerous
hickories, black walnuts, and chestnuts, interspersed
with occasional oak; and the strong lateral branches
thrown out by the walnuts, especially, spread far over
the edge of the cliff. Proceeding southwardly, the ex-
plorer saw at first the same class of trees, but less and
less lofty and Salvatorish in character; then he saw the
gentler elm, succeeded by the sassafras and locust —
these again by the softer linden, red-bud, catalpa, and
maple — these yet again by still more graceful and more
modest varieties. The whole face of the southern declivity was covered with wild shrubbery alone — an
occasional silver willow or white poplar excepted. In the
bottom of the valley itself — for it must be borne in mind
that the vegetation hitherto mentioned grew only on the
cliffs or hillsides — were to be seen three insulated trees.
One was an elm of fine size and exquisite form: it stood
guard over the southern gate of the vale. Another was a
hickory, much larger than the elm, and altogether a
much finer tree, although both were exceedingly beautiful: it seemed to have taken charge of the northwestern
entrance, springing from a group of rocks in the very
jaws of the ravine, and throwing its graceful body, at an
angle of nearly forty-five degrees, far out into the sun-

shine of the amphitheater. About thirty yards east of
this tree stood, however, the pride of the valley, and
beyond all question the most magnificent tree I have
ever seen, unless, perhaps, among the cypresses of the
Itchiatuckanee. It was a triple-stemmed tulip tree —
the *Liriodendron tulipiferum* — one of the natural order
of magnolias. Its three trunks separated from the
parent at about three feet from the soil and, diverging
very slightly and gradually, were not more than four
feet apart at the point where the largest stem shot out
into the foliage: this was at an elevation of about eighty
feet. The whole height of the principal division was one
hundred and twenty feet. Nothing can surpass in beauty
the form or the glossy, vivid green of the leaves of the
tulip tree. In the present instance they were fully eight
inches wide; but their glory was altogether eclipsed by
the gorgeous splendor of the profuse blossoms. Conceive, closely congregated, a million of the largest and
most resplendent tulips! Only thus can the reader get
any idea of the picture I would convey. And then the
stately grace of the clean, delicately granulated colum-
nar stems, the largest four feet in diameter, at twenty
from the ground. The innumerable blossoms, mingling
with those of other trees scarcely less beautiful,
although infinitely less majestic, filled the valley with
more than Arabian perfumes.

The general floor of the amphitheater was *grass* of the
same character as that I had found in the road: if anything, more deliciously soft, thick, velvety, and miracu-
lously green. It was hard to conceive how all this beauty
had been attained.

I have spoken of two openings into the vale. From
the one to the northwest issued a rivulet, which came,
gently murmuring and slightly foaming, down the ra-

vine, until it dashed against the group of rocks out of
which sprang the insulated hickory. Here, after encir-
cling the tree, it passed on, a little to the north of east,
leaving the tulip tree some twenty feet to the south, and
making no decided alteration in its course until it came
near the midway between the eastern and western boundaries of the valley. At this point, after a series of
sweeps, it turned off at right angles and pursued a generally southern direction — meandering as it went —
until it became lost in a small lake of irregular figure
(although roughly oval), that lay gleaming near the
lower extremity of the vale. This lakelet was, perhaps,
a hundred yards in diameter at its widest part. No crystal could be clearer than its waters. Its bottom, which
could be distinctly seen, consisted altogether of pebbles
brilliantly white. Its banks, of the emerald grass already described, *rounded*, rather than sloped, off into
the clear heaven below; and *so* clear was this heaven, so
perfectly, at times, did it reflect all objects above it, that
where the true bank ended and where the mimic one
commenced, it was a point of no little difficulty to determine. The trout, and some other varieties of fish, with
which this pond seemed to be almost inconveniently
crowded, had all the appearance of veritable flying-fish.
It was almost impossible to believe that they were not
absolutely suspended in the air. A light birch canoe,
that lay placidly on the water, was reflected in its
minutest fibers with a fidelity unsurpassed by the most
exquisitely polished mirror. A small island, fairly laughing with flowers in full bloom, and affording little more
space than just enough for a picturesque little building,
seemingly a fowl-house, arose from the lake not far from
its northern shore, to which it was connected by means
of an inconceivably light-looking and yet very primitive

bridge. It was formed of a single broad and thick plank
of the tulip wood. This was forty feet long, and spanned
the interval between shore and shore with a slight but
very perceptible arch, preventing all oscillation. From
the southern extreme of the lake issued a continuation
of the rivulet, which, after meandering for perhaps thirty
yards, finally passed through the "depression" (already
described) in the middle of the southern declivity, and,
tumbling down a sheer precipice of a hundred feet, made
its devious and unnoticed way to the Hudson.

The lake was deep — at some points thirty feet — but
the rivulet seldom exceeded three, while its greatest
width was about eight. Its bottom and banks were as
those of the pond — if a defect could have been attributed in point of picturesqueness, it was that of excessive
neatness.

The expanse of the green turf was relieved, here and
there, by an occasional showy shrub, such as the hydran-
gea, or the common snowball, or the aromatic syringa;
or, more frequently, by a clump of geraniums blossom-
ing gorgeously in great varieties. These latter grew in
pots which were carefully buried in the soil, so as to give
the plants the appearance of being indigenous. Besides
all this, the lawn's velvet was exquisitely spotted with
sheep — a considerable flock of which roamed about the
vale, in company with three tamed deer, and a vast number of brilliantly plumed ducks. A very large mastiff
seemed to be in vigilant attendance upon these animals,
each and all.

Along the eastern and western cliffs — where, towards
the upper portion of the amphitheater, the boundaries
were more or less precipitous — grew ivy in great profusion — so that only here and there could even a glimpse
of the naked rock be obtained. The northern precipice,

in like manner, was almost entirely clothed by grape-vines of rare luxuriance; some springing from the soil at the base of the cliff, and others from ledges on its face.

The slight elevation which formed the lower boundary of this little domain was crowned by a neat stone wall, of sufficient height to prevent the escape of the deer. Nothing of the fence kind was observable elsewhere; for nowhere else was an artificial inclosure needed: — any stray sheep, for example, which should attempt to make its way out of the vale by means of the ravine, would find its progress arrested, after a few yards' advance, by the precipitous ledge of rock over which tumbled the cascade that had arrested my attention as I first drew near the domain. In short, the only ingress or egress was through a gate occupying a rocky pass in the road, a few paces below the point at which I stopped to reconnoiter the scene.

I have described the brook as meandering very irregularly through the whole of its course. Its two *general* directions, as I have said, were first from west to east, and then from north to south. At the *turn*, the stream, sweeping backwards, made an almost circular *loop*, so as to form a peninsula, which was *very* nearly an island, and which included about the sixteenth of an acre. On this peninsula stood a dwelling-house — and when I say that this house, like the infernal terrace seen by Vathek, "*était d'une architecture inconnue dans les annales de la terre*," I mean, merely, that its *tout ensemble* struck me with the keenest sense of combined novelty and pro-priety—in a word, of *poetry*— (for, than in the words just employed, I could scarcely give, of poetry in the abstract, a more rigorous definition) — and I do *not* mean that the merely *outré* was perceptible in any respect.

In fact, nothing could well be more simple, more

utterly unpretending, than this cottage. Its marvelous *effect* lay altogether in its artistic arrangement *as a picture*. I could have fancied, while I looked at it, that some eminent landscape painter had built it with his brush.

The point of view from which I first saw the valley was not *altogether*, although it was nearly, the best point from which to survey the house. I will therefore describe it as I afterwards saw it — from a position on the stone wall at the southern extreme of the amphitheater.

The main building was about twenty-four feet long and sixteen broad — certainly not more. Its total height, from the ground to the apex of the roof, could not have exceeded eighteen feet. To the west end of this structure was attached one about a third smaller in all its proportions: — the line of its front standing back about two yards from that of the larger house; and the line of its roof, of course, being considerably depressed below that of the roof adjoining. At right angles to these buildings, and from the rear of the main one — not exactly in the middle — extended a third compartment, very small — being, in general, one third less than the western wing. The roofs of the two larger were very steep — sweeping down from the ridge-beam with a long concave curve, and extending at least four feet beyond the walls in front, so as to form the roofs of two piazzas. These latter roofs, of course, needed no support; but as they had the *air* of needing it, slight and perfectly plain pillars were inserted at the corners alone. The roof of the northern wing was merely an extension of a portion of the main roof. Between the chief building and western wing arose a very tall and rather slender square chimney of hard Dutch bricks, alternately black and red: — a slight cornice of projecting bricks at the top. Over the gables the roofs also projected very much: — in the main building, about four feet to the east and two to the west. The principal door was not exactly in the main division, being a little to the east — while the two windows were to the west. These latter did not extend to the floor, but were much longer and narrower than usual — they had single shutters like doors — the panes were of lozenge form, but quite large. The door itself had its upper half of glass, also in lozenge panes — a movable shutter secured it at night. The door to the west wing was in its gable, and quite simple — a single window looked out to the south. There was no external door to the north wing, and it, also, had only one window to the east.

The blank wall of the eastern gable was relieved by stairs (with a balustrade) running diagonally across it — the ascent being from the south. Under cover of the widely projecting eave these steps gave access to a door leading into the garret, or rather loft — for it was lighted only by a single window to the north, and seemed to have been intended as a storeroom.

The piazzas of the main building and western wing had no floors, as is usual; but at the doors and at each window, large, flat, irregular slabs of granite lay embedded in the delicious turf, affording comfortable footing in all weather. Excellent paths of the same material — not *nicely* adapted, but with the velvety sod filling frequent intervals between the stones, led hither and thither from the house, to a crystal spring about five paces off, to the road, or to one or two out-houses that lay to the north, beyond the brook, and were thoroughly concealed by a few locusts and catalpas.

Not more than six steps from the main door of the cottage stood the dead trunk of a fantastic pear tree, so clothed from head to foot in the gorgeous bignonia blossoms that one required no little scrutiny to determine what manner of sweet thing it could be. From various arms of this tree hung cages of different kinds. In one, a large wicker cylinder with a ring at top, reveled a mocking-bird; in another, an oriole; in a third, the impudent bobolink, — while three or four more delicate prisons were loudly vocal with canaries.

The pillars of the piazza were enwreathed in jasmine and sweet honeysuckle; while from the angle formed by the main structure and its west wing, in front, sprang a grape-vine of unexampled luxuriance. Scorning all restraint, it had clambered first to the lower roof — then to the higher; and along the ridge of this latter it continued to writhe on, throwing out tendrils to the right and left, until at length it fairly attained the east gable, and fell trailing over the stairs.

The whole house, with its wings, was constructed of the old-fashioned Dutch shingles — broad, and with unrounded corners. It is a peculiarity of this material to give houses built of it the appearance of being wider at bottom than at top — after the manner of Egyptian architecture; and in the present instance this exceedingly picturesque effect was aided by numerous pots of gorgeous flowers that almost encompassed the base of the buildings.

The shingles were painted a dull gray; and the happiness with which this neutral tint melted into the vivid green of the tulip tree leaves that partially overshadowed the cottage can readily be conceived by an artist.

From the position near the stone wall, as described, the buildings were seen at great advantage — for the southeastern angle was thrown forward — so that the eye took in at once the whole of the two fronts, with the picturesque eastern gable, and at the same time obtained just a sufficient glimpse of the northern wing, with parts of a pretty roof to the spring-house, and nearly half of a light bridge that spanned the brook in the near vicinity of the main buildings.

I did not remain very long on the brow of the hill, although long enough to make a thorough survey of the scene at my feet. It was clear that I had wandered from the road to the village, and I had thus good travelers' excuse to open the gate before me, and inquire my way, at all events; so, without more ado, I proceeded.

The road, after passing the gate, seemed to lie upon a natural ledge, sloping gradually down along the face of the northeastern cliffs. It led me on to the foot of the northern precipice, and thence over the bridge, round by the eastern gable to the front door. In this progress, I took notice that no sight of the out-houses could be obtained.

As I turned the corner of the gable, the mastiff bounded toward me in stern silence, but with the eye and the whole air of a tiger. I held him out my hand, however, in token of amity — and I never yet knew the dog who was proof against such an appeal to his courtesy. He not only shut his mouth and wagged his tail, but absolutely offered me his paw — afterward extending his civilities to Ponto.

As no bell was discernible, I rapped with my stick against the door, which stood half open. Instantly a figure advanced to the threshold — that of a young woman about twenty-eight years of age — slender, or rather slight, and somewhat above the medium height. As she approached, with a certain *modest decision* of step altogether indescribable, I said to myself, "Surely here I have found the perfection of natural, in contradistinction from artificial *grace*." The second impression which she made on me, but by far the more vivid of the two, was that of *enthusiasm*. So intense an expression of *romance*, perhaps I should call it, or of unworldliness, as that which gleamed from her deep-set eyes, had never so sunk into my heart of hearts before. I know not how it is, but this peculiar expression of the eye, wreathing itself occasionally into the lips, is the most powerful, if not absolutely the *sole*, spell, which rivets my interest in woman. "*Romance*," — provided my readers fully comprehend what I would here imply by the word — "romance" and "womanliness" seem to me convertible terms; and, after all, what man truly *loves* in woman, is simply, her *womanhood*. The eyes of Annie (I heard some one from the interior call her "Annie, darling!") were "spiritual gray"; her hair, a light chestnut: this is all I had time to observe of her.

At her most courteous of invitations, I entered — passing first into a tolerably wide vestibule. Having come mainly to *observe*, I took notice that to my right, as I stepped in, was a window, such as those in front of the house; to the left, a door leading into the principal room; while, opposite me, an *open* door enabled me to see a small apartment, just the size of the vestibule, arranged as a study, and having a large *bow* window looking out to the north.

Passing into the parlor, I found myself with *Mr. Landor* — for this, I afterwards found, was his name. He was civil, even cordial in his manner; but just then, I was more intent on observing the arrangements of the dwelling which had so much interested me, than the personal appearance of the tenant.

The north wing, I now saw, was a bed-chamber; its door opened into the parlor. West of this door was a single window, looking toward the brook. At the west

end of the parlor, were a fireplace, and a door leading
into the west wing — probably a kitchen.

Nothing could be more rigorously simple than the
furniture of the parlor. On the floor was an ingrain carpet, of excellent texture — a white ground, spotted with
small circular green figures. At the windows were curtains of snowy white jaconet muslin: they were tolerably
full, and hung *decisively*, perhaps rather formally, in
sharp, parallel plaits to the floor — *just* to the floor.
The walls were papered with a French paper of great
delicacy, a silver ground, with a faint green cord running
zig-zag throughout. Its expanse was relieved merely by
three of Julien's exquisite lithographs *à trois crayons*,
fastened to the wall without frames. One of these draw-
ings was a scene of Oriental luxury, or rather voluptu-
ousness; another was a "carnival piece," spirited beyond
compare; the third was a Greek female head — a face so
divinely beautiful, and yet of an expression so provok-
ingly indeterminate, never before arrested my attention.

The more substantial furniture consisted of a round
table, a few chairs (including a large rocking-chair), and
a sofa, or rather "settee": its material was plain maple
painted a creamy white, slightly interstriped with green
— the seat of cane. The chairs and table were "to
match"; but the *forms* of all had evidently been designed by the same brain which planned "the grounds":
it is impossible to conceive anything more graceful.

On the table were a few books; a large, square, crystal
bottle of some novel perfume; a plain, ground-glass *astral*
(not solar) lamp, with an Italian shade; and a large vase
of resplendently blooming flowers. Flowers, indeed, of
gorgeous colors and delicate odor formed the sole mere
decoration of the apartment. The fireplace was nearly
filled with a vase of brilliant geranium. On a triangular

shelf in each angle of the room stood also a similar vase, varied only as to its lovely contents. One or two smaller *bouquets* adorned the mantel; and late violets clustered about the open windows.

It is not the purpose of this work to do more than give, in detail, a picture of Mr. Landor's residence — *as I found it.*

THE WHEAT PIT [1]

BY FRANK NORRIS

THIS specimen of description, occurring at the close of chapter III in *The Pit*, a realistic novel of modern life, is a good example of expository setting, the purpose of which is to portray with exactness a scene playing a part in the general action of the narrative. It is noteworthy for its abundance of detail, which leaves little to the imagination, and it approximates a word-photograph of the scene presented. The reader feels not so much the process of selection as the attempt to include every possible circumstance — a characteristic of Norris's striking realism.

THE real business of the morning was over. The Pit knew it. . . . The traders stood around in expectant attitudes, looking into one another's faces, waiting for what they could not exactly say; loath to leave the Pit lest something should "turn up" the moment their backs were turned.

By degrees the clamor died away, ceased, began again irregularly, then abruptly stilled. Here and there a bid was called, an offer made, like the intermittent crack of small arms after the stopping of the cannonade.

"Sell five May at one eighth."

"Sell twenty at one quarter."

"Give one eighth for May."

For an instant the shoutings were renewed. Then suddenly the gong struck. The traders began slowly to leave the Pit. One of the floor officers, an old fellow in uniform and vizored cap, appeared, gently shouldering toward

---

[1] From chapter III of *The Pit*. By permission of the publishers, Messrs. Doubleday, Page & Co.

the door the groups wherein the bidding and offering were still languidly going on. His voice full of remonstration, he repeated continually:

"Time's up, gentlemen. Go on now and get your lunch. Lunch time now. Go on now, or I'll have to report you. Time's up."

The tide set toward the doorways. In the gallery the few visitors rose, putting on coats and wraps. Over by the check counter, to the right of the south entrance to the floor, a throng of brokers and traders jostled each other, reaching over one another's shoulders for hats and ulsters. In steadily increasing numbers they poured out of the north and south entrances, on their way to turn in their trading cards to the offices.

Little by little the floor emptied. The provision and grain pits were deserted, and as the clamor of the place lapsed away the telegraph instruments began to make themselves heard once more, together with the chanting of the messenger boys.

Swept clean in the morning, the floor itself, seen now through the thinning groups, was littered from end to end with scattered grain — oats, wheat, corn, and barley, with wisps of hay, peanut shells, apple parings, and orange peel, with torn newspapers, odds and ends of memoranda, crushed paper darts, and above all with a countless multitude of yellow telegraph forms, thousands upon thousands, crumpled and muddy under the trampling of innumerable feet. It was the débris of the battlefield, the abandoned impedimenta and broken weapons of contending armies, the detritus of conflict, torn, broken, and rent, that at the end of each day's combat encumbered the field.

At last even the click of the last of the telegraph keys died down. Shouldering themselves into their overcoats, the operators departed, calling back and forth to one another, making "dates," and cracking jokes. Washerwomen appeared with steaming pails, porters pushing great brooms before them began gathering the refuse of the floor into heaps.

Between the wheat and corn pits a band of young fellows, some of them absolute boys, appeared. These were the settlement clerks. They carried long account books. It was their duty to get the trades of the day into a "ring" — to trace the course of a lot of wheat which had changed hands perhaps a score of times during the trading — and their calls of "Wheat sold to Teller & West," "May wheat sold to Burbank & Co.," "May oats sold to Matthewson & Knight," "Wheat sold to Gretry, Converse & Co.," began to echo from wall to wall of the almost deserted room.

A cat, gray and striped, and wearing a dog collar of nickel and red leather, issued from the coat-room and picked her way across the floor. Evidently she was in a mood of the most ingratiating friendliness, and as one after another of the departing traders spoke to her, raised her tail in the air and arched her back against the legs of the empty chairs. The janitor put in an appearance, lowering the tall colored windows with a long rod. A noise of hammering and the scrape of saws began to issue from a corner where a couple of carpenters tinkered about one of the sample tables.

Then at last even the settlement clerks took themselves off. At once there was a great silence, broken only by the harsh rasp of the carpenters' saws and the voice of the janitor exchanging jokes with the washerwomen. The sound of footsteps in distant quarters re-echoed as if in a church.

The washerwomen invaded the floor, spreading soapy

and steaming water before them. Over by the sample tables a negro porter in shirt-sleeves swept entire bushels of spilled wheat, crushed, broken, and sodden, into his dustpans.

The day's campaign was over. It was past two o'clock. On the great dial against the eastern wall the indicator stood — sentinel fashion — at ninety-three. Not till the following morning would the whirlpool, the great central force that spun the Niagara of wheat in its grip, thunder and bellow again.

Later on even the washerwomen, even the porter and janitor, departed. An unbroken silence, the peacefulness of an untroubled calm, settled over the place. The rays of the afternoon sun flooded through the west windows in long parallel shafts full of floating golden motes. There was no sound; nothing stirred. The floor of the Board of Trade was deserted. Alone, on the edge of the abandoned Wheat Pit, in a spot where the sunlight fell warmest — an atom of life, lost in the immensity of the empty floor — the gray cat made her toilet, diligently licking the fur on the inside of her thigh, one leg, as if dislocated, thrust into the air above her head.

HAPPINESS [1]

(*Le Bonheur*)

BY GUY DE MAUPASSANT

It is apparent at even a first reading that the essential value of Maupassant's *Happiness* lies in its emotional appeal. But the directness and strength of this appeal receive greatly increased effectiveness by means of the setting amid which the details of the action are presented. The central theme of the story, the permanence of true love, is simple in the extreme; artificialities and social conventions are alien to its very spirit. Yet the story is set in the midst of an atmosphere of superficiality, of blindness to the deeper significance of life and human relations. The banqueters discuss love with all the shallow casuistry of those who have never experienced the emotion; in the words of George Meredith, they are but "fiddling harmonics on the strings of sensualism." Yet against this background of *dilettante* sentiment the author throws the picture of Suzanne de Sirmont's fidelity to her peasant lover. Then, too, the background of savage Corsica, still sunk in brutality and barbarism, produces an almost Rembrandtish contrast to the delicacy of the main theme.

The reader may well differentiate between the purely artistic effect of the setting in this story, its objective character, and the element of environment that belongs to Hawthorne's *The Great Stone Face*, wherein the setting is more intimately a part of the narrative, moulding and controlling the character of the hero. In the story of Ernest the setting constitutes an inherent part of the characterization; in *Happiness* it is more extrinsic, but of great value in heightening the effect sought by the author.

It was the hour for tea, just before the lights were brought in.

The villa overlooked the sea. The sun had sunk

[1] Translated for this work by the Editor.

below the horizon, and the rose-tinted sky was all flecked with gold. The Mediterranean, — not a wave or a ripple on its surface, smooth, and still aglow with the light of dying day, — looked like a gigantic polished metal plate.

Far away on the right the jagged mountains stood out in black profile against the pale purple of the western sky.

We talked of love; we discussed that familiar theme; we repeated anew the old commonplaces that have already been repeated so many, many times. Inspired by the tender melancholy of the twilight, we spoke only at intervals; our hearts thrilled with sentimental tenderness, and the word "love," constantly recurring, now in a strong man's voice and now in the lighter tones of a woman, seemed to pervade the little room, to flutter there like a bird, to hover about us like a spirit.

Can one remain in love for many years?

"Yes," asserted some.

"No," declared others.

We drew distinctions, we established limitations, we cited instances; and all of us, men and women alike, throbbed with emotions that rose to our lips, but which we could not frame in words. With enthusiasm and eager interest we discussed that commonplace but sovereign theme — the tender and mysterious union of two human hearts.

But suddenly some one, with eyes fixed upon the distant horizon, exclaimed, "Oh, look over there! What is that?"

Far away a huge gray mass was rising indistinctly over the sea.

The ladies had sprung to their feet, and were watching this surprising phenomenon which they had never seen before and which they did not understand.

One of the company said, "It is Corsica. You see it like that only two or three times a year, under certain peculiar atmospheric conditions, when the air is perfectly clear and the mists that veil the distance do not hide it from view."

We dimly made out the mountain-ridges; we thought that we could distinguish the snow of their summits. Every one was surprised, stirred, almost appalled at this sudden apparition of another world, at this phantom rising from the ocean. Perhaps those who like Columbus set out across unexplored seas had strange visions like this.

Then an old gentleman, who had thus far not spoken, said, "Listen. In that island, which is rising before us as if in response to what we were saying just now, and as if to remind me of a personal experience that I once had, — in that very island I knew of a wonderful example of faithful love, of love happy beyond belief.

"Here it is —

"Five years ago I made a visit to Corsica. That savage island is less familiar to us, even more remote than America, although it is sometimes visible from the very coast of France, as you have seen to-day.

"Picture to yourselves a world still plunged in chaos, a storm of mountains separated by narrow ravines down which plunge roaring torrents; not a single plain, but immense billows of granite and gigantic waves of hills covered with brush or lofty forests of chestnut and pine. It is a virgin soil, untilled, desert, although now and then you may see a village like a heap of rocks upon a mountain-top. No cultivation, no tilling of the soil, no art. You never chance across a bit of carved wood or of sculptured stone, never a trace to suggest that the ancestors of the inhabitants had either a crude or a refined taste for grace and beauty. In this wonderful but rude country nothing strikes one more than this hereditary indifference to the search after attractive form that men call Art.

"Italy, where every palace full of masterpieces is itself a masterpiece, where marble, wood, bronze, iron, metals, and precious stones attest man's genius, where the most insignificant antiques that lie about old houses reveal the regard for beauty, — Italy is for us all the sacred country of our love because she shows us and gives us proof of the might, the grandeur, the power, and the triumph of creative genius.

"And face to face with her, savage Corsica is still just what she was at the beginning. There a man lives in his rude hovel, indifferent to everything that does not concern his own everyday life or his own family feuds. He still betrays the vices and the virtues of the savage: he is violent, malignant, ready to commit murder without remorse; yet with these brutal instincts he is hospitable, generous, devoted, simple; he opens his door freely to the traveler, and at the slightest sign of sympathy he shows loyal friendship.

"For a month I wandered about this wonderful island with the feeling that I was at the very ends of the earth. Not an inn, not a tavern, not a road. By mule-paths you reach hamlets clinging to the mountain-sides and overlooking the winding abysses up which by night you hear ascending the continuous roar, the deep, dull voice of the cataract. You knock at the door of a house. You ask food and shelter until the next day. You sit down at the humble board; you sleep under the humble roof; and, in the morning, you grasp in farewell the outstretched hand of your host, who escorts you to the outskirts of the village.

"Now, one night, after walking for ten hours, I reached a little cottage quite apart by itself at the bottom of a narrow valley which, a league farther on, opened to the sea. Like two gloomy walls the steep slopes of the mountain, overgrown with brush, fallen rocks, and great trees, inclosed this dismal ravine.

"Around the cottage were a few vines, a little garden, and, farther on, some large chestnut trees — in a word, enough to live on, a fortune in this poverty-stricken country.

"The woman who greeted me was old, severe, and neat, — unusually so. A man, seated on a straw chair, rose to meet me, then sat down again without a word.

"'Excuse him,' said his companion; 'he is deaf now. He is eighty-two years old.'

"To my surprise, she spoke the French of France.

"'You do not belong to Corsica?' I asked.

"'No,' she replied; 'we are from the Continent. But we have lived here fifty years.'

"A shock, a feeling almost of terror, thrilled me at the thought of fifty years passed in this cheerless retreat so far from the haunts of man.

"An old shepherd came in, and we sat down to the solitary dish that constituted the meal, a thick soup of potatoes, lard, and cabbage, all boiled together.

"When we had finished our short repast, I sat down by the door, depressed by the melancholy of the gloomy surroundings, my heart weighed down with the dejection that sometimes seizes travelers on cheerless evenings and in lonely spots. It seems as if the end of everything is at hand — of life, of the universe itself. Suddenly we realize the frightful misery of existence, the isolation of self, the nothingness of all, the dreariness of a heart that deludes itself with dreams up to the very moment of death.

"The old woman joined me, and, impelled by the curiosity that lies at the bottom of even the most resigned heart, she said, 'You come from France, then?'

"'Yes, I am traveling about for pleasure.'

"'You are from Paris, perhaps?'

"'No, I am from Nancy.'

"It seemed to me that some deep emotion stirred her. How I perceived, or, rather, how I felt it, I do not know.

"'You are from Nancy?' she repeated slowly.

"The man appeared in the doorway, impassive like all deaf people.

"'Never mind him,' she said; 'he hears nothing.'

"Then, after a few seconds: 'So you know people at Nancy?'

"'Yes, indeed; nearly everybody.'

"'The family of Sainte-Allaize?'

"'Oh, yes. Very well. They were friends of my father.'

"'What is your name?'

"I told her. She looked searchingly at me; then, in the deep voice of one who is stirred by memories of the past, she said: 'Yes, yes. I remember it well. And the Brisemares, what has become of them?'

"'They are all dead.'

"'Ah! And the Sirmonts? Do you know them?'

"'Yes. The last of the family is a general.'

"Then, trembling with deep emotion, with a powerful passion that I did not understand, moved with a desire to confess to me, to reveal everything, to speak of secrets that she had long kept locked in her heart and of persons the mention of whose name had aroused her, she said, 'Yes. Henri de Sirmont. I know him well. He is my brother.'

"Aghast with surprise, I stared at her. And suddenly it all came to me.

"A long time ago it had caused a great scandal among the nobility of Lorraine. Suzanne de Sirmont, a young girl, beautiful and wealthy, had made a runaway match with a non-commissioned officer in the regiment of hussars commanded by her father.

"He was a handsome young fellow; he wore his blue uniform well, this peasant soldier who had won his colonel's daughter. She had seen him, noted him, fallen in love with him, doubtless as she watched the squadrons filing by. But how she had entered into conversation with him, how they had contrived to see each other, to hear from each other, how she had ventured to let him know that she loved him, — this no one ever knew.

"No one ever guessed the secret, never even suspected it. One evening, just as the soldier had completed his term of service, they disappeared. A careful search was made for them, but they were never found. Nothing was ever heard from them, and her family considered her as dead.

"And thus I found her in this gloomy valley.

"Then in my turn I spoke: 'Yes, I remember it well. You are Mademoiselle Suzanne.'

"She nodded 'yes.' Tears fell from her eyes. Then, indicating with a glance the old man motionless at the threshold of his hut, she said: 'That is he.'

"And I understood that she still loved him; that she still saw him with the eyes of affection.

"'Have you been happy?' I asked.

"She replied in a voice that came from her very heart,

'Oh, yes. Very happy. He has made me very happy. I have never regretted it.'

"Amazed, stirred by the power of love, I looked at her sadly. This rich young girl had followed this man, this peasant. She had become a peasant herself. She had become reconciled to a life without pleasure, without luxury, without attractiveness of any sort. She had stooped to his simple habits. And she still loved him. She had become the wife of a rustic, in a cap, in a cloth skirt. Seated on a straw chair, she ate from an earthen-ware dish on a wooden table a stew of cabbage and potatoes cooked in lard. She slept on a straw mattress by his side.

"Her only thought had been of him. She felt no regret for her former finery, her gowns, her various luxuries; no longing for soft upholsteries, for the perfumed warmth of tapestried chambers, for easy repose on beds of down. She had never felt need of aught but him; if he was near, she asked for nothing.

"While she was still young she had given up her life, her world, those who had cared for her and loved her. Alone with him she had come into this savage valley. He had been everything to her, the object of her every desire, of her dreams, of her trust, of her hopes. He had filled her life with happiness.

"She could not have been happier.

"And all that night as I listened to the heavy breath-ing of the old soldier stretched on his pallet by the side of her who had followed him so far, I thought upon this strangely simple adventure, of this happiness so com-plete but founded on so little.

"And as I went away at sunrise I pressed the hands of the aged couple."

The narrator was silent.

A lady said, "Well, her ideals were too low, her wants too easily satisfied, her needs too simple. She must have been a fool."

Another in a low voice murmured, "What of it? She was happy."

And out beyond, at the edge of the horizon, Corsica was sinking into the night, slowly dropping into the sea, effacing the great shadow that had appeared as if to tell in person the story of the two humble lovers sheltered and protected by her shores.

OF A MIRROR AND A BELL [1]

BY LAFCADIO HEARN

THIS narrative, like many of Lafcadio Hearn's translations from the Japanese, is illustrative of local color and atmosphere, reproducing in wonderfully clear and simple style the poetry of Oriental imagination. "Some of his tales are of the long ago, and yet they seem to illuminate the very souls and minds of the little men who are at this hour crowding the decks of Japan's armored cruisers. But many of the stories are about women and children, — the lovely materials from which the best fairy-tales of the world have been woven. They, too, are strange, these Japanese maidens and wives and keen-eyed, dark-haired girls and boys; they are like us and yet not like us; and the sky and the hills and the flowers are all different from ours. Yet by a magic of which Mr. Hearn, almost alone among contemporary writers, is the master, in these delicate, transparent, ghostly sketches of a world unreal to us, there is a haunting sense of spiritual reality." [2]

Throughout the selection here presented there is the air of strangeness, of something foreign to our Occidental civilization, and this atmosphere, or tone, is, perhaps, the element that gives the narrative its peculiar charm.

EIGHT centuries ago, the priests of Mugenyama, in the province of Tōtōmi, wanted a big bell for their temple; and they asked the women of their parish to help them by contributing old bronze mirrors for bell-metal.

[Even to-day, in the courts of certain Japanese temples, you may see heaps of old bronze mirrors contributed for such a purpose. The largest collection of this kind that I ever saw was in the court of a temple of the Jōdo sect, at Hakata, in Kyūshū: the mirrors had been given

---

[1] From *Kwaidan*, published by Houghton Mifflin Company.
[2] From the Preface to *Kwaidan*.

for the making of a bronze statue of Amida, thirty-three feet high.]

There was at that time a young woman, a farmer's wife, living at Mugenyama, who presented her mirror to the temple, to be used for bell-metal. But afterwards she much regretted her mirror. She remembered things that her mother had told her about it; and she remembered that it had belonged, not only to her mother but to her mother's mother and grandmother; and she remembered some happy smiles which it had reflected. Of course, if she could have offered the priests a certain sum of money in place of the mirror, she could have asked them to give back her heirloom. But she had not the money necessary. Whenever she went to the temple, she saw her mirror lying in the courtyard, behind a railing, among hundreds of other mirrors heaped there together. She knew it by the *Shō-Chiku-Bai* in relief on the back of it, — those three fortunate emblems of Pine, Bamboo, and Plumflower, which delighted her baby-eyes when her mother first showed her the mirror. She longed for some chance to steal the mirror, and hide it, — that she might thereafter treasure it always. But the chance did not come; and she became very unhappy, — felt as if she had foolishly given away a part of her life. She thought about the old saying that a mirror is the Soul of a Woman (a saying mystically expressed, by the Chinese character for Soul, upon the backs of many bronze mirrors), — and she feared that it was true in weirder ways than she had before imagined. But she could not dare to speak of her pain to anybody.

Now, when all the mirrors contributed for the Mugenyama bell had been sent to the foundry, the bell-founders discovered that there was one mirror among them which would not melt. Again and again they tried to melt it; but it resisted all their efforts. Evidently the woman who had given that mirror to the temple must have regretted the giving. She had not presented her offering with all her heart; and therefore her selfish soul, remaining attached to the mirror, kept it hard and cold in the midst of the furnace.

Of course everybody heard of the matter, and everybody soon knew whose mirror it was that would not melt. And because of this public exposure of her secret fault, the poor woman became very much ashamed and very angry. And as she could not bear the shame, she drowned herself, after having written a farewell letter containing these words: —

"When I am dead, it will not be difficult to melt the mirror and to cast the bell. But, to the person who breaks that bell by ringing it, great wealth will be given by the ghost of me."

— You must know that the last wish or promise of anybody who dies in anger, or performs suicide in anger, is generally supposed to possess a supernatural force. After the dead woman's mirror had been melted, and the bell had been successfully cast, people remembered the words of that letter. They felt sure that the spirit of the writer would give wealth to the breaker of the bell; and, as soon as the bell had been suspended in the court of the temple, they went in multitudes to ring it. With all their might and main they swung the ringing-beam; but the bell proved to be a good bell, and it bravely withstood their assaults. Nevertheless, the people were not easily discouraged. Day after day, at all hours, they continued

to ring the bell furiously, — caring nothing whatever for
the protests of the priests. So the ringing became an
affliction; and the priests could not endure it; and they
got rid of the bell by rolling it down the hill into a
swamp. The swamp was deep, and swallowed it up, —
and that was the end of the bell. Only its legend remains; and in that legend it is called the *Mugen-Kané*, or
Bell of Mugen.

. . . .

Now there are queer old Japanese beliefs in the magical efficacy of a certain mental operation implied,
though not described, by the verb *nazoraëru*. The word
itself cannot be adequately rendered by any English
word; for it is used in relation to many kinds of mimetic magic, as well as in relation to the performance
of many religious acts of faith. Common meanings of
nazoraëru, according to dictionaries, are "to imitate,"
"to compare," "to liken"; but the esoteric meaning
is *to substitute, in imagination, one object or action for
another, so as to bring about some magical or miraculous
result.*

For example:—you cannot afford to build a Buddhist
temple; but you can easily lay a pebble before the image
of the Buddha, with the same pious feeling that would
prompt you to build a temple if you were rich enough to
build one. The merit of so offering the pebble becomes
equal, or almost equal, to the merit of erecting a temple. . . . You cannot read the six thousand seven hundred and seventy-one volumes of the Buddhist texts; but
you can make a revolving library, containing them, turn
round, by pushing it like a windlass. And if you push
with an earnest wish that you could read the six thous-
and seven hundred and seventy-one volumes, you will
acquire the same merit as the reading of them would

enable you to gain. . . . So much will perhaps suffice to explain the religious meanings of *nazoraëru*.

The magical meanings could not all be explained without a great variety of examples; but, for present purposes, the following will serve. If you should make a little man of straw, for the same reason that Sister Helen made a little man of wax, — and nail it, with nails not less than five inches long, to some tree in a temple-grove at the Hour of the Ox, — and if the person, imaginatively represented by that little straw man, should die thereafter in atrocious agony, — that would illustrate one signification of *nazoraëru*. . . . Or, let us suppose that a robber has entered your house during the night, and carried away your valuables. If you can discover the footprints of that robber in your garden, and then promptly burn a very large moxa on each of them, the soles of the feet of the robber will become inflamed, and will allow him no rest until he returns, of his own accord, to put himself at your mercy. That is another kind of mimetic magic expressed by the term *nazoraëru*. And a third kind is illustrated by various legends of the Mugen-Kané.

After the bell had been rolled into the swamp, there was, of course, no more chance of ringing it in such wise as to break it. But persons who regretted this loss of opportunity would strike and break objects imaginatively substituted for the bell, — thus hoping to please the spirit of the owner of the mirror that had made so much trouble. One of these persons was a woman called Umégaë, — famed in Japanese legend because of her relation to Kajiwara Kagésué, a warrior of the Heiké clan. While the pair were traveling together, Kajiwara one day found himself in great straits for want of money;

and Umégaë, remembering the tradition of the Bell of
Mugen, took a basin of bronze, and, mentally representing it to be the bell, beat upon it until she broke it, —
crying out, at the same time, for three hundred pieces of
gold. A guest of the inn where the pair were stopping
made inquiry as to the cause of the banging and the crying, and, on learning the story of the trouble, actually
presented Umégaë with three hundred *ryō* in gold. Afterwards a song was made about Umégaë's basin of bronze;
and that song is sung by dancing-girls even to this day:—

> Umégaë no chōzubachi tataïté
> O-kané ga déru naraba,
> Mina San mi-uké wo
> Sōré tanomimasu.

["*If, by striking upon the wash-basin of Umégaë, I could make honor-
ble money come to me, then would I negotiate for the freedom of all my girl
comrades.*"]

After this happening, the fame of the Mugen-Kané
became great; and many people followed the example of
Umégaë, — thereby hoping to emulate her luck. Among
these folk was a dissolute farmer who lived near Mugenyama, on the bank of the Oïgawa. Having wasted his
substance in riotous living, this farmer made for himself,
out of the mud in his garden, a clay-model of the Mugen-
Kané; and he beat the clay-bell, and broke it, — crying
out the while for great wealth.

Then, out of the ground before him, rose up the figure
of a white-robed woman, with long, loose-flowing hair,
holding a covered jar. And the woman said: "I have
come to answer your fervent prayer as it deserves to be
answered. Take, therefore, this jar." So saying, she put
the jar into his hands, and disappeared.

Into his house the happy man rushed, to tell his wife
the good news. He set down in front of her the covered

jar, — which was heavy, — and they opened it together. And they found that it was filled, up to the very brim, with . . .

But, no! — I really cannot tell you with what it was filled.

THE FALL OF THE HOUSE OF USHER

BY EDGAR ALLAN POE

THE unity of tone that permeates *The Fall of the House of Usher* is indicated in the words, "About the whole mansion and domain there hung an atmosphere peculiar to themselves and their immediate vicinity — an atmosphere which had no affinity with the air of heaven, but which had reeked up from the decayed trees, and the gray wall, and the silent tarn — a pestilent, mystic vapor, dull, sluggish, faintly discernible, and leaden-hued." The mood of the story is that of unreclaimed dreariness, gloomy depression, sickening terror. From beginning to end this mood is unrelieved. From the first glimpse of the gray sedge, the ghostly tree-stems, and the vacant, eye-like windows inverted in the dull waters of the tarn, to the rushing asunder of the walls and their submersion beneath the sullen waters, every detail is drawn to the pattern of the one sentiment. The imaginary narrator, we are told, was of a cheerful disposition by nature, but he is not proof against the gloomy surroundings; leaden depression of soul weighs upon him throughout the narrative.

In entire accord with this dreariness of spirit, with the hideous events, and with the gruesome personalities that contribute to the action is the background of the gloomy mansion, — the decaying dilapidation of the building, the somber tapestries, the encrimsoned rays of light streaming through the narrow casements, the ghostly sounds reëchoing through the deserted halls. The story is an instance of the dramatic effects that may be secured through a masterly harmonizing of all the elements that enter into narrative.

> Son cœur est un luth suspendu;
> Sitôt qu'on le touche il résonne.
> DE BÉRANGER.

DURING the whole of a dull, dark, and soundless day in the autumn of the year, when the clouds hung oppressively low in the heavens, I had been passing alone, on horseback, through a singularly dreary tract of country; and at length found myself, as the shades of evening drew on, within view of the melancholy House of Usher. I know not how it was — but, with the first glimpse of the building, a sense of insufferable gloom pervaded my spirit. I say insufferable; for the feeling was unrelieved by any of that half-pleasurable, because poetic, sentiment, with which the mind usually receives even the sternest natural images of the desolate or terrible. I looked upon the scene before me — upon the mere house, and the simple landscape features of the domain — upon the bleak walls — upon the vacant, eye-like windows — upon a few rank sedges — and upon a few white trunks of decayed trees — with an utter depression of soul which I can compare to no earthly sensation more properly than to the after-dream of the reveler upon opium — the bitter lapse into everyday life — the hideous dropping off of the veil. There was an iciness, a sinking, a sickening of the heart — an unredeemed dreariness of thought which no goading of the imagination could torture into aught of the sublime. What was it — I paused to think — what was it that so unnerved me in the contemplation of the House of Usher? It was a mystery all insoluble; nor could I grapple with the shadowy fancies that crowded upon me as I pondered. I was forced to fall back upon the unsatisfactory conclusion, that while, beyond doubt, there *are* combinations of very simple natural objects which have the power of thus affecting us, still the analysis of this power lies among considerations beyond our depth. It was possible, I reflected, that a mere different arrangement of the particulars of the scene, of the details of the picture, would be sufficient to modify, or perhaps to annihilate its capacity for sor-

rowful impression; and, acting upon this idea, I reined
my horse to the precipitous brink of a black and lurid
tarn that lay in unruffled luster by the dwelling, and
gazed down — but with a shudder even more thrilling
than before — upon the remodeled and inverted images
of the gray sedge, and the ghastly tree-stems, and the
vacant and eye-like windows.

Nevertheless, in this mansion of gloom I now proposed to myself a sojourn of some weeks. Its proprietor,
Roderick Usher, had been one of my boon companions
in boyhood; but many years had elapsed since our last
meeting. A letter, however, had lately reached me in
a distant part of the country — a letter from him —
which, in its wildly importunate nature, had admitted of
no other than the personal reply. The manuscript gave
evidence of nervous agitation. The writer spoke of acute
bodily illness — of a mental disorder which oppressed
him — and of an earnest desire to see me, as his best,
and indeed his only personal, friend, with a view of
attempting, by the cheerfulness of my society, some
alleviation of his malady. It was the manner in which
all this, and much more, was said — it was the apparent
heart that went with his request — which allowed me no
room for hesitation; and I accordingly obeyed forthwith
what I still considered a very singular summons.

Although, as boys, we had been even intimate asso-
ciates, yet I really knew little of my friend. His reserve
had been always excessive and habitual. I was aware,
however, that his very ancient family had been noted,
time out of mind, for a peculiar sensibility of temperament, displaying itself, through long ages, in many
works of exalted art, and manifested, of late, in repeated
deeds of munificent yet unobtrusive charity, as well as
in a passionate devotion to the intricacies, perhaps even

more than to the orthodox and easily recognizable beauties, of musical science. I had learned, too, the very remarkable fact, that the stem of the Usher race, all time-honored as it was, had put forth, at no period, any enduring branch; in other words, that the entire family lay in the direct line of descent, and had always, with very trifling and very temporary variation, so lain. It was this deficiency, I considered, while running over in thought the perfect keeping of the character of the premises with the accredited character of the people, and while speculating upon the possible influence which the one, in the long lapse of centuries, might have exercised upon the other — it was this deficiency, perhaps, of collateral issue, and the consequent undeviating transmission, from sire to son, of the patrimony with the name, which had, at length, so identified the two as to merge the original title of the estate in the quaint and equivocal appellation of the "House of Usher" — an appellation which seemed to include, in the minds of the peasantry who used it, both the family and the family mansion.

I have said that the sole effect of my somewhat childish experiment — that of looking down within the tarn — had been to deepen the first singular impression. There can be no doubt that the consciousness of the rapid increase of my superstition — for why should I not so term it? — served mainly to accelerate the increase itself. Such, I have long known, is the paradoxical law of all sentiments having terror as a basis. And it might have been for this reason only, that, when I again uplifted my eyes to the house itself, from its image in the pool, there grew in my mind a strange fancy — a fancy so ridiculous, indeed, that I but mention it to show the vivid force of the sensations which oppressed me. I had

so worked upon my imagination as really to believe that
about the whole mansion and domain there hung an
atmosphere peculiar to themselves and their immediate
vicinity — an atmosphere which had no affinity with
the air of heaven, but which had reeked up from the
decayed trees, and the gray wall, and the silent tarn —
a pestilent and mystic vapor, dull, sluggish, faintly discernible, and leaden-hued.

Shaking off from my spirit what *must* have been a
dream, I scanned more narrowly the real aspect of the
building. Its principal feature seemed to be that of an
excessive antiquity. The discoloration of ages had been
great. Minute fungi overspread the whole exterior,
hanging in a fine, tangled webwork from the eaves. Yet
all this was apart from any extraordinary dilapidation.
No portion of the masonry had fallen; and there appeared to be a wild inconsistency between its still perfect
adaptation of parts and the crumbling condition of the
individual stones. In this there was much that reminded
me of the specious totality of old woodwork which has
rotted for long years in some neglected vault, with no
disturbance from the breath of the external air. Beyond
this indication of extensive decay, however, the fabric
gave little token of instability. Perhaps the eye of a
scrutinizing observer might have discovered a barely
perceptible fissure, which, extending from the roof of
the building in front, made its way down the wall in a
zigzag direction, until it became lost in the sullen waters
of the tarn.

Noticing these things, I rode over a short causeway
to the house. A servant in waiting took my horse, and
I entered the Gothic archway of the hall. A valet, of
stealthy step, thence conducted me, in silence, through
many dark and intricate passages in my progress to the

studio of his master. Much that I encountered on the way contributed, I know not how, to heighten the vague sentiments of which I have already spoken. While the objects around me — while the carvings of the ceilings, the somber tapestries of the walls, the ebon blackness of the floors, and the phantasmagoric armorial trophies which rattled as I strode, were but matters to which, or to such as which, I had been accustomed from my infancy, — while I hesitated not to acknowledge how familiar was all this, — I still wondered to find how unfamiliar were the fancies which ordinary images were stirring up. On one of the staircases I met the physician of the family. His countenance, I thought, wore a mingled expression of low cunning and perplexity. He accosted me with trepidation and passed on. The valet now threw open a door and ushered me into the presence of his master.

The room in which I found myself was very large and lofty. The windows were long, narrow, and pointed, and at so vast a distance from the black oaken floor as to be altogether inaccessible from within. Feeble gleams of encrimsoned light made their way through the trellised panes, and served to render sufficiently distinct the more prominent objects around; the eye, however, struggled in vain to reach the remoter angles of the chamber, or the recesses of the vaulted and fretted ceiling. Dark draperies hung upon the walls. The general furniture was profuse, comfortless, antique, and tattered. Many books and musical instruments lay scattered about, but failed to give any vitality to the scene. I felt that I breathed an atmosphere of sorrow. An air of stern, deep, and irredeemable gloom hung over and pervaded all.

Upon my entrance, Usher arose from a sofa on which

he had been lying at full length, and greeted me with a vivacious warmth which had much in it, I at first thought, of an overdone cordiality — of the constrained effort of the *ennuyé* man of the world. A glance, however, at his countenance, convinced me of his perfect sincerity. We sat down; and for some moments, while he spoke not, I gazed upon him with a feeling half of pity, half of awe. Surely, man had never before so terribly altered, in so brief a period, as had Roderick Usher! It was with difficulty that I could bring myself to admit the identity of the wan being before me with the companion of my early boyhood. Yet the character of his face had been at all times remarkable. A cadaverousness of complexion; an eye large, liquid, and luminous beyond comparison; lips somewhat thin and very pallid, but of a surpassingly beautiful curve; a nose of a delicate Hebrew model, but with a breadth of nostril unusual in similar formations; a finely moulded chin, speaking, in its want of prominence, of a want of moral energy; hair of a more than weblike softness and tenuity; these features, with an inordinate expansion above the regions of the temple, made up altogether a countenance not easily to be forgotten. And now in the mere exaggeration of the prevailing character of these features, and of the expression they were wont to convey, lay so much of change that I doubted to whom I spoke. The now ghastly pallor of the skin, and the now miraculous luster of the eye, above all things startled and even awed me. The silken hair, too, had been suffered to grow all unheeded, and as, in its wild gossamer texture, it floated rather than fell about the face, I could not, even with effort, connect its Arabesque expression with any idea of simple humanity.

In the manner of my friend I was at once struck with an incoherence — an inconsistency; and I soon found this to arise from a series of feeble and futile struggles to overcome an habitual trepidancy — an excessive nervous agitation. For something of this nature I had indeed, been prepared, no less by his letter than by reminiscences of certain boyish traits, and by conclusions deduced from his peculiar physical conformation and temperament. His action was alternately vivacious and sullen. His voice varied rapidly from a tremendous indecision (when the animal spirits seemed utterly in abeyance) to that species of energetic concision — that abrupt, weighty, unhurried, and hollow-sounding enunciation — that leaden, self-balanced, and perfectly modulated guttural utterance, which may be observed in the lost drunkard, or the irreclaimable eater of opium, during the periods of his most intense excitement.

It was thus that he spoke of the object of my visit, of his earnest desire to see me, and of the solace he expected me to afford him. He entered, at some length, into what he conceived to be the nature of his malady. It was, he said, a constitutional and a family evil, and one for which he despaired to find a remedy — a mere nervous affection, he immediately added, which would undoubtedly soon pass off. It displayed itself in a host of unnatural sensations. Some of these, as he detailed them, interested and bewildered me; although, perhaps, the terms, and the general manner of the narration had their weight. He suffered much from a morbid acuteness of the senses; the most insipid food was alone endurable; he could wear only garments of certain texture; the odors of all flowers were oppressive; his eyes were tortured by even a faint light; and there were but peculiar sounds, and these from stringed instruments, which did not inspire him with horror.

To an anomalous species of terror I found him a

bounden slave. "I shall perish," said he, — "I *must* perish in this deplorable folly. Thus, thus, and not otherwise, shall I be lost. I dread the events of the future, not in themselves, but in their results. I shudder at the thought of any, even the most trivial, incident, which may operate upon this intolerable agitation of soul. I have, indeed, no abhorrence of danger, except in its absolute effect — in terror. In this unnerved — in this pitiable condition — I feel that the period will sooner or later arrive when I must abandon life and reason together, in some struggle with the grim phantasm, FEAR."

I learned, moreover, at intervals, and through broken and equivocal hints, another singular feature of his mental condition. He was enchained by certain superstitious impressions in regard to the dwelling which he tenanted, and whence, for many years, he had never ventured forth — in regard to an influence whose supposititious force was conveyed in terms too shadowy here to be restated — an influence which some peculiarities in the mere form and substance of his family mansion had, by dint of long sufferance, he said, obtained over his spirit — an effect which the physique of the gray walls and turrets, and of the dim tarn into which they all looked down, had at length brought about upon the morale of his existence.

He admitted, however, although with hesitation, that much of the peculiar gloom which thus afflicted him could be traced to a more natural and far more palpable origin — to the severe and long-continued illness — indeed, to the evidently approaching dissolution — of a tenderly beloved sister — his sole companion for long years — his last and only relative on earth. "Her decease," he said, with a bitterness which I can never forget, "would leave him (him the hopeless and the frail) the last of the ancient race of the Ushers." While he spoke, the Lady Madeline (for so was she called) passed slowly through a remote portion of the apartment, and, without having noticed my presence, disappeared. I regarded her with an utter astonishment not unmingled with dread — and yet I found it impossible to account for such feelings. A sensation of stupor oppressed me, as my eyes followed her retreating steps. When a door at length closed upon her, my glance sought instinctively and eagerly the countenance of the brother — but he had buried his face in his hands, and I could only perceive that a far more than ordinary wanness had overspread the emaciated fingers through which trickled many passionate tears.

The disease of the Lady Madeline had long baffled the skill of her physicians. A settled apathy, a gradual wasting away of the person, and frequent although transient affections of a partially cataleptical character, were the unusual diagnosis. Hitherto she had steadily borne up against the pressure of her malady, and had not betaken herself finally to bed; but, on the closing in of the evening of my arrival at the house, she succumbed (as her brother told me at night with inexpressible agitation) to the prostrating power of the destroyer; and I learned that the glimpse I had obtained of her person would thus probably be the last I should obtain — that the lady, at least while living, would be seen by me no more.

For several days ensuing, her name was unmentioned by either Usher or myself; and during this period I was busied in earnest endeavors to alleviate the melancholy of my friend. We painted and read together; or I listened, as if in a dream, to the wild improvisations of his speaking guitar. And thus, as a closer and still closer intimacy admitted me more unreservedly into the recesses of his spirit, the more bitterly did I perceive the futility of all attempt at cheering a mind from which darkness, as if an inherent positive quality, poured forth upon all objects of the moral and physical universe, in one unceasing radiation of gloom.

I shall ever bear about me a memory of the many solemn hours I thus spent alone with the master of the House of Usher. Yet I should fail in any attempt to convey an idea of the exact character of the studies, or of the occupations, in which he involved me, or led me the way. An excited and highly distempered ideality threw a sulphureous luster over all. His long improvised dirges will ring forever in my ears. Among other things, I hold painfully in mind a certain singular perversion and amplification of the wild air of the last waltz of Von Weber. From the paintings over which his elaborate fancy brooded, and which grew, touch by touch, into vaguenesses at which I shuddered the more thrillingly, because I shuddered knowing not why — from these paintings (vivid as their images now are before me) I would in vain endeavor to educe more than a small portion which should lie within the compass of merely written words. By the utter simplicity, by the nakedness of his designs, he arrested and overawed attention. If ever mortal painted an idea, that mortal was Roderick Usher. For me, at least, — in the circumstances then surrounding me, — there arose out of the pure abstractions which the hypochondriac contrived to throw upon his canvas, an intensity of intolerable awe, no shadow of which felt I ever yet in the contemplation of the certainly glowing yet too concrete reveries of Fuseli.

One of the phantasmagoric conceptions of my friend, partaking not so rigidly of the spirit of abstraction, may be shadowed forth, although feebly, in words. A small picture presented the interior of an immensely long and rectangular vault or tunnel, with low walls, smooth, white, and without interruption or device. Certain accessory points of the design served well to convey the idea that this excavation lay at an exceeding depth below the surface of the earth. No outlet was observed in any portion of its vast extent, and no torch, or other artificial source of light, was discernible; yet a flood of intense rays rolled throughout, and bathed the whole in a ghastly and inappropriate splendor.

I have just spoken of that morbid condition of the auditory nerve which rendered all music intolerable to the sufferer, with the exception of certain effects of stringed instruments. It was, perhaps, the narrow limits to which he thus confined himself upon the guitar, which gave birth, in great measure, to the fantastic character of his performances. But the fervid facility of his impromptus could not be so accounted for. They must have been, and were, in the notes, as well as in the words, of his wild fantasias (for he not unfrequently accompanied himself with rhymed verbal improvisations), the result of that intense mental collectedness and concentration to which I have previously alluded as observable only in particular moments of the highest artificial excitement. The words of one of these rhapsodies I have easily remembered. I was, perhaps, the more forcibly impressed with it, as he gave it, because, in the under or mystic current of its meaning, I fancied that I perceived, and for the first time, a full consciousness on the part of Usher, of the tottering of his lofty reason upon her throne. The verses, which were entitled "The Haunted Palace," ran very nearly, if not accurately, thus: —

I

In the greenest of our valleys,
  By good angels tenanted,
Once a fair and stately palace —
  Radiant palace — reared its head.
In the monarch Thought's dominion —
  It stood there!
Never seraph spread a pinion
  Over fabric half so fair.

II

Banners yellow, glorious, golden,
  On its roof did float and flow
(This — all this — was in the olden
  Time long ago);
And every gentle air that dallied,
  In that sweet day,
Along the ramparts plumed and pallid,
  A winged odor went away.

III

Wanderers in that happy valley
  Through two luminous windows saw
Spirits moving musically
  To a lute's well-tunèd law,
Round about a throne, where sitting
  (Porphyrogene!)
In state his glory well befitting,
  The ruler of the realm was seen.

IV

And all with pearl and ruby glowing
  Was the fair palace door,
Through which came flowing, flowing, flowing
  And sparkling evermore,
A troop of Echoes, whose sweet duty
  Was but to sing,
In voices of surpassing beauty,
  The wit and wisdom of their king.

V

But evil things, in robes of sorrow,
  Assailed the monarch's high estate.
(Ah, let us mourn, for never morrow
  Shall dawn upon him, desolate!)

And, round about his home, the glory
  That blushed and bloomed
Is but a dim-remembered story
  Of the old time entombed.

VI

And travelers now within that valley,
  Through the red-litten windows, see
Vast forms that move fantastically
  To a discordant melody;
While, like a rapid ghastly river,
  Through the pale door,
A hideous throng rush out for ever,
  And laugh — but smile no more.

I well remember that suggestions arising from this ballad led us into a train of thought wherein there became manifest an opinion of Usher's, which I mention not so much on account of its novelty (for other men have thought thus), as on account of the pertinacity with which he maintained it. This opinion, in its general form, was that of the sentience of all vegetable things. But, in his disordered fancy, the idea had assumed a more daring character, and trespassed, under certain conditions, upon the kingdom of inorganization. I lack words to express the full extent, or the earnest *abandon* of his persuasion. The belief, however, was connected (as I have previously hinted) with the gray stones of the home of his forefathers. The conditions of the sentience had been here, he imagined, fulfilled in the method of collocation of these stones — in the order of their arrangement, as well as in that of the many fungi which overspread them, and of the decayed trees which stood around — above all, in the long undisturbed endurance of this arrangement, and in its reduplication in the still waters of the tarn. Its evidence — the evidence of the sentience — was to be seen, he said (and I here

started as he spoke), in the gradual yet certain condensation of an atmosphere of their own about the waters
and the walls. The result was discoverable, he added, in
that silent, yet importunate and terrible influence which
for centuries had moulded the destinies of his family,
and which made *him* what I now saw him — what he
was. Such opinions need no comment, and I will make
none.

Our books — the books which, for years, had formed
no small portion of the mental existence of the invalid
— were, as might be supposed, in strict keeping with
this character of phantasm. We pored together over
such works as the *Ververt et Chartreuse* of Gresset; the
Belphegor of Machiavelli: the *Heaven* and *Hell* of Swe-
denborg; the *Subterranean Voyage of Nicholas Klimm*,
by Holberg; the *Chiromancy of Robert Flud*, of Jean D'In-
daginé, and of De la Chambre; the *Journey into the Blue
Distance* of Tieck; and the *City of the Sun* of Campanella.
One favorite volume was a small octavo edition of the
Directorium Inquisitorium, by the Dominican Eymeric
de Gironne; and there were passages in Pomponius Mela,
about the old African satyrs and Œgipans, over which
Usher would sit dreaming for hours. His chief delight,
however, was found in the perusal of an exceedingly
rare and curious book in quarto Gothic — the manual
of a forgotten church — the *Vigiliæ Mortuorum secun-
dum Chorum Ecclesiæ Maguntinæ.*

I could not help thinking of the wild ritual of this
work, and of its probable influence upon the hypochondriac, when, one evening, having informed me abruptly
that the Lady Madeline was no more, he stated his intention of preserving her corpse for a fortnight (previously to its final interment), in one of the numerous
vaults within the main walls of the building. The worldly

reason, however, assigned for this singular proceeding, was one which I did not feel at liberty to dispute. The brother had been led to his resolution (so he told me) by consideration of the unusual character of the malady of the deceased, of certain obtrusive and eager inquiries on the part of her medical men, and of the remote and exposed situation of the burial-ground of the family. I will not deny that when I called to mind the sinister countenance of the person whom I met upon the staircase, on the day of my arrival at the house, I had no desire to oppose what I regarded as at best but a harmless, and by no means an unnatural, precaution.

At the request of Usher, I personally aided him in the arrangements for the temporary entombment. The body having been encoffined, we two alone bore it to its rest. The vault in which we placed it (and which had been so long unopened that our torches, half smothered in its oppressive atmosphere, gave us little opportunity for investigation) was small, damp, and entirely without means of admission for light; lying, at great depth, immediately beneath that portion of the building in which was my own sleeping-apartment. It had been used, apparently, in remote feudal times, for the worst purposes of a donjon-keep, and, in latter days, as a place of deposit for powder, or some other highly combustible substance, as a portion of its floor, and the whole interior of a long archway through which we reached it, were carefully sheathed with copper. The door, of massive iron, had been, also, similarly protected. Its immense weight caused an unusually sharp grating sound, as it moved upon its hinges.

Having deposited our mournful burden upon trestles within this region of horror, we partially turned aside the yet unscrewed lid of the coffin, and looked upon the face of the tenant. A striking similitude between the brother and sister now first arrested my attention; and Usher, divining, perhaps, my thoughts, murmured out some few words from which I learned that the deceased and himself had been twins, and that sympathies of a scarcely intelligible nature had always existed between them. Our glances, however, rested not long upon the dead — for we could not regard her unawed. The disease which had thus entombed the lady in the maturity of youth, had left, as usual in all maladies of a strictly cataleptical character, the mockery of a faint blush upon the bosom and the face, and that suspiciously lingering smile upon the lip which is so terrible in death. We replaced and screwed down the lid, and, having secured the door of iron, made our way, with toil, into the scarcely less gloomy apartments of the upper portion of the house.

And now, some days of bitter grief having elapsed, an observable change came over the features of the mental disorder of my friend. His ordinary manner had vanished. His ordinary occupations were neglected or forgotten. He roamed from chamber to chamber with hurried, unequal, and objectless step. The pallor of his countenance had assumed, if possible, a more ghastly hue — but the luminousness of his eye had utterly gone out. The more occasional huskiness of his tone was heard no more; and a tremulous quaver, as if of extreme terror, habitually characterized his utterance. There were times, indeed, when I thought his unceasingly agitated mind was laboring with some oppressive secret, to divulge which he struggled for the necessary courage. At times, again, I was obliged to resolve all into the mere inexplicable vagaries of madness, for I beheld him gazing upon vacancy for long hours, in an attitude of the profoundest attention, as if listening to some imaginary sound. It was no wonder that his condition terrified — that it infected me. I felt creeping upon me, by slow yet certain degrees, the wild influences of his own fantastic yet impressive superstitions.

It was, especially, upon retiring to bed late in the night of the seventh or eighth day after the placing of the Lady Madeline within the donjon, that I experienced the full power of such feelings. Sleep came not near my couch — while the hours waned and waned away. I struggled to reason off the nervousness which had dominion over me. I endeavored to believe that much if not all of what I felt was due to the bewildering influence of the gloomy furniture of the room — of the dark and tattered draperies, which, tortured into motion by the breath of a rising tempest, swayed fitfully to and fro upon the walls, and rustled uneasily about the decorations of the bed. But my efforts were fruitless. An irrepressible tremor gradually pervaded my frame; and, at length, there sat upon my very heart an incubus of utterly causeless alarm. Shaking this off with a gasp and a struggle, I uplifted myself upon the pillows, and, peering earnestly within the intense darkness of the chamber, hearkened — I know not why, except that an instinctive spirit prompted me — to certain low and indefinite sounds which came, through the pauses of the storm, at long intervals, I knew not whence. Overpowered by an intense sentiment of horror, unaccountable yet unendurable, I threw on my clothes with haste (for I felt that I should sleep no more during the night), and endeavored to arouse myself from the pitiable condition into which I had fallen, by pacing rapidly to and fro through the apartment.

I had taken but few turns in this manner, when a light

step on an adjoining staircase arrested my attention. I presently recognized it as that of Usher. In an instant afterward he rapped, with a gentle touch, at my door, and entered, bearing a lamp. His countenance was, as usual, cadaverously wan — but, moreover, there was a species of mad hilarity in his eyes — an evidently restrained hysteria in his whole demeanor. His air appalled me — but anything was preferable to the solitude which I had so long endured, and I even welcomed his presence as a relief.

"And you have not seen it?" he said abruptly, after having stared about him for some moments in silence — "you have not, then, seen it? — but, stay! you shall." Thus speaking, and having carefully shaded his lamp, he hurried to one of the casements, and threw it freely open to the storm.

The impetuous fury of the entering gust nearly lifted us from our feet. It was, indeed, a tempestuous yet sternly beautiful night, and one wildly singular in its terror and its beauty. A whirlwind had apparently collected its force in our vicinity; for there were frequent and violent alterations in the direction of the wind; and the exceeding density of the clouds (which hung so low as to press upon the turrets of the house) did not prevent our perceiving the lifelike velocity with which they flew careering from all points against each other, without passing away into the distance. I say that even their exceeding density did not prevent our perceiving this — yet we had no glimpse of the moon or stars — nor was there any flashing forth of the lightning. But the under surfaces of the huge masses of agitated vapor, as well as all terrestrial objects immediately around us, were glowing in the unnatural light of a faintly luminous and distinctly visible gaseous exhalation which hung about and enshrouded the mansion.

"You must not — you shall not behold this!" said I, shudderingly, to Usher, as I led him, with a gentle violence, from the window to a seat. "These appearances, which bewilder you, are merely electrical phenomena not uncommon — or it may be that they have their ghastly origin in the rank miasma of the tarn. Let us close this casement — the air is chilling and dangerous to your frame. Here is one of your favorite romances. I will read, and you shall listen — and so we will pass away this terrible night together."

The antique volume which I had taken up was the *Mad Trist* of Sir Launcelot Canning; but I had called it a favorite of Usher's more in sad jest than in earnest; for, in truth, there is little in its uncouth and unimaginative prolixity which could have had interest for the lofty and spiritual ideality of my friend. It was, however, the only book immediately at hand; and I indulged a vague hope that the excitement which now agitated the hypochondriac might find relief (for the history of mental disorder is full of similar anomalies) even in the extremeness of the folly which I should read. Could I have judged, indeed, by the wild, overstrained air of vivacity with which he hearkened, or apparently hearkened, to the words of the tale, I might well have congratulated myself upon the success of my design.

I had arrived at that well-known portion of the story where Ethelred, the hero of the Trist, having sought in vain for peaceable admission into the dwelling of the hermit, proceeds to make good an entrance by force. Here, it will be remembered, the words of the narrative run thus: —

"And Ethelred, who was by nature of a doughty heart, and who was now mighty withal, on account of the powerfulness of the wine which he had drunken,

waited no longer to hold parley with the hermit, who, in
sooth, was of an obstinate and maliceful turn, but, feeling the rain upon his shoulders, and fearing the rising of
the tempest, uplifted his mace outright, and, with blows,
made quickly room in the plankings of the door for his
gauntleted hand; and now pulling therewith sturdily, he
so cracked, and ripped, and tore all asunder, that the
noise of the dry and hollow-sounding wood alarummed
and reverberated throughout the forest."

At the termination of this sentence I started, and for
a moment paused; for it appeared to me (although I at
once concluded that my excited fancy had deceived me)
— it appeared to me that, from some very remote portion of the mansion, there came, indistinctly, to my ears,
what might have been, in its exact similarity of character, the echo (but a stifled and dull one certainly) of the
very cracking and ripping sound which Sir Launcelot
had so particularly described. It was, beyond doubt,
the coincidence alone which had arrested my attention;
for, amid the rattling of the sashes of the casements, and
the ordinary commingled noises of the still increasing
storm, the sound, in itself, had nothing, surely, which
should have interested or disturbed me. I continued the
story: —

"But the good champion Ethelred, now entering
within the door, was sore enraged and amazed to perceive no signal of the maliceful hermit; but, in the stead
thereof, a dragon of a scaly and prodigious demeanour,
and of a fiery tongue, which sate in guard before a palace of gold, with a floor of silver; and upon the wall
there hung a shield of shining brass with this legend
enwritten: —

'Who entereth herein, a conqueror hath bin;
Who slayeth the dragon, the shield he shall win.'

And Ethelred uplifted his mace, and struck upon the head of the dragon, which fell before him, and gave up his pesty breath, with a shriek so horrid and harsh, and withal so piercing, that Ethelred had fain to close his ears with his hands against the dreadful noise of it, the like whereof was never before heard."

Here again I paused abruptly, and now with a feeling of wild amazement — for there could be no doubt whatever that, in this instance, I did actually hear (although from what direction it proceeded I found it impossible to say) a low and apparently distant, but harsh, protracted, and most unusual screaming or grating sound — the exact counterpart of what my fancy had already conjured up for the dragon's unnatural shriek as described by the romancer.

Oppressed as I certainly was, upon the occurrence of this second and most extraordinary coincidence, by a thousand conflicting sensations, in which wonder and extreme terror were predominant, I still retained sufficient presence of mind to avoid exciting, by any observation, the sensitive nervousness of my companion. I was by no means certain that he had noticed the sound in question; although, assuredly, a strange alteration had, during the last few minutes, taken place in his demeanor. From a position fronting my own, he had gradually brought round his chair, so as to sit with his face to the door of the chamber; and thus I could but partially perceive his features, although I saw that his lips trembled as if he were murmuring inaudibly. His head had dropped upon his breast — yet I knew that he was not asleep, from the wide and rigid opening of the eye as I caught a glance of it in profile. The motion of his body, too, was at variance with this idea — for he rocked from side to side with a gentle yet constant and uniform sway. Having rapidly taken notice of all this, I resumed the narrative of Sir Launcelot, which thus proceeded: —

"And now, the champion, having escaped from the terrible fury of the dragon, bethinking himself of the brazen shield, and of the breaking up of the enchantment which was upon it, removed the carcass from out of the way before him, and approached valorously over the silver pavement of the castle to where the shield was upon the wall; which in sooth tarried not for his full coming, but fell down at his feet upon the silver floor, with a mighty great and terrible ringing sound."

No sooner had these syllables passed my lips, than — as if a shield of brass had, indeed, at the moment, fallen heavily upon a floor of silver — I became aware of a distinct, hollow, metallic, and clangorous, yet apparently muffled, reverberation. Completely unnerved, I leaped to my feet; but the measured, rocking movement of Usher was undisturbed. I rushed to the chair in which he sat. His eyes were bent fixedly before him, and throughout his whole countenance there reigned a stony rigidity. But, as I placed my hand upon his shoulder, there came a strong shudder over his whole person; a sickly smile quivered on his lips; and I saw that he spoke in a low, hurried, and gibbering murmur, as if unconscious of my presence. Bending closely over him, I at length drank in the hideous import of his words.

"Not hear it?—yes, I hear it, and *have* heard it. Long —long—long— many minutes, many hours, many days, have I heard it — yet I dared not — oh, pity me, miserable wretch that I am!—I dared not — I *dared* not speak! *We have put her living in the tomb!* Said I not that my senses were acute? I *now* tell you that I heard her first feeble movements in the hollow coffin. I heard them — many, many days ago — yet I dared not — *I dared not speak!* And now, — to-night — Ethelred — ha! ha! — the breaking of the hermit's door, and the death-cry of the dragon, and the clangor of the shield! — say, rather, the rending of her coffin, and the grating of the iron hinges of her prison, and her struggles within the coppered archway of the vault! Oh, whither shall I fly? Will she not be here anon? Is she not hurrying to upbraid me for my haste? Have I not heard her footstep on the stair? Do I not distinguish that heavy and horrible beating of her heart? Madman!" — here he sprang furiously to his feet, and shrieked out his syllables, as if in the effort he were giving up his soul — "*Madman! I tell you that she now stands without the door!*"

As if in the superhuman energy of his utterance there had been found the potency of a spell — the huge antique panels to which the speaker pointed threw slowly back, upon the instant, their ponderous and ebony jaws. It was the work of the rushing gust — but then without those doors there *did* stand the lofty and enshrouded figure of the Lady Madeline of Usher. There was blood upon her white robes, and the evidence of some bitter struggle upon every portion of her emaciated frame. For a moment she remained trembling and reeling to and fro upon the threshold — then, with a low, moaning cry, fell heavily inward upon the person of her brother, and in her violent and now final death-agonies, bore him to the floor a corpse, and a victim to the terrors he had anticipated.

From that chamber, and from that mansion, I fled aghast. The storm was still abroad in all its wrath as I found myself crossing the old causeway. Suddenly there shot along the path a wild light, and I turned to see whence a gleam so unusual could have issued; for the vast house and its shadows were alone behind me. The radiance was that of the full, setting, and blood-red moon, which now shone vividly through that once barely discernible fissure, of which I have before spoken as extending from the roof of the building, in a zigzag direction, to the base. While I gazed, this fissure rapidly widened — there came a fierce breath of the whirlwind — the entire orb of the satellite burst at once upon my sight — my brain reeled as I saw the mighty walls rushing asunder — there was a long, tumultuous shouting sound like a voice of a thousand waters — and the deep and dank tarn at my feet closed sullenly and silently over the fragments of the "House of Usher."

CHARACTER

FRANCISCO PIZARRO [1]

BY WILLIAM H. PRESCOTT

THIS selection is a good example of various elements that enter into characterization. In the delineation of Pizarro we have the external portraiture of the man — his dress, stature, and other similar personal details. We also have a direct exposition of the traits of his character — his avarice and ambition, his perfidy and personal courage. The exposition of these various qualities is attended by the citation of many illustrative examples, presenting data from which the reader may more effectively draw his conclusions. Pizarro's invariable custom of saying "No" to every applicant for favor, his simplicity of dress on public occasions, his perfidy in the case of Atahuallpa — these and other concrete cases alluded to in the passage and developed at greater length elsewhere in the history, constitute indirect characterization, although the selection in general makes use of the direct method.

One of the most noteworthy qualities of the selection is the subjective attitude of the author, whose own individuality is apparent throughout. For instance, in the paragraph concerning the perfidy of Pizarro, we read: "Yet nothing is more opposed to sound policy. The act of perfidy fully established becomes the ruin of its author. The man who relinquishes confidence in his good faith gives up the best basis for future operations. Who will knowingly build on a quicksand?" This is, of course, a mere intercalation of the narrator's attitude to life and to the conduct of his hero. The same tendency is found at the close in the words: "Who does not shudder at the thought of what his own fate might have been, trained in such a school? The amount of crime does not necessarily show the criminality of the agent. History, indeed, is concerned with the former, that it may be recorded as a warning to

[1] From chapter v, book iv, of *The Conquest of Peru*. By permission of J. B. Lippincott Company.

mankind; but it is He alone who knoweth the heart, the strength of the temptation, and the means of resisting it, that can determine the measure of the guilt." This subjective attitude marks a distinct difference between the method of earlier historians and those of the later so-called "scientific" school, who so polarize their facts as to make them wholly impersonal: their function is to search out the material and present it, not to moralize about it and color it with the various shades of personal opinion. The same general distinction appears in fiction. Maupassant, for instance, as may be seen in *Happiness*, sets forth his characters without personal comment: his approval or disapproval forms no part of the exposition. Thackeray, on the other hand, buttonholes the reader, genially discussing with him the various personages, and gives to the whole characterization an atmosphere of familiar intercourse between creator and reader.

PIZARRO was, probably, not far from sixty-five years of age at the time of his death; though this, it must be added, is but loose conjecture, since there exists no authentic record of the date of his birth. He was never married; but by an Indian princess of the Inca blood, daughter of the Atahuallpa and granddaughter of the great Huayna Capac, he had two children, a son and a daughter. Both survived him; but the son did not live to manhood. Their mother, after Pizarro's death, wedded a Spanish cavalier, named Ampuero, and removed with him to Spain. Her daughter Francisca accompanied her, and was there subsequently married to her uncle Hernando Pizarro, then a prisoner in the Mota del Medina. Neither the title nor estates of the Marquess Francisco descended to his illegitimate offspring. But in the third generation, in the reign of Philip IV, the title was revived in favor of Don Juan Hernando Pizarro, who, out of gratitude for the services of his ancestor, was created Marquess of the Conquest (Marques de la Conquista), with a liberal pension from Government. His descendants bearing the same title of nobility are still to be found, it is said, at Truxillo, in the ancient province of Estremadura, the original birthplace of the Pizarros.

Pizarro's person has been already described. He was tall in stature, well-proportioned, and with a countenance not unpleasing. Bred in camps, with nothing of the polish of a court, he had a soldier-like bearing, and the air of one accustomed to command. But though not polished, there was no embarrassment or rusticity in his address, which, where it served his purpose, could be plausible and even insinuating. The proof of it is the favorable impression made by him, on presenting himself, after his second expedition — stranger as he was to all its forms and usages — at the punctilious court of Castile.

Unlike many of his countrymen, he had no passion for ostentatious dress, which he regarded as an imcumbrance. The costume which he most affected on public occasions was a black coat, with a white hat, and shoes of the same color; the last, it is said, being in imitation of the Great Captain, whose character he had early learned to admire in Italy, but to which his own, certainly, bore very faint resemblance.

He was temperate in eating, drank sparingly, and usually rose an hour before dawn. He was punctual in attendance to business, and shrank from no toil. He had, indeed, great powers of patient endurance. Like most of his nation, he was fond of play, and cared little for the quality of those with whom he played; though, when his antagonist could not afford to lose, he would allow himself, it is said, to be the loser, a mode of conferring an obligation much commended by a Castilian writer for its delicacy.

Though avaricious, it was in order to spend, and not to hoard. His ample treasures, more ample than those, probably, that ever before fell to the lot of an adventurer, were mostly dissipated in his enterprises, his architectural works and schemes of public improvement, which, in a country where gold and silver might be said to have lost their value from their abundance, absorbed an incredible amount of money. While he regarded the whole country, in a manner, as his own, and distributed it freely among his captains, it is certain that the princely grant of a territory with twenty thousand vassals, made to him by the Crown, was never carried into effect; nor did his heirs ever reap the benefit of it.

To a man possessed of the active energies of Pizarro, sloth was the greatest evil. The excitement of play was in a manner necessary to a spirit accustomed to the habitual stimulants of war and adventure. His uneducated mind had no relish for more refined, intellectual recreation. The deserted foundling had neither been taught to read nor write. This has been disputed by some, but it is attested by unexceptionable authorities. Mentesinos says, indeed, that Pizarro, on his first voyage, tried to learn to read; but the impatience of his temper prevented it, and he contented himself with learning to sign his name. But Montesinos was not a contemporary historian. Pedro Pizarro, his companion in arms, expressly tells us he could neither read nor write; and Zarate, another contemporary, well acquainted with the Conquerors, confirms this statement, and adds, that Pizarro could not so much as sign his name. This was done by his secretary — Picado, in his later years — while the governor merely made the customary rubrica or flourish at the sides of his name. This is the case with the instruments I have examined, in which his signature, written probably by his secretary, or his title of Marques, in later life substituted for his name, is garnished with a flourish at the ends, executed in as bungling a manner as if done by the hand of a ploughman. Yet we must not estimate this deficiency as we should in this period of general illumination — general, at least, in our own fortunate country. Reading and writing, so universal now, in the beginning of the sixteenth century might be regarded in the light of accomplishments; and all who have occasion to consult the autograph memorials of that time will find the execution of them, even by persons of the highest rank, too often such as would do little credit to a schoolboy of the present day.

Though bold in action and not easily turned from his purpose, Pizarro was slow in arriving at a decision. This gave him an appearance of irresolution foreign to his character. Perhaps the consciousness of this led him to adopt the custom of saying "No," at first, to applicants for favor; and afterwards, at leisure, to revise his judgment, and grant what seemed to him expedient. He took the opposite course from his comrade Almagro, who, it was observed, generally said "Yes," but too often failed to keep his promise. This was characteristic of the careless and easy nature of the latter, governed by impulse rather than principle.

It is hardly necessary to speak of the courage of a man pledged to such a career as that of Pizarro. Courage, indeed, was a cheap quality among the Spanish adventurers, for danger was their element. But he possessed something higher than mere animal courage, in that constancy of purpose which was rooted too deeply in his nature to be shaken by the wildest storms of fortune. It was this inflexible constancy which formed the key to his character, and constituted the secret of his success. A remarkable evidence of it was given in his first expedition among the mangroves and dreary marshes of Choco. He saw his followers pining around him under the blighting malaria, wasting before an invisible enemy, and unable to strike a stroke in their own defense. Yet his spirit did not yield, nor did he falter in his enterprise.

There is something oppressive to the imagination in this war against nature. In the struggle of man against man, the spirits are raised by a contest conducted on equal terms; but in a war with the elements, we feel that, however bravely we may contend, we can have no power to control. Nor are we cheered on by the prospect of glory in such a contest; for, in the capricious estimate of human glory, the silent endurance of privations, however painful, is little, in comparison with the ostentatious trophies of victory. The laurel of the hero — alas for humanity that it should be so! — grows best on the battle-field.

This inflexible spirit of Pizarro was shown still more strongly, when, in the little island of Gallo, he drew the line on the sand, which was to separate him and his handful of followers from their country and from civilized man. He trusted that his own constancy would give strength to the feeble, and rally brave hearts around him for the prosecution of his enterprise. He looked with confidence to the future, and he did not miscalculate. This was heroic, and wanted only a nobler motive for its object to constitute the true moral sublime.

Yet the same feature in his character was displayed in a manner scarcely less remarkable, when, landing on the coast, and ascertaining the real strength and civilization of the Incas, he persisted in marching into the in-

terior at the head of a force of less than two hundred
men. In this he undoubtedly proposed to himself the
example of Cortes, so contagious to the adventurous
spirits of that day, and especially to Pizarro, engaged,
as he was, in a similar enterprise. Yet the hazard assumed by Pizarro was far greater than that of the Conqueror of Mexico, whose force was nearly three times
as large, while the terrors of the Inca name — however
justified by the result — were as widely spread as those
of the Aztecs.

It was doubtless in imitation of the same capitivating
model that Pizarro planned the seizure of Atahuallpa.
But the situations of the two Spanish captains were as
dissimilar as the manner in which their acts of violence
were conducted. The wanton massacre of the Peruvians
resembled that perpetrated by Alvarado in Mexico, and
might have been attended with consequences as disastrous, if the Peruvian character had been as fierce as
that of the Aztecs. But the blow which roused the latter
to madness broke the tamer spirits of the Peruvians. It
was a bold stroke which left so much to chance that it
scarcely merits the name of policy.

When Pizarro landed in the country, he found it dis-
tracted by a contest for the crown. It would seem to
have been for his interest to play off one party against
the other, throwing his own weight into the scale that
suited him. Instead of this, he resorted to an act of
audacious violence which crushed them both at a blow.
His subsequent career afforded no scope for the profound policy displayed by Cortes, when he gathered
conflicting nations under his banner, and directed them
against a common foe. Still less did he have the opportunity of displaying the tactics and admirable strat-
egy of his rival. Cortes conducted his military opera-

tions on the scientific principles of a great captain at the head of a powerful host. Pizarro appears only as an adventurer, a fortunate knight-errant. By one bold stroke he broke the spell which had so long held the land under the dominion of the Incas. The spell was broken, and the airy fabric of their empire, built on the superstition of ages, vanished at a touch. This was good fortune, rather than the result of policy.

Pizarro was eminently perfidious. Yet nothing is more opposed to sound policy. One act of perfidy fully established becomes the ruin of its author. The man who relinquishes confidence in his good faith gives up the best basis for future operations. Who will knowingly build on a quicksand? By his perfidious treatment of Almagro, Pizarro alienated the minds of the Spaniards. By his perfidious treatment of Atahuallpa, and subsequently of the Inca Manco, he disgusted the Peruvians. The name of Pizarro became a by-word for perfidy. Almagro took his revenge in a civil war; Manco in an insurrection which nearly cost Pizarro his dominion. The civil war terminated in a conspiracy which cost him his life. Such were the fruits of his policy. Pizarro may be regarded as a cunning man; but not, as he has been often eulogized by his countrymen, as a politic one.

When Pizarro obtained possession of Cuzco, he found a country well advanced in the arts of civilization: institutions under which the people lived in tranquillity and personal safety; the mountains and the uplands whitened with flocks; the valleys teeming with the fruits of a scientific husbandry; the granaries and warehouses filled to overflowing; the whole land rejoicing in its abundance; and the character of the nation, softened under the influence of the mildest and most innocent form of superstition, well prepared for the reception of a higher and a Christian civilization. But, far from introducing this, Pizarro delivered up the conquered races to his brutal soldiery; the sacred cloisters were abandoned to their lust; the towns and villages were given up to pillage; the wretched natives were parceled out like slaves, to toil for their conquerors in the mines; the flocks were scattered, and wantonly destroyed; the granaries were dissipated; the beautiful contrivances for the more perfect culture of the soil were suffered to fall into decay; the paradise was converted into a desert. Instead of profiting by the ancient forms of civilization, Pizarro preferred to efface every vestige of them from the land, and on their ruin to erect the institutions of his own country. Yet these institutions did little for the poor Indian, held in iron bondage. It was little to him that the shores of the Pacific were studded with rising communities and cities, the marts of a flourishing commerce. He had no share in the goodly heritage. He was an alien in the land of his fathers.

The religion of the Peruvian, which directed him to the worship of that glorious luminary which is the best representative of the might and beneficence of the Creator, is perhaps the purest form of superstition that has existed among men. Yet it was much, that, under the new order of things, and through the benevolent zeal of the missionaries, some glimmerings of a nobler faith were permitted to dawn on his darkened soul. Pizarro, himself, cannot be charged with manifesting any overweening solicitude for the propagation of the Faith. He was no bigot, like Cortes. Bigotry is the perversion of the religious principle; but the principle itself was wanting in Pizarro. The conversion of the heathen was a predominant motive with Cortes in his expedition. It was not a vain boast. He would have sacrificed his life for it at any time; and more than once, by his indiscreet zeal, he actually did place his life and the success of his enterprise in jeopardy. It was his great purpose to purify the land from the brutish abominations of the Aztecs, by substituting the religion of Jesus. This gave to his expedition the character of a crusade. It furnished the best apology of the Conquest, and does more than all other considerations towards enlisting our sympathies on the side of the Conquerors.

But Pizarro's ruling motives, so far as they can be scanned by human judgment, were avarice and ambition. The good missionaries, indeed, followed in his train to scatter the seeds of spiritual truth, and the Spanish Government, as usual, directed its beneficent legislation to the conversion of the natives. But the moving power with Pizarro and his followers was the lust of gold. This was the real stimulus to their toil, the price of perfidy, the true guerdon of their victories. This gave a base and mercenary character to their enterprise; and, when we contrast the ferocious cupidity of the Conquerors with the mild and inoffensive manners of the conquered, our sympathies, the sympathies even of the Spaniard, are necessarily thrown into the scale of the Indian.

But as no picture is without its lights, we must not, in justice to Pizarro, dwell exclusively on the darker features of his portrait. There was no one of her sons to whom Spain was under larger obligations for extent of empire; for his hand won for her the richest of the Indian jewels that once sparkled in her imperial diadem. When we contemplate the perils he braved, the sufferings he patiently endured, the incredible obstacles he overcame, the magnificent results he effected with his single arm, as it were, unaided by the Government —

though neither a good, nor a great man in the highest sense of that term — it is impossible not to regard him as a very extraordinary one.

Nor can we fairly omit to notice in extenuation of his errors, the circumstances of his early life; for, like Almagro, he was the son of sin and sorrow, early cast upon the world to seek his fortunes as he might. In his young and tender age he was to take the impression of those into whose society he was thrown. And when was it the lot of the needy outcast to fall into that of the wise and the virtuous? His lot was cast among the licentious inmates of a camp, the school of rapine, whose only law was the sword, and who looked on the wretched Indian and his heritage as their rightful spoil.

Who does not shudder at the thought of what his own fate might have been, trained in such a school? The amount of crime does not necessarily show the criminality of the agent. History, indeed, is concerned with the former, that it may be recorded as a warning to mankind; but it is He alone who knoweth the heart, the strength of the temptation, and the means of resisting it, that can determine the measure of the guilt.

THE GREAT STONE FACE [1]

BY NATHANIEL HAWTHORNE

STRUCTURALLY this story is of interest for two principal reasons: as illustrating character moulded by background, and as a "key narrative," or allegory. The Great Stone Face was an important element in the formation of Ernest's personality; the constant contemplation of the noble and benign features was in itself, as the narrator tells us, an education to all who dwelt in the valley under its shadow. Among these was Ernest, and, as he grew from youth through manhood to old age, the presence of the Face was ever an inspiration to him, until at last he himself became the impersonation of all that the majestic features signified.

The symbolism implied within the narrative is not difficult of solution. In the young man moulded by the constant contemplation of the titanic features on the mountain-side, Hawthorne shows how the attainment of all that is best in character may be secured through unswerving fidelity to the ideal.

The plot structure is simple in the extreme, being merely of the successive episodic sort; and the setting is of interest mainly in so far as it enters into the shaping of Ernest's personality. The main structural concern lies in the characterization.

ONE afternoon, when the sun was going down, a mother and her little boy sat at the door of their cottage, talking about the Great Stone Face. They had but to lift their eyes, and there it was plainly to be seen, though miles away, with the sunshine brightening all its features.

And what was the Great Stone Face?

[1] From Hawthorne's *Complete Works*. Published by Houghton Mifflin Company.

Embosomed amongst a family of lofty mountains, there was a valley so spacious that it contained many thousand inhabitants. Some of these good people dwelt in log huts, with the black forest all around them, on the steep and difficult hillsides. Others had their homes in comfortable farmhouses, and cultivated the rich soil on the gentle slopes or level surfaces of the valley. Others, again, were congregated into populous villages, where some wild, highland rivulet, tumbling down from its birthplace in the upper mountain region, had been caught and tamed by human cunning, and compelled to turn the machinery of cotton-factories. The inhabitants of this valley, in short, were numerous, and of many modes of life. But all of them, grown people and children, had a kind of familiarity with the Great Stone Face, although some possessed the gift of distinguishing this grand natural phenomenon more perfectly than many of their neighbors.

The Great Stone Face, then, was a work of Nature in her mood of majestic playfulness, formed on the perpendicular side of a mountain by some immense rocks, which had been thrown together in such a position as, when viewed at a proper distance, precisely to resemble the features of the human countenance. It seemed as if an enormous giant, or a Titan, had sculptured his own likeness on the precipice. There was the broad arch of the forehead, a hundred feet in height; the nose, with its long bridge; and the vast lips, which, if they could have spoken, would have rolled their thunder accents from one end of the valley to the other. True it is, that if the spectator approached too near, he lost the outline of the gigantic visage, and could discern only a heap of ponderous and gigantic rocks, piled in chaotic ruin one upon another. Retracing his steps, however, the wondrous features would again be seen; and the farther he withdrew from them, the more like a human face, with all its original divinity intact, did they appear; until, as it grew dim in the distance, with the clouds and glorified vapor of the mountains clustering about it, the Great Stone Face seemed positively to be alive.

It was a happy lot for children to grow up to manhood or womanhood with the Great Stone Face before their eyes, for all the features were noble, and the expression was at once grand and sweet, as if it were the glow of a vast, warm heart, that embraced all mankind in its affections, and had room for more. It was an education only to look at it. According to the belief of many people, the valley owed much of its fertility to this benign aspect that was continually beaming over it, illuminating the clouds, and infusing its tenderness into the sunshine.

As we began with saying, a mother and her little boy sat at their cottage-door, gazing at the Great Stone Face, and talking about it. The child's name was Ernest.

"Mother," said he, while the Titanic visage smiled on him, "I wish that it could speak, for it looks so very kindly that its voice must needs be pleasant. If I were to see a man with such a face, I should love him dearly."

"If an old prophecy should come to pass," answered his mother, "we may see a man, some time or other, with exactly such a face as that."

"What prophecy do you mean, dear mother?" eagerly inquired Ernest. "Pray tell me all about it!"

So his mother told him a story that her own mother had told to her, when she herself was younger than little Ernest; a story, not of things that were past, but of what was yet to come; a story, nevertheless, so very old, that even the Indians, who formerly inhabited this valley, had heard it from their forefathers, to whom, as they affirmed, it had been murmured by the mountain streams, and whispered by the wind among the tree-tops. The purport was, that, at some future day, a child should be born hereabouts, who was destined to become the greatest and noblest personage of his time, and whose countenance, in manhood, should bear an exact resemblance to the Great Stone Face. Not a few old-fashioned people, and young ones likewise, in the ardor of their hopes, still cherished an enduring faith in this old prophecy. But others, who had seen more of the world, had watched and waited till they were weary, and had beheld no man with such a face, nor any man that proved to be much greater or nobler than his neighbors, concluded it to be nothing but an idle tale. At all events, the great man of the prophecy had not yet appeared.

"O mother, dear mother!" cried Ernest, clapping his hands above his head, "I do hope that I shall live to see him!"

His mother was an affectionate and thoughtful woman, and felt that it was wisest not to discourage the generous hopes of her little boy. So she only said to him, "Perhaps you may."

And Ernest never forgot the story that his mother told him. It was always in his mind, whenever he looked upon the Great Stone Face. He spent his childhood in the log cottage where he was born, and was dutiful to his mother, and helpful to her in many things, assisting her much with his little hands, and more with his loving heart. In this manner, from a happy yet often pensive child, he grew up to be a mild, quiet, unobtrusive boy, and sun-browned with labor in the fields, but with more intelligence brightening his aspect than is seen in many lads who have been taught at famous schools. Yet

Ernest had had no teacher, save only that the Great
Stone Face became one to him. When the toil of the day
was over, he would gaze at it for hours, until he began to
imagine that those vast features recognized him, and
gave him a smile of kindness and encouragement, re-
sponsive to his own look of veneration. We must not
take upon us to affirm that this was a mistake, although
the Face may have looked no more kindly at Ernest
than at all the world besides. But the secret was that
the boy's tender and confiding simplicity discerned what
other people could not see; and thus the love, which was
meant for all, became his peculiar portion.

About this time there went a rumor throughout the
valley, that the great man, foretold from ages long ago,
who was to bear a resemblance to the Great Stone Face,
had appeared at last. It seems that, many years before,
a young man had migrated from the valley and settled
at a distant seaport, where, after getting together a little
money, he had set up as a shopkeeper. His name — but
I could never learn whether it was his real one, or a nickname that had grown out of his habits and success in
life — was Gathergold. Being shrewd and active, and
endowed by Providence with that inscrutable faculty
which develops itself in what the world calls luck, he became an exceedingly rich merchant, and owner of a whole
fleet of bulky-bottomed ships. All the countries of the
globe appeared to join hands for the mere purpose of
adding heap after heap to the mountainous accumula-
tion of this one man's wealth. The cold regions of the
north, almost within the gloom and shadow of the Arctic
Circle, sent him their tribute in the shape of furs; hot
Africa sifted for him the golden sands of her rivers, and
gathered up the ivory tusks of her great elephants out of
the forests; the East came bringing him the rich shawls,

and spices, and teas, and the effulgence of diamonds, and the gleaming purity of large pearls. The ocean, not to be behindhand with the earth, yielded up her mighty whales, that Mr. Gathergold might sell their oil, and make a profit on it. Be the original commodity what it might, it was gold within his grasp, It might be said of him, as of Midas in the fable, that whatever he touched with his finger immediately glistened, and grew yellow, and was changed at once into sterling metal, or, which suited him still better, into piles of coin. And, when Mr. Gathergold had become so very rich that it would have taken him a hundred years only to count his wealth, he bethought himself of his native valley, and resolved to go back thither, and end his days where he was born. With this purpose in view, he sent a skillful architect to build him such a palace as should be fit for a man of his vast wealth to live in.

As I have said above, it had already been rumored in the valley that Mr. Gathergold had turned out to be the prophetic personage so long and vainly looked for, and that his visage was the perfect and undeniable similitude of the Great Stone Face. People were the more ready to believe that this must needs be the fact, when they beheld the splendid edifice that rose, as if by enchantment, on the site of his father's old weather-beaten farmhouse. The exterior was of marble, so dazzlingly white that it seemed as though the whole structure might melt away in the sunshine, like those humbler ones which Mr. Gathergold, in his young play-days, before his fingers were gifted with the touch of transmutation, had been accustomed to build of snow. It had a richly ornamented portico, supported by tall pillars, beneath which was a lofty door, studded with silver knobs, and made of a kind of variegated wood that had been brought from beyond the sea. The windows, from the floor to the ceiling of each stately apartment, were composed, respectively, of but one enormous pane of glass, so transparently pure that it was said to be a finer medium than even the vacant atmosphere. Hardly anybody had been permitted to see the interior of this palace; but it was reported, and with good semblance of truth, to be far more gorgeous than the outside, insomuch that whatever was iron or brass in other houses was silver or gold in this; and Mr. Gathergold's bedchamber, especially, made such a glittering appearance that no ordinary man would have been able to close his eyes there. But, on the other hand, Mr. Gathergold was now so inured to wealth, that perhaps he could not have closed his eyes unless where the gleam of it was certain to find its way beneath his eyelids.

In due time, the mansion was finished; next came the upholsterers, with magnificent furniture; then a whole troop of black and white servants, the harbingers of Mr. Gathergold, who, in his own majestic person, was expected to arrive at sunset. Our friend Ernest, meanwhile, had been deeply stirred by the idea that the great man, the noble man, the man of prophecy, after so many ages of delay, was at length to be made manifest to his native valley. He knew, boy as he was, that there were a thousand ways in which Mr. Gathergold, with his vast wealth, might transform himself into an angel of beneficence, and assume a control over human affairs as wide and benignant as the smile of the Great Stone Face. Full of faith and hope, Ernest doubted not that what the people said was true, and that now he was to behold the living likeness of those wondrous features on the mountainside. While the boy was still gazing up the valley, and fancying, as he always did, that the Great Stone Face returned his gaze and looked kindly at him, the rumbling of wheels was heard, approaching swiftly along the winding road.

"Here he comes!" cried a group of people who were assembled to witness the arrival. "Here comes the great Mr. Gathergold!"

A carriage, drawn by four horses, dashed round the turn of the road. Within it, thrust partly out of the window, appeared the physiognomy of the old man, with a skin as yellow as if his own Midas-hand had transmuted it. He had a low forehead, small, sharp eyes, puckered about with innumerable wrinkles, and very thin lips, which he made still thinner by pressing them forcibly together.

"The very image of the Great Stone Face!" shouted the people. "Sure enough, the old prophecy is true; and here we have the great man come, at last!"

And, what greatly perplexed Ernest, they seemed actually to believe that here was the likeness which they spoke of. By the roadside there chanced to be an old beggar-woman and two little beggar-children, stragglers from some far-off region, who, as the carriage rolled onward, held out their hands and lifted up their doleful voices, most piteously beseeching charity. A yellow claw — the very same that had clawed together so much wealth — poked itself out of the coach-window, and dropped some copper coins upon the ground; so that, though the great man's name seems to have been Gathergold, he might just as suitably have been nicknamed Scattercopper. Still, nevertheless, with an earnest shout, and evidently with as much good faith as ever, the people bellowed, —

"He is the very image of the Great Stone Face!"

But Ernest turned sadly from the wrinkled shrewdness of that sordid visage, and gazed up the valley, where, amid a gathering mist, gilded by the last sun-beams, he could still distinguish those glorious features which had impressed themselves into his soul. Their aspect cheered him. What did the benign lips seem to say?

"He will come! Fear not, Ernest; the man will come!"

The years went on, and Ernest ceased to be a boy. He had grown to be a young man now. He attracted little notice from the other inhabitants of the valley; for they saw nothing remarkable in his way of life, save that, when the labor of the day was over, he still loved to go apart and gaze and meditate upon the Great Stone Face. According to their idea of the matter, it was a folly, indeed, but pardonable, inasmuch as Ernest was industrious, kind, and neighborly, and neglected no duty for the sake of indulging this idle habit. They knew not that the Great Stone Face had become a teacher to him, and that the sentiment which was expressed in it would enlarge the young man's heart, and fill it with wider and deeper sympathies than other hearts. They knew not that thence would come a better wisdom than could be learned from books, and a better life than could be moulded on the defaced example of other human lives. Neither did Ernest know that the thoughts and affections which came to him so naturally, in the fields and at the fireside, and wherever he communed with himself, were of a higher tone than those which all men shared with him. A simple soul, — simple as when his mother first taught him the old prophecy, — he beheld the marvelous features beaming adown the valley, and still wondered that their human counterpart was so long in making his appearance.

By this time poor Mr. Gathergold was dead and buried; and the oddest part of the matter was, that his wealth, which was the body and spirit of his existence, had disappeared before his death, leaving nothing of him but a living skeleton, covered over with a wrinkled, yellow skin. Since the melting away of his gold, it had been very generally conceded that there was no such striking resemblance, after all, betwixt the ignoble features of the ruined merchant and that majestic face upon the mountain-side. So the people ceased to honor him during his lifetime, and quietly consigned him to forgetfulness after his decease. Once in a while, it is true, his memory was brought up in connection with the magnificent palace which he had built, and which had long ago been turned into a hotel for the accommodation of strangers, multitudes of whom came, every summer, to visit that famous natural curiosity, the Great Stone Face. Thus, Mr. Gathergold being discredited and thrown into the shade, the man of prophecy was yet to come.

It so happened that a native-born son of the valley, many years before, had enlisted as a soldier, and, after a great deal of hard fighting, had now become an illustrious commander. Whatever he may be called in history, he was known in camps and on the battle-field under the nickname of Old Blood-and-Thunder. This war-worn veteran, being now infirm with age and wounds, and weary of the turmoil of a military life, and of the roll of the drum and the clangor of the trumpet, that had so long been ringing in his ears, had lately signified a purpose of returning to his native valley, hoping to find repose where he remembered to have left it. The inhabitants, his old neighbors and their grown-up children, were resolved to welcome the renowned warrior with a salute of cannon and a public dinner; and all the more enthusiastically, it being affirmed that now, at last, the likeness of the Great Stone Face had actually appeared. An aide-de-camp of Old Blood-and-Thunder, traveling through the valley, was said to have been struck with the resemblance. Moreover, the schoolmates and early acquaintances of the general were ready to testify, on oath, that, to the best of their recollection, the aforesaid general had been exceedingly like the majestic image, even when a boy, only that the idea had never occurred to them at that period. Great, therefore, was the excitement throughout the valley; and many people, who had never once thought of glancing at the Great Stone Face for years before, now spent their time in gazing at it, for the sake of knowing exactly how General Blood-and-Thunder looked.

On the day of the great festival, Ernest, with all the other people of the valley, left their work, and proceeded to the spot where the sylvan banquet was prepared. As he approached, the loud voice of the Rev. Dr. Battle-blast was heard, beseeching a blessing on the good things set before them, and on the distinguished friend of peace in whose honor they were assembled. The tables were arranged in a cleared space of the woods, shut in by the surrounding trees, except where a vista opened eastwards and afforded a distant view of the Great Stone Face. Over the general's chair, which was a relic from the home of Washington, there was an arch of verdant boughs, with the laurel profusely intermixed, and surmounted by his country's banner, beneath which he had won his victories. Our friend Ernest raised himself on his tiptoes, in hopes to get a glimpse of the celebrated guest; but there was a mighty crowd about the tables anxious to hear the toasts and speeches, and to catch any word that might fall from the general in reply; and a volunteer company, doing duty as a guard, pricked ruthlessly with their bayonets at any particularly quiet person among the throng. So Ernest, being of an unobtrusive character, was thrust quite into the background, where he could see no more of Old Blood-and-Thunder's physiognomy than if it had been still blazing on the battle-field. To console himself, he turned towards the Great Stone Face, which, like a faithful and long-remembered friend, looked back and smiled upon him through the vista of the forest. Meantime, however, he could overhear the remarks of various individuals, who were comparing the features of the hero with the face on the distant mountain-side.

"'T is the same face, to a hair!" cried one man, cutting a caper for joy.

"Wonderfully like, that 's a fact!" responded another.

"Like! why, I call it Old Blood-and-Thunder himself, in a monstrous looking-glass!" cried a third. "And why not? He 's the greatest man of this or any other age, beyond a doubt."

And then all three of the speakers gave a great shout, which communicated electricity to the crowd, and called forth a roar from a thousand voices, that went reverberating for miles among the mountains, until you might have supposed that the Great Stone Face had poured its thunder-breath into the cry. All these comments, and this vast enthusiasm, served the more to interest our friend; nor did he think of questioning that now, at length, the mountain-visage had found its human counterpart. It is true, Ernest had imagined that this long-looked-for personage would appear in the character of a man of peace, uttering wisdom, and doing good, and making people happy. But, taking an habitual breadth of view, with all his simplicity, he contended that Providence should choose its own method of blessing mankind, and could conceive that this great end might be effected even by a warrior and a bloody sword, should inscrutable wisdom see fit to order matters so.

"The general! the general!" was now the cry. "Hush! silence! Old Blood-and-Thunder's going to make a speech."

Even so; for, the cloth being removed, the general's health had been drunk, amid shouts of applause, and he now stood upon his feet to thank the company. Ernest saw him. There he was, over the shoulders of the crowd, from the two glittering epaulets and embroidered collar upward, beneath the arch of green boughs with intertwined laurel, and the banner drooping as if to shade his brow! And there, too, visible in the same glance, through the vista of the forest, appeared the Great Stone Face! And was there, indeed, such a resemblance as the crowd had testified? Alas, Ernest could not recognize it! He beheld a war-worn and weather-beaten countenance, full of energy, and expressive of an iron will; but the gentle wisdom, the deep, broad, tender sympathies, were altogether wanting in Old Blood-and-Thunder's visage; and even if the Great Stone Face had assumed his look of stern command, the milder traits would still have tempered it.

"This is not the man of prophecy," sighed Ernest to himself, as he made his way out of the throng. "And must the world wait longer yet?"

The mists had congregated about the distant mountain-side, and there were seen the grand and awful features of the Great Stone Face, awful but benignant, as if a mighty angel were sitting among the hills, and enrobing himself in a cloud-vesture of gold and purple. As he looked, Ernest could hardly believe but that a smile beamed over the whole visage, with a radiance still brightening, although without motion of the lips. It was probably the effect of the western sunshine, melting through the thinly diffused vapors that had swept between him and the object that he gazed at. But — as it always did — the aspect of his marvelous friend made Ernest as hopeful as if he had never hoped in vain.

"Fear not, Ernest," said his heart, even as if the Great Face were whispering him, — "fear not, Ernest; he will come."

More years sped swiftly and tranquilly away. Ernest still dwelt in his native valley, and was now a man of middle age. By imperceptible degrees, he had become known among the people. Now, as heretofore, he labored for his bread, and was the same simple-hearted man that he had always been. But he had thought and felt so much, he had given so many of the best hours of his life to unworldly hopes for some great good to mankind, that it seemed as though he had been talking with the angels, and had imbibed a portion of their wisdom unawares. It was visible in the calm and well-considered beneficence of his daily life, the quiet stream of which had made a wide green margin all along its course. Not a day passed by, that the world was not the better because this man, humble as he was, had lived. He never stepped aside from his own path, yet would always reach a blessing to his neighbor. Almost involuntarily, too, he had become a preacher. The pure and high simplicity of his thought, which, as one of its manifestations, took shape in the good deeds that dropped silently from his hand, flowed also forth in speech. He uttered truths that wrought upon and moulded the lives of those who heard him. His auditors, it may be, never suspected that Ernest, their own neighbor and familiar friend, was more than an ordinary man; least of all did Ernest himself suspect it; but, inevitably as the murmur of a rivulet came thoughts out of his mouth that no other human lips had spoken.

When the people's minds had had a little time to cool, they were ready enough to acknowledge their mistake in imagining a similarity between General Blood-and-Thunder's truculent physiognomy and the benign visage on the mountain-side. But now, again, there were reports and many paragraphs in the newspapers, affirming that the likeness of the Great Stone Face had appeared upon the broad shoulders of a certain eminent statesman. He, like Mr. Gathergold and Old Blood-and-Thunder, was a native of the valley, but had left it in his early days, and had taken up the trades of law and politics. Instead of the rich man's wealth and the warrior's sword, he had but a tongue, and it was mightier than both together. So wonderfully eloquent was he, that whatever he might choose to say, his auditors had no choice but to believe him; wrong looked like right, and right like wrong; for when it pleased him, he could make a kind of illuminated fog with his mere breath, and obscure the natural daylight with it. His tongue, indeed, was a magic instrument: sometimes it rumbled like the thunder; sometimes it warbled like the sweetest music. It was the blast of war, — the song of peace; and it seemed to have a heart in it, when there was no such matter. In good truth, he was a wondrous man; and when his tongue had acquired him all other imaginable success, — when it had been heard in halls of state, and in the courts of princes and potentates, — after it had made him known all over the world, even as a voice crying from shore to shore, — it finally persuaded his countrymen to elect him for the Presidency. Before this time, — indeed, as soon as he began to grow celebrated, — his admirers had found out the resemblance between him and the Great Stone Face; and so much were they struck by it, that throughout the country this distinguished gentleman was known by the name of Old Stony Phiz. The phrase was considered as giving a highly favorable aspect to his political prospects; for, as is likewise the case with the Popedom, nobody ever becomes President without taking a name other than his own.

While his friends were doing their best to make him President, Old Stony Phiz, as he was called, set out on a visit to the valley where he was born. Of course, he had no other object than to shake hands with his fellow-citizens, and neither thought nor cared about any effect which his progress through the country might have upon the election. Magnificent preparations were made to receive the illustrious statesman; a cavalcade of horsemen set forth to meet him at the boundary line of the State, and all the people left their business and gathered along the wayside to see him pass. Among these was Ernest. Though more than once disappointed, as we have seen, he had such a hopeful and confiding nature, that he was always ready to believe in whatever seemed beautiful and good. He kept his heart continually open, and thus was sure to catch the blessing from on high when it should come. So now again, as buoyantly as ever, he went forth to behold the likeness of the Great Stone Face.

The cavalcade came prancing along the road, with a great clattering of hoofs and a mighty cloud of dust, which rose up so dense and high that the visage of the mountain-side was completely hidden from Ernest's eyes. All the great men of the neighborhood were there on horseback; militia officers, in uniform; the member of Congress; the sheriff of the county; the editors of newspapers; and many a farmer, too, had mounted his patient steed, with his Sunday coat upon his back. It really was a very brilliant spectacle, especially as there were numerous banners flaunting over the cavalcade, on some of which were gorgeous portraits of the illustrious statesman and the Great Stone Face, smiling familiarly at one another, like two brothers. If the pictures were to be trusted, the mutual resemblance, it must be confessed, was marvelous. We must not forget to mention that there was a band of music, which made the echoes of the mountains ring and reverberate with the loud triumph of its strains; so that airy and soul-thrilling melodies broke out among all the heights and hollows, as if every nook of his native valley had found a voice, to welcome the distinguished guest. But the grandest effect was when the far-off mountain precipice flung back the music; for then the Great Stone Face itself seemed to be swelling the triumphant chorus, in acknowledgment that, at length, the man of prophecy was come.

All this while the people were throwing up their hats and shouting, with enthusiasm so contagious that the heart of Ernest kindled up, and he likewise threw up his hat, and shouted, as loudly as the loudest, "Huzza for the great man! Huzza for Old Stony Phiz!" But as yet he had not seen him.

"Here he is, now!" cried those who stood near Ernest. "There! There! Look at Old Stony Phiz and then at the Old Man of the Mountain, and see if they are not as like as two twin-brothers!"

In the midst of all this gallant array came an open barouche, drawn by four white horses; and in the barouche, with his massive head uncovered, sat the illustrious statesman, Old Stony Phiz himself.

"Confess it," said one of Ernest's neighbors to him, "the Great Stone Face has met its match at last!"

Now, it must be owned that, at his first glimpse of the countenance which was bowing and smiling from the barouche, Ernest did fancy that there was a resemblance between it and the old familiar face upon the mountainside. The brow, with its massive depth and loftiness, and all the other features, indeed, were boldly and strongly hewn, as if in emulation of a more than heroic, of a Titanic model. But the sublimity and stateliness, the grand expression of a divine sympathy, that illuminated the mountain visage and etherealized its ponderous granite substance into spirit, might here be sought in vain. Something had been originally left out, or had departed. And therefore the marvelously gifted statesman had always a weary gloom in the deep caverns of his eyes, as of a child that has outgrown its playthings or a man of mighty faculties and little aims, whose life, with all its high performances, was vague and empty, because no high purpose had endowed it with reality.

Still, Ernest's neighbor was thrusting his elbow into his side, and pressing him for an answer.

"Confess! confess! Is not he the very picture of your Old Man of the Mountain?"

"No!" said Ernest bluntly, "I see little or no likeness."

"Then so much the worse for the Great Stone Face!" answered his neighbor; and again he set up a shout for Old Stony Phiz.

But Ernest turned away, melancholy, and almost despondent: for this was the saddest of his disappointments, to behold a man who might have fulfilled the prophecy, and had not willed to do so. Meantime, the cavalcade, the banners, the music, and the barouches swept past him, with the vociferous crowd in the rear, leaving the dust to settle down, and the Great Stone

Face to be revealed again, with the grandeur that it had worn for untold centuries.

"Lo, here I am, Ernest!" the benign lips seemed to say. "I have waited longer than thou, and am not yet weary. Fear not; the man will come."

The years hurried onward, treading in their haste on one another's heels. And now they began to bring white hairs, and scatter them over the head of Ernest; they made reverend wrinkles across his forehead, and furrows in his cheeks. He was an aged man. But not in vain had he grown old: more than the white hairs on his head were the sage thoughts in his mind; his wrinkles and furrows were inscriptions that Time had graved, and in which he had written legends of wisdom that had been tested by the tenor of a life. And Ernest had ceased to be obscure. Unsought for, undesired, had come the fame which so many seek, and made him known in the great world, beyond the limits of the valley in which he had dwelt so quietly. College professors, and even the active men of cities, came from far to see and converse with Ernest; for the report had gone abroad that this simple husbandman had ideas unlike those of other men, not gained from books, but of a higher tone, — a tranquil and familiar majesty, as if he had been talking with the angels as his daily friends. Whether it were sage, statesman, or philanthropist, Ernest received these visitors with the gentle sincerity that had characterized him from boyhood, and spoke freely with them of whatever came uppermost, or lay deepest in his heart or their own. While they talked together, his face would kindle, unawares, and shine upon them, as with a mild evening light. Pensive with the fullness of such discourse, his guests took leave and went their way; and passing up the valley, paused to look at the Great Stone Face, imagining that they had seen its likeness in a human countenance, but could not remember where.

While Ernest had been growing up and growing old, a bountiful Providence had granted a new poet to this earth. He, likewise, was a native of the valley, but had spent the greater part of his life at a distance from that romantic region, pouring out his sweet music amid the bustle and din of cities. Often, however, did the mountains which had been familiar to him in his childhood lift their snowy peaks into the clear atmosphere of his poetry. Neither was the Great Stone Face forgotten, for the poet had celebrated it in an ode, which was grand enough to have been uttered by its own majestic lips. This man of genius, we may say, had come down from heaven with wonderful endowments. If he sang of a mountain, the eyes of all mankind beheld a mightier grandeur reposing on its breast, or soaring to its summit, than had before been seen there. If his theme were a lovely lake, a celestial smile had now been thrown over it, to gleam forever on its surface. If it were the vast old sea, even the deep immensity of its dread bosom seemed to swell the higher, as if moved by the emotions of the song. Thus the world assumed another and a better aspect from the hour that the poet blessed it with his happy eyes. The Creator had bestowed him, as the last best touch to his own handiwork. Creation was not finished till the poet came to interpret, and so complete it.

The effect was no less high and beautiful, when his human brethren were the subject of his verse. The man or woman, sordid with the common dust of life, who crossed his daily path, and the little child who played in it, were glorified if he beheld them in his mood of poetic faith. He showed the golden links of the great chain that intertwined them with an angelic kindred; he brought out the hidden traits of a celestial birth that made them worthy of such kin. Some, indeed, there were, who thought to show the soundness of their judgment by affirming that all the beauty and dignity of the natural world existed only in the poet's fancy. Let such men speak for themselves, who undoubtedly appear to have been spawned forth by Nature with a contemptuous bitterness; she having plastered them up out of her refuse stuff, after all the swine were made. As respects all things else, the poet's ideal was the truest truth.

The songs of this poet found their way to Ernest. He read them after his customary toil, seated on the bench before his cottage-door, where for such a length of time he had filled his repose with thought, by gazing at the Great Stone Face. And now as he read stanzas that caused the soul to thrill within him, he lifted his eyes to the vast countenance beaming on him so benignantly.

"O majestic friend," he murmured, addressing the Great Stone Face, "is not this man worthy to resemble thee?"

The Face seemed to smile, but answered not a word.

Now it happened that the poet, though he dwelt so far away, had not only heard of Ernest, but had meditated much upon his character, until he deemed nothing so desirable as to meet this man, whose untaught wisdom walked hand in hand with the noble simplicity of his life. One summer morning, therefore, he took passage by the railroad, and, in the decline of the afternoon, alighted from the cars at no great distance from Ernest's cottage. The great hotel, which had formerly been the palace of Mr. Gathergold, was close at hand, but the poet, with his carpet-bag on his arm, inquired at once where Ernest dwelt, and was resolved to be accepted as his guest.

Approaching the door, he there found the good old man, holding a volume in his hand, which alternately he read, and then, with a finger between the leaves, looked lovingly at the Great Stone Face.

"Good-evening," said the poet. "Can you give a traveler a night's lodging?"

"Willingly," answered Ernest; and then he added, smiling, "Methinks I never saw the Great Stone Face look so hospitably at a stranger."

The poet sat down on the bench beside him, and he and Ernest talked together. Often had the poet held intercourse with the wittiest and the wisest, but never before with a man like Ernest, whose thoughts and feelings gushed up with such a natural freedom, and who made great truths so familiar by his simple utterance of them. Angels, as had been so often said, seemed to have wrought with him at his labor in the fields; angels seemed to have sat with him by the fireside; and, dwelling with angels as friend with friends, he had imbibed the sublimity of their ideas, and imbued it with the sweet and lowly charm of household words. So thought the poet. And Ernest, on the other hand, was moved and agitated by the living images which the poet flung out of his mind, and which peopled all the air above the cottage-door with shapes of beauty, both gay and pensive. The sympathies of these two men instructed them with a profounder sense than either could have attained alone. Their minds accorded into one strain, and made delightful music which neither of them could have claimed as all his own, nor distinguished his own share from the other's. They led one another, as it were, into a high pavilion of their thoughts, so remote, and hitherto so dim, that they had never entered it before, and so beautiful that they desired to be there always.

As Ernest listened to the poet, he imagined that the Great Stone Face was bending forward to listen too. He gazed earnestly into the poet's glowing eyes.

"Who are you, my strangely gifted guest?" he said.

The poet laid his finger on the volume that Ernest had been reading.

"You have read these poems," said he. "You know me, then, — for I wrote them."

Again, and still more earnestly than before, Ernest examined the poet's features; then turned towards the Great Stone Face; then back, with an uncertain aspect, to his guest. But his countenance fell; he shook his head, and sighed.

"Wherefore are you sad?" inquired the poet.

"Because," replied Ernest, "all through life I have awaited the fulfillment of a prophecy; and, when I read these poems, I hoped that it might be fulfilled in you."

"You hoped," answered the poet, faintly smiling, "to find in me the likeness of the Great Stone Face. And you are disappointed, as formerly was Mr. Gathergold, and Old Blood-and-Thunder, and Old Stony Phiz. Yes, Ernest, it is my doom. You must add my name to the illustrious three, and record another failure of your hopes. For — in shame and sadness do I speak it, Ernest — I am not worthy to be typified by yonder benign and majestic image."

"And why?" asked Ernest. He pointed to the volume. "Are not those thoughts divine?"

"They have a strain of the Divinity," replied the

poet. "You can hear in them the far-off echo of a heav-enly song. But my life, dear Ernest, has not corre-sponded with my thought. I have had grand dreams, but they have been only dreams, because I have lived — and that, too, by my own choice — among poor and mean realities. Sometimes even — shall I dare to say it? — I lack faith in the grandeur, the beauty, and the goodness, which my own works are said to have made more evident in nature and in human life. Why, then, pure seeker of the good and true, shouldst thou hope to find me, in yonder image of the divine?"

The poet spoke sadly, and his eyes were dim with tears. So, likewise, were those of Ernest.

At the hour of sunset, as had long been his frequent custom, Ernest was to discourse to an assemblage of the neighboring inhabitants in the open air. He and the poet, arm in arm, still talking together as they went along, proceeded to the spot. It was a small nook among the hills, with a gray precipice behind, the stern front of which was relieved by the pleasant foliage of many creeping plants that made a tapestry for the naked rock, by hanging their festoons from all its rugged angles. At a small elevation above the ground, set in a rich frame-work of verdure, there appeared a niche, spacious enough to admit a human figure, with freedom for such gestures as spontaneously accompany earnest thought and genuine emotion. Into this natural pulpit Ernest ascended, and threw a look of familiar kindness around upon his audience. They stood, or sat, or reclined upon the grass, as seemed good to each, with the departing sunshine falling obliquely over them, and mingling its subdued cheerfulness with the solemn-ity of a grove of ancient trees, beneath and amid the boughs of which the golden rays were constrained to pass. In another direction was seen the Great Stone Face, with the same cheer, combined with the same solemnity, in its benignant aspect.

Ernest began to speak, giving to the people of what was in his heart and mind. His words had power, because they accorded with his thoughts; and his thoughts had reality and depth, because they harmonized with the life which he had always lived. It was not mere breath that this preacher uttered; they were the words of life, because a life of good deeds and holy love was melted into them. Pearls, pure and rich, had been dissolved into this precious draught. The poet, as he listened, felt that the being and character of Ernest were a nobler strain of poetry than he had ever written. His eyes glistening with tears, he gazed reverentially at the venerable man, and said within himself that never was there an aspect so worthy of a prophet and a sage as that mild, sweet, thoughtful countenance, with the glory of white hair diffused about it. At a distance, but distinctly to be seen, high up in the golden light of the setting sun, appeared the Great Stone Face, with hoary mists around it, like the white hairs around the brow of Ernest. Its look of grand beneficence seemed to embrace the world.

At that moment, in sympathy with a thought which he was about to utter, the face of Ernest assumed a grandeur of expression, so imbued with benevolence, that the poet, by an irresistible impulse, threw his arms aloft, and shouted, —

"Behold! Behold! Ernest is himself the likeness of the Great Stone Face!"

Then all the people looked, and saw that what the deep-sighted poet said was true. The prophecy was fulfilled. But Ernest, having finished what he had to say, took the poet's arm, and walked slowly homeward, still hoping that some wiser and better man than himself would by and by appear, bearing a resemblance to the GREAT STONE FACE.

MISS ESTHER'S GUEST [1]

BY SARAH ORNE JEWETT

THE author of this narrative is well known as the writer of New England stories, in which she presents a sympathetic and realistic portrayal of the "characters" peculiar to that portion of the country. This selection is illustrative of local color and atmosphere, but the main interest is, after all, in Miss Esther herself, who is in perfect harmony with her environment. Indeed, the element of environment is an essential part of the characterization. Miss Porley's little conventionalities — pathetic in considerable degree — were the natural results of her straitened circumstances and of her Puritan upbringing. And, on the other hand, the universal respect that she enjoyed in Daleham and the general atmosphere of her cottage with its humble but immaculate "homelikeness," were of her own creation. The portrayal presents in typical form both the active and the passive phases of characterization.

I

OLD MISS PORLEY put on her silk shawl, and arranged it carefully over her thin shoulders, and pinned it with a hand that shook a little as if she were much excited. She bent forward to examine the shawl in the mahogany-framed mirror, for there was a frayed and tender spot in the silk where she had pinned it so many years. The shawl was very old; it had been her mother's, and she disliked to wear it too often, but she never could make up her mind to go out into the street in summer, as some of her neighbors did, with nothing over her shoulders at all. Next she put on her bonnet

[1] From *A Native of Winby and Other Tales*. Published by Houghton Mifflin Company.

and tried to set it straight, allowing for a wave in the looking-glass that made one side of her face appear much longer than the other; then she drew on a pair of well-darned silk gloves; one had a wide crack all the way up the back of the hand, but they were still neat and decent for everyday wear, if she were careful to keep her left hand under the edge of the shawl. She had discussed the propriety of drawing the raveled silk together, but a thick seam would look very ugly, and there was something accidental about the crack.

Then, after hesitating a few moments, she took a small piece of folded white letter-paper from the table and went out of the house, locking the door and trying it, and stepped away bravely down the village street. Everybody said, "How do you do, Miss Porley?" or "Good-mornin', Esther." Every one in Daleham knew the good woman; she was one of the unchanging persons, always to be found in her place, and always pleased and friendly and ready to take an interest in old and young. She and her mother, who had early been left a widow, had been for many years the village tailoresses and makers of little boys' clothes. Mrs. Porley had been dead three years, however, and her daughter "Easter," as old friends called our heroine, had lived quite alone. She was made very sorrowful by her loneliness, but she never could be persuaded to take anybody to board: she could not bear to think of any one's taking her mother's place.

It was a warm summer morning, and Miss Porley had not very far to walk, but she was still more shaky and excited by the time she reached the First Church parsonage. She stood at the gate undecidedly, and, after she pushed it open a little way, she drew back again, and felt a curious beating at her heart and a

general reluctance of mind and body. At that moment
the minister's wife, a pleasant young woman with a
smiling, eager face, looked out of the window and asked
the tremulous visitor to come in. Miss Esther straight-
ened herself and went briskly up the walk; she was very
fond of the minister's wife, who had only been in Daleham a few months.

"Won't you take off your shawl?" asked Mrs. Wayton affectionately; "I have just been making ginger-
bread, and you shall have a piece as soon as it
cools."

"I don't know 's I ought to stop," answered Miss
Esther, flushing quickly. "I came on business; I won't
keep you long."

"Oh, please stay a little while," urged the hostess.
"I'll take my sewing, if you don't mind; there are two
or three things that I want to ask you about."

"I've thought and flustered a sight over taking
this step," said good old Esther abruptly. "I had to
conquer a sight o' reluctance, I must say. I've got so
used to livin' by myself that I sha'n't know how to consider another. But I see I ain't got common feelin' for
others unless I can set my own comfort aside once in
a while. I've brought you my name as one of those
that will take one o' them city folks that needs a spell
o' change. It come straight home to me how I should
be feeling it by this time, if my lot had been cast in
one o' them city garrets that the minister described
so affecting. If 't had n't been for kind consideration
somewheres, mother an' me might have sewed all them
pleasant years away in the city that we enjoyed so in
our own home, and our garding to step right out into
when our sides set in to ache. And I ain't rich, but we
was able to save a little something, and now I'm eatin'

of it up all alone. It come to me I should like to have somebody take a taste out o' mother's part. Now, don't you let 'em send me no rampin' boys like them Barnard's folks had come last year, that vexed dumb creatur's so; and I don't know how to cope with no kind o' men-folks or strange girls, but I should know how to do for a woman that's getting well along in years, an' has come to feel kind o' spent. P'r'aps we ain't no right to pick an' choose, but I should know best how to make that sort comfortable on 'count of doin' for mother and studying what she preferred."

Miss Esther rose with quaint formality and put the folded paper, on which she had neatly written her name and address, into Mrs. Wayton's hand. Mrs. Wayton rose soberly to receive it, and then they both sat down again.

"I'm sure that you will feel more than repaid for your kindness, dear Miss Esther," said the minister's wife. "I know one of the ladies who have charge of the arrangements for the Country Week, and I will explain as well as I can the kind of guest you have in mind. I quite envy her: I have often thought, when I was busy and tired, how much I should like to run along the street and make you a visit in your dear old-fashioned little house."

"I should be more than pleased to have you, I'm sure," said Miss Esther, startled into a bright smile and forgetting her anxiety. "Come any day, and take me just as I am. We used to have a good deal o' company years ago, when there was a number of mother's folks still livin' over Ashfield way. Sure as we had a pile o' work on hand and was hurryin' for dear life an' limb, a wagon-load would light down at the front gate to spend the day an' have an early tea. Mother never was one to get flustered same's I do 'bout everything. She was a lovely cook, and she'd fill 'em up an' cheer 'em, and git 'em off early as she could, an' then we'd be kind o' waked up an' spirited ourselves, and would set up late sewin' and talkin' the company over, an' I'd have things saved up to tell her that had been said while she was out o' the room. I make such a towse over everything myself, but mother was waked right up and felt pleased an' smart, if anything unexpected happened. I miss her more every year," and Miss Esther gave a great sigh. "I s'pose 't wa'n't reasonable to expect that I could have her to help me through with old age, but I'm a poor tool alone."

"Oh, no, you must n't say that!" exclaimed the minister's wife. "Why, nobody could get along without you. I wish I had come to Daleham in time to know your mother too."

Miss Esther shook her head sadly. "She would have set everything by you and Mr. Wayton. Now I must be getting back in case I'm wanted, but you let 'em send me somebody right away, while my bush beans is so nice. An' if any o' your little boy's clothes wants repairin', just give 'em to me; 't will be a real pleasant thing to set a few stitches. Or the minister's; ain't there something needed for him?"

Mrs. Wayton was about to say no, when she became conscious of the pleading old face before her. "I'm sure you are most kind, dear friend," she answered, "and I do have a great deal to do. I'll bring you two or three things to-night that are beyond my art, as I go to evening meeting. Mr. Wayton frayed out his best coat sleeve yesterday, and I was disheartened, for we had counted upon his not having a new one before the fall."

"'T would be mere play to me," said Miss Esther, and presently she went smiling down the street.

II

The Committee for the Country Week in a certain ward of Boston were considering the long list of children, and mothers with babies, and sewing-women, who were looking forward, some of them for the first time in many years, to a country holiday. Some were to go as guests to hospitable, generous farmhouses that opened their doors willingly now and then to tired city people; for some persons board could be paid.

The immediate arrangements of that time were settled at last, except that Mrs. Belton, the chairman, suddenly took a letter from her pocket. "I had almost forgotten this," she said; "it is another place offered in dear quiet old Daleham. My friend, the minister's wife there, writes me a word about it: 'The applicant desires especially an old person, being used to the care of an aged parent and sure of her power of making such a one comfortable, and she would like to have her guest come as soon as possible.' My friend asks me to choose a person of some refinement, — 'one who would appreciate the delicate simplicity and quaint ways of the hostess.'"

Mrs. Belton glanced hurriedly down the page. "I believe that's all," she said. "How about that nice old sewing-woman, Mrs. Connolly, in Bantry Street?"

"Oh, no!" some one entreated, looking up from her writing. "Why is n't it just the place for my old Mr. Rill, the dear old Englishman who lives alone up four flights in Town Court and has the bullfinch. He used to engrave seals, and his eyes gave out, and he is so thrifty with his own bit of savings and an atom of a pension. Some one pays his expenses to the country, and this sounds like a place he would be sure to like. I've been watching for the right chance."

"Take it, then," said the busy chairman, and there was a little more writing and talking, and then the committee meeting was over which settled Miss Esther Porley's fate.

III

The journey to Daleham was a great experience to Mr. Rill. He was a sensible old person, who knew well that he was getting stiffer and clumsier than need be in his garret, and that, as certain friends had said, a short time spent in the country would cheer and invigorate him. There had been occasional propositions that he should leave his garret altogether and go to the country to live, or at least to the suburbs of the city. He could not see things close at hand so well as he could take a wide outlook, and as his outlook from the one garret window was a still higher brick wall and many chimneys, he was losing a great deal that he might have had. But so long as he was expected to take an interest in the unseen and unknown he failed to accede to any plans about the country home, and declared that he was well enough in his high abode. He had lost a sister a few years before who had been his mainstay, but with his hands so well used to delicate work he had been less bungling in his simple household affairs than many another man might have been. But he was very lonely and was growing anxious; as he was rattled along in the train toward Daleham he held the chirping bullfinch's cage fast with both hands, and said to himself now and then, "This may lead to something; the country air smells very good to me."

The Daleham station was not very far out of the village, so that Miss Esther Porley put on her silk shawl and bonnet and everyday gloves just before four o'clock that afternoon, and went to meet her Country Week guest. Word had come the day before that the person for Miss Porley's would start two days in advance of the little company of children and helpless women, and since this message had come from the parsonage Miss Esther had worked diligently, late and early, to have her house in proper order. Whatever her mother had liked was thought of and provided. There were going to be rye shortcakes for tea, and there were some sprigs of thyme and sweet-balm in an old-fashioned wine-glass on the keeping-room table; mother always said they were so freshening. And Miss Esther had taken out a little shoulder-shawl and folded it over the arm of the rocking-chair by the window that looked out into the small garden where the London-pride was in full bloom, and the morning-glories had just begun to climb. Miss Esther was sixty-four herself, but still looked upon age as well in the distance.

She was always a prompt person, and had some minutes to wait at the station; then the time passed and the train was late. At last she saw the smoke far in the distance, and her heart began to sink. Perhaps she would not find it easy to get on with the old lady, and — well it was only for a week, and she had thought it right and best to take such a step, and now it would soon be over.

The train stopped, and there was no old lady at all.

Miss Esther had stood far back to get away from the smoke and roar, — she was always as afraid of the cars as she could be, — but as they moved away she took a few steps forward to scan the platform. There

was no black bonnet with a worn lace veil, and no old
lady with a burden of bundles; there were only the
station master and two or three men, and an idle boy
or two, and one clean-faced, bent old man with a bird-
cage in one hand and an old carpet-bag in the other.
She thought of the rye shortcakes for supper and all
that she had done to make her small home pleasant,
and her fire of excitement suddenly fell into ashes.

The old man with the bird-cage suddenly turned toward her. "Can you direct me to Miss Esther Porley's?" said he.

"I can," replied Miss Esther, looking at him with
curiosity.

"I was directed to her house," said the pleasant old
fellow, "by Mrs. Belton, of the Country Week Committee. My eyesight is poor. I should be glad if anybody would help me to find the place."

"You step this way with me, sir," said Miss Esther.
She was afraid that the men on the platform heard
every word they said, but nobody took particular
notice, and off they walked down the road together.
Miss Esther was enraged with the Country Week
Committee.

"*You* were sent to — Miss Porley's?" she asked
grimly, turning to look at him.

"I was, indeed," said Mr. Rill.

"I am Miss Porley, and I expected an old lady,"
she managed to say; and they both stopped and looked
at each other with apprehension.

"I do declare!" faltered the old seal-cutter anxiously. "What had I better do, ma'am? They most
certain give me your name. Maybe you could recommend me somewheres else, an' I can get home to-morrow
if 't ain't convenient."

They were standing under a willow tree in the shade; Mr. Rill took off his heavy hat, — it was a silk hat of by-gone shape; a golden robin began to sing, high in the willow, and the old bullfinch twittered and chirped in the cage. Miss Esther heard some footsteps coming behind them along the road. She changed color; she tried to remember that she was a woman of mature years and considerable experience.

"'T ain't a mite o' matter, sir," she said cheerfully. "I guess you 'll find everything comfortable for you"; and they turned, much relieved, and walked along together.

"That's Lawyer Barstow's house," she said calmly, a minute afterward, "the handsomest place in town, we think 't is"; and Mr. Rill answered politely that Daleham was a pretty place; he had not been out of the city for so many years that everything looked beautiful as a picture.

IV

Miss Porley rapidly recovered her composure, and bent her energies to the preparing of an early tea. She showed her guest to the snug bedroom under the low gambrel roof, and when she apologized for his having to go upstairs, he begged her to remember that it was nothing but a step to a man who was used to four long flights. They were both excited at finding a proper nail for the bird-cage outside the window, though Miss Esther said that she should love to have the pretty bird downstairs where they could see it and hear it sing. She said to herself over and over that if she could have her long-lost brother come home from sea, she should like to have him look and behave as gentle and kind as Mr. Rill. Somehow she found herself singing a cheerful hymn as she mixed and stirred the shortcakes. She could not help wishing that her mother were there to enjoy this surprise, but it did seem very odd, after so many years, to have a man in the house. It had not happened for fifteen years, at least, when they had entertained Deacon Sparks and wife, delegates from the neighboring town of East Wilby to the County Conference.

The neighbors did not laugh at Miss Esther openly or cause her to blush with self-consciousness, however much they may have discussed the situation and smiled behind her back. She took the presence of her guest with delighted simplicity, and the country week was extended to a fortnight, and then to a month. At last, one day Miss Esther and Mr. Rill were seen on their way to the railroad station, with a large bundle apiece beside the carpet-bag, though some one noticed that the bullfinch was left behind. Miss Esther came back alone, looking very woebegone and lonely, and if the truth must be known, she found her house too solitary. She looked into the woodhouse, where there was a great store of kindlings, neatly piled, and her water-pail was filled to the brim, her garden-paths were clean of weeds and swept, and yet everywhere she looked it seemed more lonely than ever. She pinned on her shawl again and went along the street to the parsonage.

"My old lady 's just gone," she said to the minister's wife. "I was so lonesome I could not stay in the house."

"You found him a very pleasant visitor, did n't you, Miss Esther?" asked Mrs. Wayton, laughing a little.

"I did so; he wa'n't like other men, — kind and friendly and fatherly, and never stayed round when I was occupied, but entertained himself down street considerable, an' was as industrious as a bee, always

asking me if there wa'n't something he could do about
house. He and a sister some years older used to keep
house together, and it was her long sickness used up
what they'd saved, and yet he's got a little somethin',
and there are friends he used to work for, jewelers, a
big firm, that gives him somethin' regular. He's goin'
to see," — and Miss Esther blushed crimson, — "he's
goin' to see if they'd be willing to pay it just the same
if he come to reside in Daleham. He thinks the air
agrees with him here."

"Does he, indeed?" inquired the minister's wife,
with deep interest and a look of amusement.

"Yes'm," said Miss Esther simply; "but don't you
go an' say nothin' yet. I don't want folks to make a
joke of it. Seems to me if he does feel to come back, and
remains of the same mind he went away, we might be
judicious to take the step —"

"Why, Miss Esther!" exclaimed the listener.

"Not till fall, — not till fall," said Miss Esther
hastily. "I ain't goin' to count on it too much any-
way. I expect we could get along; there's considerable
goodness left in me, and you can always work better
when you've got somebody beside yourself to work for.
There, now I've told you, I feel as if I was blown away
in a gale."

"Why, I don't know what to say at such a piece of
news!" exclaimed Mrs. Wayton again.

"I don't know 's there's anything *to* say," gravely
answered Miss Esther. "But I did laugh just now
comin' in the gate to think what a twitter I got into
the day I fetched you that piece of paper."

"Why, I must go right and tell Mr. Wayton!" said
the minister's wife.

"Oh, don't you, Mis' Wayton; no, no!" begged

Miss Esther, looking quite coy and girlish. "I really don't know 's it's quite settled,—it don't seem 's if it could be. I'm going to hear from him in the course of a week. But I suppose *he* thinks it's settled; he's left the bird."

THE PROPRIETOR OF THE CAFÉ
SAINT-ANTOINE [1]

BY HARRY JAMES SMITH

THIS little episode, complete in itself, is essentially a character sketch of two aged people, — the proprietor of the once famous Café Saint-Antoine at Rouen, and his admiring wife. It is to be noted that the characterization is accomplished without direct exposition. Individuality is developed by actions, words, and the manner of speech — especially the last. The rebellious rapping of the old man's cane as he comments angrily upon Torine's severity with the "aged ones," his complaisant smile as he accepts his wife's tribute to his skill, the Gallic flourish with which he places his masterpiece in the oven, the last quavering wish for Torine's return — these are but a few examples of the delicate touches with which the author realistically sets his actors before the reader as revealing their own characters.

It is also to be observed that this method of indirect characterization possesses the distinct advantage of constant appeal to the reader's interpretative faculties, and, in consequence, — perhaps unconsciously, — the narrative holds the interest more consistently. It is one thing to tell us bluntly and directly that the old restaurateur was still crafty, and that he secretly rebelled against the domination of his capable daughter. The thought is far more effectively conveyed by implication : —

"Torine! Always Torine!" — He snapped his fingers contemptuously. "I'm not afraid of Torine."

The little woman drew a tremulous breath of admiration. "Ah, you never were a man for being afraid, my Victor." . . .

A blush of new life had appeared in her sunken little cheeks. Her two hands, freely gesticulating, shook with excitement. The old Victor agreed with her, rapping his stick on the floor. And then a look of Machiavellian subtlety came into his glittering eye.

"Attend, my wife," he whispered significantly. "I know some-

[1] Chapter XIII of *Enchanted Ground*. Published by Houghton Mifflin Company.

thing about Victorine, and she suspects that I know it. How did the dog of Monsieur Philippe run away yesterday? He did not get out on the street himself. Neither did the grocer boy let him out, as Torine declare. — *I know how he get out !*"

The reader will also find the selection singularly illustrative of the pathos that often lies close by the sources of humor. This is a quality more readily felt than expounded, and it pervades this characterization of the aged couple in their abortive attempt to declare their independence against the ravages of increasing years.

FROM young Victor, Victorine and her sister-in-law, Jenny La Bergère, alias Shepherd (or, as Victorine stoutly maintained, Shepherdess), had received the present of two balcony tickets to the Hippodrome, for the afternoon after Thanksgiving. Victorine, who was rarely to be found outside her kitchen, was declaring that she did not see how she could possibly arrange to go to that place, leaving the old papa and the old maman all to themselves.

"What does my brother think, I wonder!" she demanded. — "That I have nothing to do but go running around after mermaids and trick horses and all those foolish things? If you will tell me how I can find time for that, I will be thankful."

Although she did not deign to look up from the kitchen table which she was vigorously scrubbing with a pumice-stone, her challenge was presumably addressed to Jenny, who stood languidly in the doorway, dressed in a much-beruffled morning-wrapper, her red hair still in crimpers. The two old ones occupied their customary stations, the papa at one side of the range, his two gnarled hands resting on a stout cane, his head trembling slightly, as always, on its pipestem of a neck; the maman Susanne deep in her padded chair in the corner. The energetic scrape of the pumice-stone and the scrub-brush, ocular proof of her immense business, belonged properly to Victorine's sentence. The muscles stood out on her large arms; her face was red with exertion and defiance.

For an instant only she relaxed her labor, to rest her hands on her hips and accord a rapid, contemptuous scrutiny to Jenny's matutinal attire.

"For some people," she announced, crisply, with a little snort, "who have nothing to do in the world but dress stylish and spend money, those Hippodromes may be all very well."

Between the Shepherdess and the thrifty, indefatigable Victorine existed an ever-smouldering hostility which sometimes came near to flame. The two were well matched, however. If Victorine had her contemptuous little snort, Jenny had her supercilious little sniff, and used it with especial readiness because she knew that it was excessively well-bred.

"Yes, my dear," she added, with a smile of superior amusement. "I know just how hard it must be for you to get off. Perhaps, after all, it will not be worth the trouble. I hope you will feel perfectly free to give it up."

Victorine gave her a crushing look. "Will you tell me," she demanded, "you who know all about such things, if it would be good manners for me to give it up, when my poor brother has already bought the ticket for me?"

To give it up was, indeed, the last thought in Victorine's head. She was consumed with curiosity in regard to these wonderful soaring ladies, diving mermaids, and dancing flowers of which she had heard so often, and which Jenny authoritatively declared to be the swellest thing that had ever hit New York. But to make admission of that curiosity was by no means Victorine's way.

"Oh, for that matter," said Jenny, with mordant gentleness, "I'm sure Victor would n't mind if you returned the ticket, my dear, and spent the money for some useful thing. He is very sweet in those ways. Though I can't tell you how I'd hate to have to go without you."

Victorine clicked her teeth together, and seemed to speak without so much as opening her mouth. "At half-past one I shall be ready, *my dear*. Voilà!"

The scrubbing was resumed so vindictively that Jenny's final retort — if she made one: she probably did — was quite lost in the uproar. At last, however, the labor of cleanliness was completed, and a strange quiet supervened. Jenny had disappeared. Victorine's temper had evidently worked itself out.

Turning solicitously to her father from the sink, over which she had just replaced her housewife's battery, she inquired, —

"You will be comfortable, mon père? Since it appears to be necessary for me to go to that Hippodrome of theirs, you promise that you will be good — très, très sage — that you will not go to the corner?"

The old man nodded with the most irreproachable docility.

"Oui, ma Torine," he replied, reassuringly. "You may trust the old papa. He will not do anything."

"Good," she commented. "And is the little mother going to be sage, too? She will not get to coughing — no? — while her Torine is away?"

"Non, ma Torine," came the thin, faithful response. "You may trust the old maman. She is going to be good, good."

"Well, then," said Mademoiselle, with a sigh of seeming reluctance, "well, then, I suppose it will be all right if I let them persuade me to go, since Victor wishes it."

"Yes, indeed, ma Torine," urged the old man. "You must go for Victor's sake. We promise to be sage — eh, Susanne?"

"Victorine can trust the old ones," agreed the Norman coiffe. "They are going to be sage, sage."

Promptly, therefore, at the appointed moment, Mademoiselle was in readiness. She entered the kitchen magnificent, incredible, in a black suit that seemed on the point of bursting for the extreme snugness of its fit, and a broad hat towering with white plumes.

The old man rubbed his hands together with paternal admiration.

"You are beautiful, my Victorine! Eh, Susanne, are not you proud to be the mother of our Torine there?"

"She could have five husbands any day if she wanted them," chimed in the little creature.

Victorine gave a smiling grunt, as she struggled with a refractory glove. "I know too much about husbands," she said.

"There is plenty time yet," put in the papa, knowingly. "But, however, you are going to enjoy yourself well this afternoon."

"Oh, as for that," conceded Victorine doubtfully, "I do not care much about all those absurd things at the Hippodrome. But Victor will be pleased, I hope. I am doing it for him. — You may light the gas, father, at half-past four."

"Very well, my Torine. At half-past four. You can trust us to be sage."

In another minute the ancient pair heard the shutting of the front door. They were alone.

"Eh bien," observed old Victor, taking a little pinch of snuff. "The young people must have their good times, I suppose. One of these days the good times will come to an end. They will grow feeble and old and have to sit beside the stove all day."

"Yes, my Victor," sighed Susanne. "Life is not gay. For a little time there is singing and happiness; but not for long. Well, one must bear it with patience."

The papa Victor gave a rebellious rap of his cane. "But for all that," he remarked, "it seems to me that Torine is a little too severe with the old ones. Why does she refuse to let me get a little glass sometimes at the corner? Why, I say? — Even at my age I might have a little pleasure in that."

"For one thing, my Victor, she does not like to have you spend money."

"A little glass — that is only ten sous."

"Yes, my dear man, if it would only be one little glass. But always where there is one, there is two, sometimes three. That costs."

"Nevertheless, Torine is too severe," reiterated the papa Victor, in an injured voice. "She forget the days of the Café Antoine. She think she owe nothing to her poor old father."

Susanne, perceiving that nothing was to be gained by argument, only sighed a little ghost of a sigh, and continued her knitting.

"But an idea has come to me," pursued the octogenarian, darkly. "I am thinking about it since two days. Surely there can be no harm in amusing ourselves a little when they have gone off like that and left us all alone."

"If Torine would not object," put in Susanne, timidly.

"Torine! Always Torine!" — He snapped his fingers contemptuously. "I am not afraid of Torine."

The little woman drew a tremulous breath of admiration. "Ah, you never were a man for being afraid, my Victor."

The old papa smiled complaisantly. "No," he agreed. "I do not believe anybody ever accused the proprietor of the Café Antoine of being timid; and all Rouen knew the Café Antoine. — Besides, in her heart, Torine would be glad. She would only pretend to be angry."

"What do you mean, mon ami?" inquired Susanne, scenting evil.

The old man gave a confident toss to his head. "She does not like to have him out there," he said, with a gesture of a long bony finger toward the yard. "He will never fly, that is certain. His wing is not going to be strong again. He only eats and eats and grows fat, — oh, my Susanne, so fat! so fat! — a veritable marvel!"

He produced a curiously succulent sound between his scanty teeth. A first clear hint of the devilish design flashed into the old maman's brain.

"The pigeon!" she gasped. "Oh, my friend, you would never dare!"

"No?" — The papa Victor drew himself up imperially. "Who says I would not dare? — Listen, my Susanne, do you remember the famous pigeon-pasties of the Café Antoine? Do you remember the universal admiration they evoked? Do you remember how Victor Napoléon La Bergère, who is now an old, old man, huddling by the stove with his cane, used to create them in that fine little cuisine behind the restaurant? Ah, those were the good days. There was glory then!"

"Glory! Ah, my man!" exclaimed Susanne, with an outburst of febrile enthusiasm. "In all Rouen one used to hear, 'Oh, the wonderful pâtés de pigeon of the Café Antoine! Oh, the lovely sauces of the Café Antoine! Oh, the fried potatoes, so delicate, so tender, of the

Café Antoine!' No one talked in Rouen of anything else!"

A flush of new life had appeared in her sunken little cheeks. Her two hands, freely gesticulating, shook with excitement. The old Victor agreed with her, rapping his stick on the floor. And then a look of Machiavellian subtlety came into his glittering eyes.

"Attend, my wife," he whispered, significantly. "I know something about Victorine, and she suspects that I know it. — How did the dog of Monsieur Philippe run away yesterday? He did not get out on the street himself. Neither did the grocer boy let him out, as Torine declare. — *I know how he get out!*"

She gazed at him with eyes wide-set, comprehending, reasoning.

"Go, my Victor," she directed, with sudden resolution. "Take the pigeon. Yes, yes, why should we not amuse ourselves a little? We will tell Monsieur Philippe that it flew away while you were feeding it."

"That is what I am going to do," announced the hero of the Café Antoine. "We will have once more a little pâté — just me and you, hein? — Wait, I am going for him. Will you get ready the little black kettle, my dear? We will boil him for fifteen minute in water with a small little onion and some salt."

It was a labor of but a half-hour to prepare Columba for the pot. Susanne sat close by during the entire process, proudly, eagerly watching, until the last joint had been separated by the old man's skilled fingers, and put over to seethe. Next the paste must be mixed, and sauce prepared. With excited, fevered devotion she responded to his every request, hovering about like a timid winter bird. She fetched flour and butter, fetched stock, whole cloves, mace, cayenne, bay leaves, and a precious dark little bottle of herb-extract that had come from Rouen twenty years ago; she buttered a tiny baking-dish, found a piece of brown paper to cover the pie, and stood with raised, tremulous hands beside the old Victor while the pâté was compounded. He was a general; she his devoted adjutant.

"Ah, my Victor, you are a marvel of men," she protested, while her sunken eyes glowed with adoration. "One would believe you were not a day older than thirty to see the address with which you work. It is the Café Antoine once more alive!"

The old man gave a deprecatory shrug. "Oh, this is nothing," he asserted, magnificently. "This is the simplest of all my creations. However, it *is* something, my friend, to be free once more. Torine will never remember that her father is an artist supreme. She believe he is the same as any old man."

"Torine forget the Café Antoine," put in Susanne, antiphonally.

"But it is going to be all different in the future," declared the papa Victor, defiantly. "After this I am going to have my own way whenever I want it. It will be, 'Torine, this!' — 'Torine, that!' She will soon learn that things have changed."

There were two bright red spots at his cheek-bones; his eyes flashed with authority; his voice had lost its old-time tremolo, and was once more that of a commander of men's stomachs. The years had rolled from him like magic. Even Susanne seemed a quarter-century younger.

"Voilà!" he announced, grandly, as he put the last decorative touch to the crimped edge of the pasty. "Voilà! It is done! — Open the oven!"

The oven was opened. In went the masterpiece of the

Café Antoine. Click shut the heavy door. The deed was accomplished. The inspiration had come to its fruition. The genius of the papa Victor, evoked from its long slumber, had been vindicated.

"And now, my man," said Susanne, with hectic briskness, "we will have a little wee rest for one minute in our chairs; and then we will gather up the cooking things and put them away. Later we will eat the pie."

"Yes," said the papa Victor. "A minute or two of rest; and then we will finish."

They resumed their accustomed places; and a silence fell upon the room, broken only by the ticking of the clock. The afternoon was slipping away. Already the basement kitchen had grown a little dusky. A great fatigue began to envelop the ex-proprietor of the Café Antoine. His limbs, that so short a time before had thrilled with imperial energy, felt like dead things. He wondered how he could ever get up from his chair again.

The fire began to glow with a ruddier gleam through the little chinks of the stove. The kettle hummed with a soft, insistent monotony. And still the clock ticked on. The shadows were ranked deep in the corners of the room. It was almost time to light the gas. The dishes and utensils were still lying in disorder on the table. The thought suddenly came to him that before very, very long Victorine would be coming home; and with the thought a pall of dread fell upon his spirit. Victorine would be oh, so angry! She would scold him. Perhaps she would refuse to give him his little glass of cognac before he went to bed!

Oh, they must clear away the dishes at once. Victorine must not find things in disorder.

"Susanne," he called feebly. "We have had our rest now, hein? We must be putting away the things."

For the space of several seconds he waited for an answer. It was very dark in the corner where Susanne was sitting. He could not see her.

"Susanne," he called again. "Do you hear? We must be putting away the things now."

The reply came so faint as scarcely to be audible. "Yes, my friend. We must put away the things at once, — at once, — in just a little minute."

But neither made any movement to get up. The room grew darker. It was night in the corners. Victorine's white apron hanging on the back of the door looked like a ghostly visitant, come upon them unawares. The shadows were full of things that got on one's nerves.

"Susanne," he said, finally, in a strange, muffled voice that tried to be resolute. "It is time to light the gas now. We must be busying ourselves. The dishes must be washed and put away now."

"Yes, my Victor," came the response, scarcely louder than the whirr of an insect's wing. "We must not sit here any longer like this. We have had our rest."

There was a little break in her words; while the clock ticked tyrannically.

"Ah, my friend," she concluded. "Life is very hard. It is not an easy thing for the poor old ones."

The room was all dark now, save for the mocking little chinks of the fire. The pâté was surely burned to a crisp. Even the kettle was beginning to boil away, as you could tell by its eager, hoarse song. Decidedly old age had once more claimed its victims.

The maman Susanne sat huddled among the cushions of her deep chair, gazing at nothing out of vague, frightened eyes. She began to feel cold. She knew that soon she would begin to cough. Ah, life was not gay at all, just now. She wished they would come and put her to bed. She was very tired.

"Why does not our Victorine come back?" she murmured, feebly, at last. "I am getting frightened, it is so dark. And I am very tired."

"Yes," came the papa's voice, quaveringly, through the darkness. "I wish she would come. I wish she would come and light the gas. I do not like to sit here so long, just us two, in the dark. It is not kind to leave the old ones so long without attention."

A LIBERAL EDUCATION [1]

BY ANTHONY HOPE HAWKINS ("ANTHONY HOPE")

DIALOGUE is one of the various methods of indirect characterization, — whereby the reader is enabled to gain knowledge of personality through implication rather than by direct exposition. This is sometimes known as the *dramatic method*, as the drama, from the very nature of the conditions, renders direct exposition impossible and proceeds by means of conversation between the actors. Excellent illustration is furnished by the *Dolly Dialogues*, from which the selection is taken. After reading *A Liberal Education* one is in possession of a very definite picture of Miss Dolly Foster and of Mr. Carter, yet it is through the process of inference, by "reading between the lines," that the impression is secured.

"THERE's ingratitude for you!" Miss Dolly Foster exclaimed suddenly.

"Where?" I asked, rousing myself from meditation.

She pointed at a young man who had just passed where we sat. He was dressed very smartly, and was walking with a lady attired in the height of the fashion.

"I *made* that man," said Dolly, "and now he cuts me dead before the whole of the Row! It's atrocious. Why, but for me, do you suppose he'd be at this moment engaged to three thousand a year and — and the plainest girl in London?"

"Not that," I pleaded; "think of —"

"Well, very plain, anyhow. I was quite ready to bow to him. I almost did."

"In fact, you did!"

[1] From *The Dolly Dialogues*. Printed by permission of Henry Holt & Co.

"I did n't. I declare I did n't."

"Oh, well, you did n't then. It only looked like it."

"I met him," said Miss Dolly, "three years ago. At that time he was — oh, quite unpresentable. He was everything he should n't be. He was a teetotaler, you know, and he did n't smoke, and he was always going to concerts. Oh, and he wore his hair long, and his trousers short, and his hat on the back of his head. And his umbrella —"

"Where did he wear that?"

"He *carried* that, Mr. Carter. Don't be silly! Carried it unrolled, you know, and generally a paper parcel in the other hand; and he had spectacles, too."

"He has certainly changed outwardly, at least."

"Yes, I know; well, I did that. I took him in hand, and I just taught him, and now —!"

"Yes, I know that. But how did you teach him? Give him Saturday evening lectures, or what?"

"Oh, every-evening lectures, and most-morning walks. And I taught him to dance, and I broke his wretched fiddle with my own hands!"

"What very arbitrary distinctions you draw!"

"I don't know what you mean. I do like a man to be smart, anyhow. Don't you, Mr. Carter? You 're not so smart as you might be. Now, shall I take you in hand?" And she smiled upon me.

"Let 's hear your method. What did you do to him?"

"To Phil Meadows? Oh, nothing. I just slipped in a remark here and there, whenever he talked nonsense. I used to speak just at the right time, you know."

"But how had your words such influence, Miss Foster?"

"Oh, well, you know, Mr. Carter, I made it a *condi-*

tion that he should do just what I wanted in little things like that. Did he think I was going to walk about with a man carrying a brown-paper parcel — as if we had been to the shop for a pound of tea?"

"Still, I don't see why he should alter all his —"

"Oh, you are stupid! Of course, he liked me, you know."

"Oh, did he? I see."

"You seem to think that very funny."

"Not that he did — but that, apparently, he does n't."

"Well, you got out of that rather neatly — for you. No, he does n't now. You see, he misunderstood my motive. He thought — well, I do believe he thought I cared for him, you know. Of course, I did n't."

"Not a bit?"

"Just as a friend — and a pupil, you know. And when he'd had his hair cut and bought a frock-coat (fancy! he'd never had one!), he looked quite nice. He has nice eyes. Did you notice them?"

"Lord, no!"

"Well, you're so unobservant."

"Oh, not always. I've observed that your —"

"Please don't! It's no use, is it?"

I looked very unhappy. There is an understanding that I am very unhappy since Miss Foster's engagement to the Earl of Mickleham was announced.

"What was I saying before — before you — you know — oh, about Phil Meadows, of course. I did like him very much, you know, or I should n't have taken all that trouble. Why, his own mother thanked me!"

"I have no more to say," said I.

"But she wrote me a horrid letter afterwards."

"You're so very elliptical."

"So very what, Mr. Carter?"

"You leave so much out, I mean. After what?"

"Why, after I sent him away. Did n't I tell you? Oh, we had the most awful scene. He *raved*, Mr. Carter. He called me the most horrid names, and —"

"Tore his hair?"

"It was n't long enough to get hold of," she tittered. "But don't laugh. It was really dreadful. And so unjust! And then, next day, when I thought it was comfortably over, you know, he came back, and — and apologized, and called himself the most awful names, and — well, that was really worse."

"What did the fellow complain of?" I asked in wondering tones.

"Oh, he said I 'd destroyed his faith in women, you know, and that I 'd led him on, and that I was — well, he was very rude, indeed. And he went on writing me letters like that for a whole year! It made me quite uncomfortable."

"But he did n't go back to short trousers and a fiddle, did he?" I asked anxiously.

"Oh, no. But he forgot all he owed me, and he told me that his heart was dead, and that he should never love any one again."

"But he 's going to marry that girl."

"Oh, he does n't care about her," said Miss Dolly, reassuringly. "It 's the money, you know. He had n't a farthing of his own. Now he 'll be set up for life."

"And it 's all due to you!" said I, admiringly.

"Well, it is, really."

"I don't call her such a bad-looking girl, though." (I had n't seen her face.)

"Mr. Carter! She 's *hideous!*"

I dropped that subject.

"And now," said Miss Dolly again, "he cuts me dead!"

"It is the height of ingratitude. Why, to love you was a liberal education!"

"Yes, was n't it? How nicely you put that! 'A liberal education!' I shall tell Archie." (Archie is Lord Mickleham.)

"What, about Phil Meadows?"

"Goodness me, no, Mr. Carter. Just what you said, you know."

"But why not tell Mickleham about Phil Meadows?" I urged. "It's all to your credit, you know."

"Yes, I know, but men are so foolish. You see, Archie thinks —"

"Of course he does."

"You might let me finish."

"Archie thinks you were never in love before."

"Yes, he does. Well, of course, I was n't in love with Phil —"

"Not a little bit?"

"Oh, well —"

"Nor with any one else?"

Miss Dolly prodded the path with her parasol.

"Nor with any one else?" I asked again.

Miss Dolly looked for an instant in my direction.

"Nor with any one else?" said I.

Miss Dolly looked straight in front of her.

"Nor with —" I began.

"Hullo, old chappie, where did you spring from?"

"Why, Archie!" cried Miss Dolly.

"Oh, how are you, Mickleham, old man? Take this seat; I'm just off — just off. Yes, I was, upon my honor — got to meet a man at the club. Good-bye, Miss Foster. Jove! I'm late!"

And as I went I heard Miss Dolly say, "I thought you were *never* coming, Archie, dear!"

Well, she did n't think he was coming just then. No more did I.

THE OUTCASTS OF POKER FLAT[1]

BRET HARTE

The Outcasts of Poker Flat presents evident exemplification of the three fundamentals of narrative writing, — setting, characterization, and plot, — but the ultimate value of the story lies in its realistic portrayal of human emotion; it is therefore, essentially a story of character. In the evolution of John Oakhurst's true and better self, in the revelation of the Duchess's underlying womanhood, in the characterization of all the actors, one notes the difference between the two senses in which the word "character" is used: that of *personage* and *personality.* Uncle Billy, for example, is introduced as a "suspected sluice-robber and confirmed drunkard." To this extent he is a mere personage, nothing more than an actor in the drama. He is in no sense individualized, differentiated from other similar rascals. But when Oakhurst awakens on the morning after Tom and Piney's arrival to find the little encampment threatened with a blizzard, and to discover that the villainous Uncle Billy has made off during the night with the mules, — their sole hope of escape, — then the suspected sluice-robber and confirmed drunkard ceases to be but one of a class: he is now essentially himself, one who, to save his own worthless skin, will deprive others of their single chance for life. In this sense Uncle Billy is raised from the level of a personage, a mere *dramatis persona*, to that of a personality. Similarly the other characters of the story are developed, each with particular reference to the particular trait that constitutes what we term individuality, or the personal equation.

The author sets forth the various characters of the story mainly by the indirect method: that is, by word and action. In the case of Oakhurst, — to take one instance, — beyond a brief paragraph and an occasional sentence here and there, one finds little direct exposition of the gambler's character;

[1] From the *Complete Works of Bret Harte.* Published by Houghton Mifflin Company.

yet at the close of the story the personality of John Oakhurst is clearly and distinctly defined. The kick administered to Uncle Billy when, upon Tom and Piney's arrival, that degenerate is about to give expression to thoughts that were better left unspoken, the parting kiss to the Duchess, the quiet departure from the camp when food is running low, and the final act of the dissipated life, — these and other external indications make it easy for the reader to draw definite inferences regarding him "who was at once the strongest and yet the weakest of the outcasts of Poker Flat."

The reader will observe also the generally objective attitude that the author assumes toward his narrative. In the closing sentence characterizing Oakhurst, quoted at the end of the preceding paragraph, there is, indeed, a suggestion of the personal attitude toward the gambler's heroism; yet passages of this character are infrequent, and the story is presented from the impersonal point of view, without sentiment, without expressed disapproval or approval of the various personages as they perform their respective parts in the action.

As Mr. John Oakhurst, gambler, stepped into the main street of Poker Flat on the morning of the 23d of November, 1850, he was conscious of a change in its moral atmosphere since the preceding night. Two or three men, conversing earnestly together, ceased as he approached, and exchanged significant glances. There was a Sabbath lull in the air, which, in a settlement unused to Sabbath influences, looked ominous.

Mr. Oakhurst's calm, handsome face betrayed small concern in these indications. Whether he was conscious of any predisposing cause was another question. "I reckon they're after somebody," he reflected; "likely it's me." He returned to his pocket the handkerchief with which he had been wiping away the red dust of Poker Flat from his neat boots, and quietly discharged his mind of any further conjecture.

In point of fact, Poker Flat was "after somebody." It

had lately suffered the loss of several thousand dollars, two valuable horses, and a prominent citizen. It was experiencing a spasm of virtuous reaction, quite as lawless and ungovernable as any of the acts that had provoked it. A secret committee had determined to rid the town of all improper persons. This was done permanently in regard of two men who were then hanging from the boughs of a sycamore in the gulch, and temporarily in the banishment of certain other objectionable characters. I regret to say that some of these were ladies. It is but due to the sex, however, to state that their impropriety was professional, and it was only in such easily established standards of evil that Poker Flat ventured to sit in judgment.

Mr. Oakhurst was right in supposing that he was included in this category. A few of the committee had urged hanging him as a possible example and a sure method of reimbursing themselves from his pockets of the sums he had won from them. "It's ag'in' justice," said Jim Wheeler, "to let this yer young man from Roaring Camp — an entire stranger — carry away our money." But a crude sentiment of equity residing in the breasts of those who had been fortunate enough to win from Mr. Oakhurst overruled this narrower local prejudice.

Mr. Oakhurst received his sentence with philosophic calmness, none the less coolly that he was aware of the hesitation of his judges. He was too much of a gambler not to accept fate. With him life was at best an uncertain game, and he recognized the usual percentage in favor of the dealer.

A body of armed men accompanied the deported wickedness of Poker Flat to the outskirts of the settlement. Besides Mr. Oakhurst, who was known to be a coolly desperate man, and for whose intimidation the armed escort was intended, the expatriated party consisted of a young woman familiarly known as "The Duchess"; another who had won the title of "Mother Shipton"; and "Uncle Billy," a suspected sluice-robber and confirmed drunkard. The cavalcade provoked no comments from the spectators, nor was any word uttered by the escort. Only when the gulch which marked the uttermost limit of Poker Flat was reached, the leader spoke briefly and to the point. The exiles were forbidden to return at the peril of their lives.

As the escort disappeared, their pent-up feelings found vent in a few hysterical tears from the Duchess, some bad language from Mother Shipton, and a Parthian volley of expletives from Uncle Billy. The philosophic Oakhurst alone remained silent. He listened calmly to Mother Shipton's desire to cut somebody's heart out, to the repeated statements of the Duchess that she would die in the road, and to the alarming oaths that seemed to be bumped out of Uncle Billy as he rode forward. With the easy good humor characteristic of his class, he insisted upon exchanging his own riding-horse, "Five-spot," for the sorry mule which the Duchess rode. But even this act did not draw the party into any closer sympathy. The young woman readjusted her somewhat draggled plumes with a feeble, faded coquetry; Mother Shipton eyed the possessor of "Five-Spot" with malevolence, and Uncle Billy included the whole party in one sweeping anathema.

The road to Sandy Bar — a camp that, not having as yet experienced the regenerating influences of Poker Flat, consequently seemed to offer some invitation to the emigrants — lay over a steep mountain range. It was distant a day's severe travel. In that advanced season the party soon passed out of the moist, temperate regions of the foothills into the dry, cold, bracing air of the Sierras. The trail was narrow and difficult. At noon the Duchess, rolling out of her saddle upon the ground, declared her intention of going no farther, and the party halted.

The spot was singularly wild and impressive. A wooded amphitheater surrounded on three sides by precipitous cliffs of naked granite, sloped gently toward the crest of another precipice that overlooked the valley. It was, undoubtedly, the most suitable spot for a camp, had camping been advisable. But Mr. Oakhurst knew that scarcely half the journey to Sandy Bar was accomplished, and the party were not equipped or provisioned for delay. This fact he pointed out to his companions curtly, with a philosophic commentary on the folly of "throwing up their hand before the game was played out." But they were furnished with liquor, which in this emergency stood them in place of food, fuel, rest, and prescience. In spite of his remonstrances, it was not long before they were more or less under its influence. Uncle Billy passed rapidly from a bellicose state into one of stupor, the Duchess became maudlin, and Mother Shipton snored. Mr. Oakhurst alone remained erect, leaning against a rock, calmly surveying them.

Mr. Oakhurst did not drink. It interfered with a profession which required coolness, impassiveness, and presence of mind, and, in his own language, he "couldn't afford it." As he gazed at his recumbent fellow exiles, the loneliness begotten of his pariah trade, his habits of life, his very vices, for the first time seriously oppressed him. He bestirred himself in dusting his black clothes, washing his hands and face, and other acts characteristic of his studiously neat habits, and for a moment forgot his annoyance. The thought of deserting his weaker and more pitiable companions never perhaps occurred to him. Yet he could not help feeling the want of that excitement which, singularly enough, was most conducive to that calm equanimity for which he was notorious. He looked at the gloomy walls that rose a thousand feet sheer above the circling pines around him, at the sky ominously clouded, at the valley below, already deepening into shadow; and, doing so, suddenly he heard his own name called.

A horseman slowly ascended the trail. In the fresh, open face of the newcomer Mr. Oakhurst recognized Tom Simson, otherwise known as "The Innocent," of Sandy Bar. He had met him some months before over a "little game," and had, with perfect equanimity, won the entire fortune — amounting to some forty dollars — of that guileless youth. After the game was finished, Mr. Oakhurst drew the youthful speculator behind the door and thus addressed him: "Tommy, you 're a good little man, but you can't gamble worth a cent. Don't try it over again." He then handed him his money back, pushed him gently from the room, and so made a devoted slave of Tom Simson.

There was a remembrance of this in his boyish and enthusiastic greeting of Mr. Oakhurst. He had started, he said, to go to Poker Flat to seek his fortune. "Alone?" No, not exactly alone; in fact (a giggle), he had run away with Piney Woods. Did n't Mr. Oakhurst remember Piney? She that used to wait on the table at the Temperance House? They had been engaged a long time, but old Jake Woods had objected, and so they had run away, and were going to Poker Flat to be married, and here they were. And they were tired out, and how lucky it was they had found a place to camp, and company. All this the Innocent delivered rapidly, while Piney, a stout, comely damsel of fifteen, emerged from behind the pine tree, where she had been blushing unseen, and rode to the side of her lover.

Mr. Oakhurst seldom troubled himself with sentiment, still less with propriety; but he had a vague idea that the situation was not fortunate. He retained, however, his presence of mind sufficiently to kick Uncle Billy, who was about to say something, and Uncle Billy was sober enough to recognize in Mr. Oakhurst's kick a superior power that would not bear trifling. He then endeavored to dissuade Tom Simson from delaying further, but in vain. He even pointed out the fact that there was no provision, nor means of making a camp. But, unluckily, the Innocent met this objection by assuring the party that he was provided with an extra mule loaded with provisions, and by the discovery of a rude attempt at a log house near the trail. "Piney can stay with Mrs. Oakhurst," said the Innocent, pointing to the Duchess, "and I can shift for myself."

Nothing but Mr. Oakhurst's admonishing foot saved Uncle Billy from bursting into a roar of laughter. As it was, he felt compelled to retire up the cañon until he could recover his gravity. There he confided the joke to the tall pine trees, with many slaps of his leg, contortions of his face, and the usual profanity. But when he returned to the party, he found them seated by a fire — for the air had grown strangely chill and the sky overcast — in apparently amicable conversation. Piney was actually talking in an impulsive girlish fashion to the Duchess, who was listening with an interest and animation she had not shown for many days. The Innocent was holding forth, apparently with equal effect, to Mr.

Oakhurst and Mother Shipton, who was actually re-laxing into amiability. "Is this yer a d—d picnic?" said Uncle Billy, with inward scorn, as he surveyed the sylvan group, the glancing firelight, and the tethered animals in the foreground. Suddenly an idea mingled with the alcoholic fumes that disturbed his brain. It was appar-ently of a jocular nature, for he felt impelled to slap his leg again and cram his fist into his mouth.

As the shadows crept slowly up the mountain, a slight breeze rocked the tops of the pine trees and moaned through their long and gloomy aisles. The ruined cabin, patched and covered with pine boughs, was set apart for the ladies. As the lovers parted, they unaffectedly exchanged a kiss, so honest and sincere that it might have been heard above the swaying pines. The frail Duchess and the malevolent Mother Shipton were prob-ably too stunned to remark upon this last evidence of simplicity, and so turned without a word to the hut. The fire was replenished, the men lay down before the door, and in a few minutes were asleep.

Mr. Oakhurst was a light sleeper. Toward morning he awoke benumbed and cold. As he stirred the dying fire, the wind, which was now blowing strongly, brought to his cheek that which caused the blood to leave it, — snow!

He started to his feet with the intention of awakening the sleepers, for there was no time to lose. But turning to where Uncle Billy had been lying, he found him gone. A suspicion leaped to his brain, and a curse to his lips. He ran to the spot where the mules had been teth-ered — they were no longer there. The tracks were al-ready rapidly disappearing in the snow.

The momentary excitement brought Mr. Oakhurst back to the fire with his usual calm. He did not waken the sleepers. The Innocent slumbered peaccfully, with a smile on his good-humored, freckled face; the virgin Piney slept beside her frailer sisters as sweetly as though attended by celestial guardians; and Mr. Oakhurst, drawing his blanket over his shoulders, stroked his mustaches and waited for the dawn. It came slowly in a whirling mist of snowflakes that dazzled and confused the eye. What could be seen of the landscape appeared magically changed. He looked over the valley, and summed up the present and future in two words, "Snowed in!"

A careful inventory of the provisions, which, fortunately for the party, had been stored within the hut, and so escaped the felonious fingers of Uncle Billy, disclosed the fact that with care and prudence they might last ten days longer. "That is," said Mr. Oakhurst *sotto voce* to the Innocent, "if you're willing to board us. If you ain't — and perhaps you'd better not — you can wait till Uncle Billy gets back with provisions." For some occult reason, Mr. Oakhurst could not bring himself to disclose Uncle Billy's rascality, and so offered the hypothesis that he had wandered from the camp and had accidentally stampeded the animals. He dropped a warning to the Duchess and Mother Shipton, who, of course, knew the facts of their associate's defection. "They'll find out the truth about us *all* when they find out anything," he added significantly, "and there's no good frightening them now."

Tom Simson not only put all his worldly store at the disposal of Mr. Oakhurst, but seemed to enjoy the prospect of their enforced seclusion. "We'll have a good camp for a week, and then the snow'll melt, and we'll all go back together." The cheerful gayety of the young man and Mr. Oakhurst's calm infected the others. The

Innocent, with the aid of pine boughs, extemporized a thatch for the roofless cabin, and the Duchess directed Piney in the rearrangement of the interior with a taste and tact that opened the blue eyes of that provincial maiden to their fullest extent. "I reckon now you're used to fine things at Poker Flat," said Piney. The Duchess turned away sharply to conceal something that reddened her cheeks through their professional tint, and Mother Shipton requested Piney not to "chatter." But when Mr. Oakhurst returned from a weary search for the trail, he heard the sound of happy laughter echoed from the rocks. He stopped in some alarm, and his thoughts first naturally reverted to the whiskey, which he had prudently cachéd. "And yet it don't somehow sound like whiskey," said the gambler. It was not until he caught sight of the blazing fire through the still blinding storm, and the group around it, that he settled to the conviction that it was "square fun."

Whether Mr. Oakhurst had cachéd his cards with the whiskey as something debarred the free access of the community, I cannot say. It was certain that, in Mother Shipton's words, he "did n't say 'cards' once" during that evening. Haply the time was beguiled by an accordion, produced somewhat ostentatiously by Tom Simson from his pack. Notwithstanding some difficulties attending the manipulation of this instrument, Piney Woods managed to pluck several reluctant melodies from its keys, to an accompaniment by the Innocent on a pair of bone castanets. But the crowning festivity of the evening was reached in a rude camp-meeting hymn, which the lovers, joining hands, sang with great earnestness and vociferation. I fear that a certain defiant tone and Covenanter's swing to its chorus, rather than any devotional quality, caused it speedily to infect the others, who at last joined in the refrain: —

> "I'm proud to live in the service of the Lord,
>   And I'm bound to die in his army."

The pines rocked, the storm eddied and whirled above the miserable group, and the flames of their altar leaped heavenward, as if in token of the vow.

At midnight the storm abated, the rolling clouds parted, and the stars glittered keenly above the sleeping camp. Mr. Oakhurst, whose professional habits had enabled him to live on the smallest possible amount of sleep, in dividing the watch with Tom Simson somehow managed to take upon himself the greater part of that duty. He excused himself to the Innocent by saying that he had "often been a week without sleep." "Doing what?" asked Tom. "Poker!" replied Oakhurst sententiously. "When a man gets a streak of luck, — nigger-luck, — he don't get tired. The luck gives in first. Luck," contined the gambler reflectively, "is a mighty queer thing. All you know about it for certain is that it's bound to change. And it's finding out when it's going to change that makes you. We've had a streak of bad luck since we left Poker Flat, — you come along, and slap you get into it, too. If you can hold your cards right along you're all right. For," added the gambler, with cheerful irrelevance —

> "'I'm proud to live in the service of the Lord,
>   And I'm bound to die in his army.'"

The third day came, and the sun, looking through the white-curtained valley, saw the outcasts divide their slowly decreasing store of provisions for the morning meal. It was one of the peculiarities of that mountain climate that its rays diffused a kindly warmth over the wintry landscape, as if in regretful commiseration of the past. But it revealed drift on drift of snow piled high around the hut, — a hopeless, uncharted, trackless sea of white lying below the rocky shores to which the castaways still clung. Through the marvelously clear air the smoke of the pastoral village of Poker Flat rose miles away. Mother Shipton saw it, and from a remote pinnacle of her rocky fastness hurled in that direction a final malediction. It was her last vituperative attempt, and perhaps for that reason was invested with a certain degree of sublimity. It did her good, she privately informed the Duchess. "Just you go out there and cuss, and see." She then set herself to the task of amusing "the child," as she and the Duchess were pleased to call Piney. Piney was no chicken, but it was a soothing and original theory of the pair thus to account for the fact that she did n't swear and was n't improper.

When night crept up again through the gorges, the reedy notes of the accordion rose and fell in fitful spasms and long-drawn gasps by the flickering camp-fire. But music failed to fill entirely the aching void left by insufficient food, and a new diversion was proposed by Piney, — story-telling. Neither Mr. Oakhurst nor his female companions caring to relate their personal experiences, this plan would have failed too, but for the Innocent. Some months before he had chanced upon a stray copy of Mr. Pope's ingenious translation of the Iliad. He now proposed to narrate the principal incidents of that poem — having thoroughly mastered the argument and fairly forgotten the words — in the current vernacular of Sandy Bar. And so for the rest of that night the Homeric demigods again walked the earth. Trojan bully and wily Greek wrestled in the winds, and the great pines in the cañon seemed to bow to the wrath of the son

of Peleus. Mr. Oakhurst listened with quiet satisfaction.
Most especially was he interested in the fate of "Ash-
heels," as the Innocent persisted in denominating the
"swift-footed Achilles."

So, with small food and much of Homer and the accordion, a week passed over the heads of the outcasts.
The sun again forsook them, and again from leaden skies
the snowflakes were sifted over the land. Day by day
closer around them drew the snowy circle, until at last
they looked from their prison over drifted walls of daz-
zling white, that towered twenty feet above their heads.
It became more and more difficult to replenish their fires,
even from the fallen trees beside them, now half hidden
in the drifts. And yet no one complained. The lovers
turned from the dreary prospect and looked into each
other's eyes, and were happy. Mr. Oakhurst settled himself coolly to the losing game before him. The Duchess,
more cheerful than she had been, assumed the care of
Piney. Only Mother Shipton — once the strongest of
the party — seemed to sicken and fade. At midnight on
the tenth day she called Oakhurst to her side. "I'm going," she said, in a voice of querulous weakness, "but
don't say anything about it. Don't waken the kids.
Take the bundle from under my head, and open it."
Mr. Oakhurst did so. It contained Mother Shipton's
rations for the last week, untouched. "Give 'em to the
child," she said, pointing to the sleeping Piney. "You've
starved yourself," said the gambler. "That's what they
call it," said the woman querulously, as she lay down
again, and, turning her face to the wall, passed quietly
away.

The accordion and the bones were put aside that day,
and Homer was forgotten. When the body of Mother
Shipton had been committed to the snow, Mr. Oakhurst

took the Innocent aside, and showed him a pair of snow-shoes, which he had fashioned from the old pack-saddle. "There's one chance in a hundred to save her yet," he said, pointing to Piney; "but it's there," he added, pointing toward Poker Flat. "If you can reach there in two days, she's safe." "And you?" asked Tom Simson. "I'll stay here," was the curt reply.

The lovers parted with a long embrace. "You are not going, too?" said the Duchess, as she saw Mr. Oakhurst apparently waiting to accompany him. "As far as the cañon," he replied. He turned suddenly and kissed the Duchess, leaving her pallid face aflame, and her trembling limbs rigid with amazement.

Night came, but not Mr. Oakhurst. It brought the storm again and the whirling snow. Then the Duchess, feeding the fire, found that some one had quietly piled beside the hut enough fuel to last a few days longer. The tears rose to her eyes, but she hid them from Piney.

The women slept but little. In the morning, looking into each other's faces, they read their fate. Neither spoke, but Piney, accepting the position of the stronger, drew near and placed her arm around the Duchess's waist. They kept this attitude for the rest of the day. That night the storm reached its greatest fury, and, rending asunder the protecting vines, invaded the very hut.

Toward morning they found themselves unable to feed the fire, which gradually died away. As the embers slowly blackened, the Duchess crept closer to Piney, and broke the silence of many hours: "Piney, can you pray?" "No, dear," said Piney simply. The Duchess, without knowing exactly why, felt relieved, and, putting her head upon Piney's shoulder, spoke no more. And so reclining, the younger and purer pillowing the head of her soiled sister upon her virgin breast, they fell asleep.

The wind lulled as if it feared to waken them. Feathery drifts of snow, shaken from the long pine boughs, flew like white winged birds, and settled about them as they slept. The moon through the rifted clouds looked down upon what had been the camp. But all human stain, all trace of earthly travail, was hidden beneath the spotless mantle mercifully flung from above.

They slept all that day and the next, nor did they waken when voices and footsteps broke the silence of the camp. And when pitying fingers brushed the snow from their wan faces, you could scarcely have told from the equal peace that dwelt upon them which was she that had sinned. Even the law of Poker Flat recognized this, and turned away, leaving them still locked in each other's arms.

But at the head of the gulch, on one of the largest pine trees, they found the deuce of clubs pinned to the bark with a bowie-knife. It bore the following, written in pencil in a firm hand: —

†

BENEATH THIS TREE

LIES THE BODY

OF

JOHN OAKHURST

WHO STRUCK A STREAK OF BAD LUCK

ON THE 23D OF NOVEMBER 1850,

AND

HANDED IN HIS CHECKS

ON THE 7TH DECEMBER 1850.

↓

And pulseless and cold, with a derringer by his side and a bullet in his heart, though still calm as in life, beneath the snow lay he who was at once the strongest and yet the weakest of the outcasts of Poker Flat.

A COWARD [1]

(*Un Lâche*)

BY GUY DE MAUPASSANT

THIS story is a careful and detailed study of a mental state. The "event," which in this case constitutes the basis of the narrative, is the overthrow of De Signolles's mind under the strain of the prospective duel with Lamil; and the "chronological details" are the successive steps which lead up to the tragedy chronicled in the closing paragraphs. The cumulative character of these details is one of the notable elements in the story. They proceed by almost imperceptible degrees from the hero's first sense of fine energy, of satisfaction over a disagreeable act creditably performed, through the scale of anger, faint uneasiness, nervousness, dread, increasing physical agitation, up to utter desperation, under the influence of which, the victim of his own morbid imagination, he suddenly puts an end to it all. The gradually increasing violence of the emotions gives to the narrative a climactic effect unusual in characterization. Not only are clearness, unity, and coherence well exemplified, but force is also an important structural quality.

The story suggests also the condensation of details by which the narrative may approximate the time actually consumed in the accomplishment of the facts chronicled — somewhat after the method of the classic drama, wherein the unities of time and place played so important a part. An examination of the other stories included in this volume will show that most of them cover considerable periods of time; it is only by a careful process of selection and by bridging over lapses in the action and rendering them as inconspicuous as possible that the narratives are condensed within the limits of the conventional short-story. In *A Coward*, however, the entire action covers but a few hours, and during most of that time the hero is before the reader, and every successive step leading up to the

[1] Translated for this work by the Editor.

terminal tragedy is developed in minute detail. In this respect the story may well be contrasted with Hawthorne's *The Great Stone Face* or with Maupassant's *The Necklace*.

HE was known in society as the "handsome Signolles." His name was Viscount Gontran-Joseph de Signolles.

An orphan and possessed of a considerable fortune, he "cut quite a figure," as the saying goes. He was well built; he carried himself well; he was gifted with sufficient conversational power to be credited with cleverness; he had a certain natural grace about him, an air of distinction and pride, a gallant mustache, a gentle glance, — and this pleased the women.

In the drawing-rooms he was a general favorite; he was much sought after as a partner in the waltz; and he aroused among men that half-hearted hostility so often felt toward persons of energy. He was suspected of several successful love-affairs. He lived a happy, uneventful life, completely at peace with himself and with the world. He was known to be a good fencer and an even better shot.

"If ever I fight," said he, "I shall choose the pistol. With this weapon I am sure of killing my man."

Well, one evening, after he had attended the theater in company with two young women of his acquaintance and their husbands, he invited them, at the close of the performance, to take an ice at Tortoni's. They had been there several minutes when he observed that a gentleman seated at a table near by was staring at one of his companions. She seemed annoyed and nervous, and dropped her eyes.

Finally she said to her husband, "That man is staring me out of countenance. I don't know him; do you?"

Her husband, who had noticed nothing, looked up and said, "No. I never saw him in my life."

The young woman, half smiling, half annoyed, replied, "It is very embarrassing; the fellow is spoiling my ice."

Her husband shrugged his shoulders. "Nonsense! Don't pay any attention to him. If one were to notice every impudent fellow that he meets, there would be no end of trouble."

But the viscount suddenly rose from his chair. He could not allow this stranger to spoil an ice that he had offered. The insult was addressed to him, as it was in his company and at his invitation that his friends had entered the café. The affair consequently concerned him alone.

He stepped up to the man and said, "You are staring at these ladies, sir, in a manner that I cannot allow. I beg that you have the goodness to put an end to it."

"Mind your own business," exclaimed the other.

The viscount hissed through his teeth, "Be careful, sir. You will force me to take extreme measures."

The man replied with one word, a foul one, which rang from one end of the café to the other, and caused every one in the room to jump. Those whose backs were turned wheeled around; the others looked up; three waiters spun around on their heels like three tops; the two girls at the desk started and turned about like two automata moved by a common impulse.

A deep silence fell upon the room. Then suddenly a sharp sound smote the air. The viscount had slapped his adversary's face. Every one leaped up to interfere. Cards were exchanged.

When the viscount reached his own apartments he paced up and down the length of his room several times with long, nervous strides. He was too much agitated

to think connectedly. One single thought haunted him:
" A duel"; but as yet it aroused no particular emotion.
He had done his duty. People would talk about it; they
would approve of what he had done; they would con-
gratulate him.

In the voice of one deeply aroused he said aloud to
himself, "What a brute that fellow was!"

Then he sat down, and began to reflect. The first
thing in the morning he must secure his seconds. Whom
should he choose? He thought over the most celebrated
men of his acquaintance, those of the best social standing. Finally he selected the Marquis de la Tour-Noire
and Colonel Bourdin, a nobleman and an officer. An
excellent choice. Their names would look well in the
papers.

He found that he was thirsty, and he drained off three
glasses of water, one after another; then he began once
more to pace up and down the room. He felt as if he was
full of energy. If he blustered a little, if he showed himself determined at every point, if he insisted on strict,
dangerous conditions, if he demanded that the duel be
serious, very serious, terrific, his opponent would probably withdraw and offer his apologies.

He picked up the card which he had drawn from his
pocket and had thrown on the table, and read it again,
as he had already read it with a glance in the café and
in the cab by the light of every street-lamp on his way
home.

"George Lamil, 51 Rue Moncy."

Nothing more.

He scrutinized the letters; they seemed charged with
mystery, full of hidden significance. George Lamil.
Who was this fellow? What had he done? Why had he
stared so at the woman? Was it not outrageous that

a total stranger should suddenly disturb one's life in this fashion because he had taken a fancy to stare at a woman?

And once more the viscount exclaimed aloud, "What a brute!"

Then he stood still and thought, his glance still fixed on the card. Anger surged up within him at this bit of paper, a feeling of resentment in which was mingled an odd sensation of uneasiness. What a stupid piece of business this was! He picked up an open penknife which lay near, and stuck it into the very middle of the printed name, as if he had stabbed some one.

Well, they would have to fight. Should he choose swords or pistols? — for he considered himself the injured party. The risk was less with swords, but if he chose pistols there was a chance that his opponent might back out. It is only on rare occasions that a duel with swords is mortal, as mutual prudence prevents the combatants from standing near enough to each other for the point of the blade to inflict a deep wound. With pistols, indeed, he ran serious risk of his life, but then he might get out of the affair with all the honors of the situation and without coming to an actual meeting.

He said, "I must be firm. He will be afraid."

The sound of his own voice gave him a start, and he glanced about him. He felt very nervous. He tossed off another glass of water, and began to prepare for bed.

As soon as he was in bed, he extinguished his light and closed his eyes.

"I have all day to-morrow to think over my affairs," he thought. "I will get some sleep first to quiet my nerves."

He felt very warm under the clothes, but he could not

get to sleep. He tossed about; for five minutes he lay on his back; then on his left side; then on his right.

He was still thirsty. He got up to drink. Then an awful thought struck him: —

"Suppose I should be afraid!"

Why did his heart begin to beat madly at every familiar sound in the room? When the clock was about to strike, the whirring of the spring made him start; and for several seconds he had to keep his mouth open in order to breathe, so oppressed was he.

He began to reason with himself on the possibility of the idea, "Suppose I should be afraid!"

Certainly he should not be afraid; had he not made up his mind to carry the affair through to the end? Had he not firmly determined to fight, to fear nothing? But he felt so thoroughly upset that he asked himself, "Can a man be frightened in spite of himself?"

And doubt, anxiety, terror began to creep over him. What would happen if some power stronger than his own indomitable will should get the better of him? Yes, what would happen? He certainly should appear on the ground, for he had made up his mind to do so. But what if he should tremble? What if he should faint? And he thought of his position, of his reputation, of his good name.

And suddenly he was seized with a strange desire to get up and look at himself in the glass. He lighted his candle. When he saw the reflection of his face in the polished mirror, he scarcely recognized himself; it seemed as if he were looking at a stranger. His eyes appeared enormous; and he was pale; there was no doubt about it, he was certainly pale, very pale.

He continued to stand before the mirror; he thrust out his tongue as if to test the state of his health; and suddenly this thought struck him like a shot: "The day after to-morrow at this time perhaps I shall be dead."

And his heart began to beat again like mad.

"The day after to-morrow at this time perhaps I shall be dead. This man whom I see before me in this glass will no longer be alive. The thought of it! Here I am. I am looking at myself, and in twenty-four hours I shall be lying in this bed, dead, my eyes closed, cold, lifeless, gone."

He turned toward the bed, and he distinctly saw himself stretched out at full length under the very sheets that he had that moment left. He had the hollow features and the lax hands of a corpse.

Then he grew afraid of his bed, and went through into his smoking-room that he might not see it any longer. Mechanically he took a cigar, lighted it, and began to pace up and down. He was cold. He started toward the bell to arouse his valet, but he stopped suddenly, his hand extended toward the bell-rope.

"The man will see that I am afraid."

And he did not ring; he made the fire himself. His hands trembled slightly, nervously, when they touched anything. His mind wandered; his troubled thoughts became disconnected, flurried, melancholy; dizziness swept over him as if he had been drinking.

And he kept asking himself, "What shall I do? What will become of me?"

His whole frame shook with jerky convulsions; he got up again, and, approaching the window, drew the curtains.

Day was breaking, a summer's day. The rosy sky was tinting the roofs and walls of the city with pink. The light, like a caress from the rising sun, enveloped the awakening world; and with this gleam a sensation of inspiring hope swept swiftly and fiercely through the viscount's heart. Had he been mad thus to be dismayed by fear, before a thing had been settled, before his seconds had seen those of George Lamil, before he even knew whether he was going to fight at all?

He made his toilet, dressed himself, and went out with a firm step.

As he walked along he kept saying to himself, "I must be firm, very firm. I must prove that I am not afraid."

His seconds, the marquis and the colonel, put themselves at his disposal, and, after shaking hands with him vigorously, they discussed the conditions.

"You want a serious duel, don't you?" asked the colonel.

"Very serious," answered the viscount.

"You insist on pistols?" said the marquis.

"Yes."

"You leave the rest to us?"

In a dry, hesitant voice the viscount managed to say, "Twenty paces; at the word; raising the arm instead of lowering it; shots to be exchanged until one party is seriously wounded."

"Those are excellent conditions," said the colonel in a tone of satisfaction. "You are a good shot; all the chances are in your favor."

And they departed.

The viscount returned home to wait for them. His agitation increased every moment. Along his arms, along his legs, in his chest, he felt a sort of trembling, a sense of continuous vibration; he could not stand nor sit in one place two consecutive minutes. There was not a drop of moisture in his mouth, and he kept making audible sounds with his tongue as if he were trying to unglue it from his palate.

He made up his mind to have breakfast, but he could not eat. Then it occurred to him that he would drink in order to give him courage, and he had a carafe of rum brought in, and swallowed in quick succession six small glasses.

A warmth like that of a burn spread through his veins, followed immediately by a sensation of dullness.

"That's the idea," thought he. "Now things are going all right."

But at the end of an hour he had emptied the carafe, and his nervousness again became intolerable. He felt a mad inclination to roll on the floor, to shriek, to bite.

Evening drew on.

The ringing of his doorbell gave him such a sense of suffocation that he had not the strength to get up and greet his seconds.

He no longer dared to speak, to say, "How are you?" — to utter a single word, for fear that they would guess everything from the alteration in his voice.

"It's all settled in accordance with your own conditions," said the colonel. "Your opponent at first demanded the privilege of the insulted party, but he yielded almost immediately and agreed to everything. His seconds are two officers."

"Thanks," said the viscount.

"Excuse us if we only drop in on you and run away," said the marquis, "but we still have a thousand things to attend to. We must have a good surgeon, for the duel is not to stop until one of you is seriously hurt, and bullets, you know, are no joke. We must choose a place near some house so that, if necessary, we can carry the wounded party there, and all that. We have two hours for it yet."

A second time the viscount managed to say "Thanks."

"You are all right?" asked the colonel. "You are calm?"

"Yes, very calm, thanks."

The two men withdrew.

When he realized that he was alone again, it seemed as if he was losing his mind. The servant had lighted the lamps, and he seated himself at the table to write some letters. Having written at the top of one page "This is my will," he got up suddenly and moved away, feeling incapable of putting two ideas together, of taking a single resolution, of coming to any decision.

And so he was going to fight. There was no longer any escape from that. What, then, ailed him? He wanted to fight; he had the firm intention and resolution of doing so; yet he realized that, in spite of every effort of his mind and all the power of his will, he should not retain even the strength necessary to go to the scene of the encounter. He tried to picture to himself the duel, his own attitude, and the bearing of his adversary.

From time to time his teeth chattered with a dry sound. He determined to read, and he picked up Châteauvillard's dueling code. Then he asked himself the question, "Has my opponent frequented the shooting galleries? Is he well known? What is his class? How can I find out?"

He recollected Baron de Vaux's book on experts with the pistol, and he ran through it from one end to the other. George Lamil was not mentioned. Yet if the man were not an expert, would he have accepted without hesitation this dangerous weapon and these mortal conditions?

He opened a box by Gastinne Renette, which lay on a table, and picked up one of the pistols; then he took position as if he were going to fire, and raised his arm. But he trembled from head to foot, and the barrel shook in every direction.

"This is impossible," said he. "I cannot fight in this condition."

He looked into the end of the barrel, at the deep little black hole that spits death; he thought of the dishonor, of the whispers at the clubs, of the scorn of the women, of the allusions in the daily papers, of the insults that cowards would cast at him.

He continued to stare at the weapon, and, raising the hammer, he suddenly saw the priming gleaming under it like a little red flame. By an oversight the pistol had been left loaded. And at this he felt a vague and inexplicable sense of joy.

If, face to face with his enemy, he had not the noble and calm bearing which was to be expected, he should be lost forever. He should be tainted, branded with infamy, driven from society. And he should not have this noble and calm bearing: — he knew it; he felt it. Yet he was brave, for he wanted to fight. . . . He was brave, for . . .

The thought that began to take form in his mind was never completed; but, opening his mouth wide, he suddenly thrust the barrel of the pistol deep into the back of his throat, and pressed the trigger. . . .

When his valet, alarmed by the report, rushed in, he found him lying on his back, dead. A jet of blood had spattered the white paper on the table, and made a great red stain above these four words: —

"This is my will."

PLOT

MURAD THE UNLUCKY[1]

BY MARIA EDGEWORTH

THIS tale is presented as an excellent type of plot in its simplest form, — that known as the picaresque plot. This consists of a single strand wholly, or almost wholly, free from complication. The general course of the action in such cases may be represented as follows: —

Here we have merely a succession of episodes (×) following one after another in chronological order. Of this sort are most of the old English chronicle tales that preceded the prose fiction of the eighteenth century. The type is familiar to us in the adventure tales of our childhood, such as *Jack the Giant Killer*, *Little Red Riding Hood*, and *Robinson Crusoe*, — stories in which the phrase "and then," frequently repeated, constitutes the principal bond between the constituent portions. Many of the great masterpieces of prose fiction are but extensive instances of the same type: *Gil Blas* and *Don Quixote*, for example.

In these chronicle narratives the original interest is a matter of plot; that is, it lies mainly in the course of the events recorded. And, while they may sometimes present noteworthy characterization, — as in the case of *Don Quixote*, — yet even in such instances the simple adventure interest has the precedence. The unity of these narratives must depend upon the narrator's ability to keep before the reader the central personage about whom the various episodes cluster, as is done in the events that set forth the isolation of Robinson Crusoe, or, as in the present case, in those that emphasize the fatalities of Murad the Imprudent and the good fortune of Saladin the Prudent. In other words, the unity of the picaresque narrative is peculiarly dependent upon coherence.

[1] From *Popular Tales*.

I

It is well known that the grand seignior amuses himself by going at night, in disguise, through the streets of
Constantinople; as the caliph, Haroun Alraschid, used
formerly to do in Bagdad.

One moonlight night, accompanied by his grand vizier,
he traversed several of the principal streets of the city,
without seeing anything remarkable. At length, as they
were passing a ropemaker's, the sultan recollected the
Arabian story of Cogia-Hassan Alhabal, the ropemaker,
and his two friends, Saad and Saadi, who differed so
much in their opinion concerning the influence of fortune over human affairs.

"What is your opinion on this subject?" said the
grand seignior to his vizier.

"I am inclined, please Your Majesty," replied the vizier, "to think that success in the world depends more
upon prudence than upon what is called luck, or fortune."

"And I," said the sultan, "am persuaded that fortune
does more for men than prudence. Do you not every
day hear of persons who are said to be fortunate or unfortunate? How comes it that this opinion should prevail amongst men, if it be not justified by experience?"

"It is not for me to dispute with Your Majesty," replied the prudent vizier.

"Speak your mind freely; I desire and command
it," said the sultan.

"Then I am of opinion," answered the vizier, "that
people are often led to believe others fortunate or unfortunate, merely because they only know the general outline of their histories; and are ignorant of the incidents
and events in which they have shown prudence or imprudence. I have heard, for instance, that there are at pres-

ent in this city two men, who are remarkable for their good and bad fortune: one is called 'Murad the Unlucky,' and the other 'Saladin the Lucky.' Now I am inclined to think, if we could hear their stories, we should find that one is a prudent and the other an imprudent character."

"Where do these men live?" interrupted the sultan. "I will hear their histories from their own lips, before I sleep."

"Murad the Unlucky lives in the next square," said the vizier.

The sultan desired to go thither immediately. Scarcely had they entered the square, when they heard the cry of loud lamentations. They followed the sound till they came to a house of which the door was open, and where there was a man tearing his turban and weeping bitterly. They asked the cause of his distress, and he pointed to the fragments of a china vase, which lay on the pavement at his door.

"This seems undoubtedly to be beautiful china," said the sultan, taking up one of the broken pieces; "but can the loss of a china vase be the cause of such violent grief and despair?"

"Ah, gentlemen," said the owner of the vase, suspending his lamentations, and looking at the dress of the pretended merchants, "I see that you are strangers: you do not know how much cause I have for grief and despair! You do not know that you are speaking to Murad the Unlucky! Were you to hear all the unfortunate accidents that have happened to me, from the time I was born till this instant, you would perhaps pity me, and acknowledge I have just cause for despair."

Curiosity was strongly expressed by the sultan; and the hope of obtaining sympathy inclined Murad to gratify it, by the recital of his adventures. "Gentlemen," said he, "I scarcely dare invite you into the house of such an unlucky being as I am; but, if you will venture to take a night's lodging under my roof, you shall hear at your leisure the story of my misfortunes."

The sultan and the vizier excused themselves from spending the night with Murad; saying that they were obliged to proceed to their khan, where they should be expected by their companions: but they begged permission to repose themselves for half an hour in his house, and besought him to relate the history of his life, if it would not renew his grief too much to recollect his misfortunes.

Few men are so miserable as not to like to talk of their misfortunes, where they have, or where they think they have, any chance of obtaining compassion. As soon as the pretended merchants were seated, Murad began his story in the following manner: —

"My father was a merchant of this city. The night before I was born, he dreamed that I came into the world with the head of a dog and the tail of a dragon; and that, in haste to conceal my deformity, he rolled me up in a piece of linen, which unluckily proved to be the grand seignior's turban; who, enraged at his insolence in touching his turban, commanded that his head should be struck off.

"My father awaked before he lost his head, but not before he had lost half his wits from the terror of his dream. He considered it as a warning sent from above, and consequently determined to avoid the sight of me. He would not stay to see whether I should really be born with the head of a dog and the tail of a dragon; but he set out, the next morning, on a voyage to Aleppo.

"He was absent for upwards of seven years; and

during that time my education was totally neglected. One day I inquired from my mother why I had been named Murad the Unlucky. She told me that this name was given to me in consequence of my father's dream; but she added that perhaps it might be forgotten, if I proved fortunate in my future life. My nurse, a very old woman, who was present, shook her head, with a look which I shall never forget, and whispered to my mother loud enough for me to hear, 'Unlucky he was, and is, and ever will be. Those that are born to ill luck cannot help themselves; nor can any, but the great prophet Mahomet himself, do anything for them. It is a folly for an unlucky person to strive with his fate: it is better to yield to it at once.'

"This speech made a terrible impression upon me, young as I then was; and every accident that happened to me afterwards confirmed my belief in my nurse's prognostic. I was in my eighth year when my father returned from abroad. The year after he came home my brother Saladin was born, who was named Saladin the Lucky, because the day he was born a vessel freighted with rich merchandise for my father arrived safely in port.

"I will not weary you with a relation of all the little instances of good fortune by which my brother Saladin was distinguished, even during his childhood. As he grew up, his success in everything he undertook was as remarkable as my ill luck in all that I attempted. From the time the rich vessel arrived, we lived in splendor; and the supposed prosperous state of my father's affairs was of course attributed to the influence of my brother Saladin's happy destiny.

"When Saladin was about twenty, my father was taken dangerously ill; and as he felt that he should not recover, he sent for my brother to the side of his bed, and, to his great surprise, informed him that the magnificence in which we had lived had exhausted all his wealth; that his affairs were in the greatest disorder; for, having trusted to the hope of continual success, he had embarked in projects beyond his powers.

"The sequel was, he had nothing remaining to leave to his children, but two large china vases, remarkable for their beauty, but still more valuable on account of certain verses inscribed upon them in an unknown character, which was supposed to operate as a talisman or charm in favor of their possessors.

"Both these vases my father bequeathed to my brother Saladin; declaring he could not venture to leave either of them to me, because I was so unlucky that I should inevitably break it. After his death, however, my brother Saladin, who was blessed with a generous temper, gave me my choice of the two vases; and endeavored to raise my spirits, by repeating frequently that he had no faith either in good fortune or ill fortune.

"I could not be of his opinion, though I felt and acknowledged his kindness in trying to persuade me out of my settled melancholy. I knew it was in vain for me to exert myself, because I was sure that, do what I would, I should still be Murad the Unlucky. My brother, on the contrary, was nowise cast down, even by the poverty in which my father left us: he said he was sure he should find some means of maintaining himself, and so he did.

"On examining our china vases, he found in them a powder of a bright scarlet color; and it occurred to him that it would make a fine dye. He tried it, and after some trouble, it succeeded to admiration.

"During my father's lifetime, my mother had been

supplied with rich dresses by one of the merchants who was employed by the ladies of the grand seignior's seraglio. My brother had done this merchant some trifling favors; and, upon application to him, he readily engaged to recommend the new scarlet dye. Indeed, it was so beautiful, that, the moment it was seen, it was preferred to every other color. Saladin's shop was soon crowded with customers; and his winning manners and pleasant conversation were almost as advantageous to him as his scarlet dye. On the contrary, I observed that the first glance at my melancholy countenance was sufficient to disgust every one who saw me. I perceived this plainly; and it only confirmed me the more in my belief in my own evil destiny.

"It happened one day that a lady, richly apparelled and attended by two female slaves, came to my brother's house to make some purchases. He was out, and I alone was left to attend to the shop. After she had looked over some goods, she chanced to see my china vase, which was in the room. She took a prodigious fancy to it, and offered me any price if I would part with it; but this I declined doing, because I believed that I should draw down upon my head some dreadful calamity, if I voluntarily relinquished the talisman. Irritated by my refusal, the lady, according to the custom of her sex, became more resolute in her purpose; but neither entreaties nor money could change my determination. Provoked beyond measure at my obstinacy, as she called it, she left the house.

"On my brother's return, I related to him what had happened, and expected that he would have praised me for my prudence; but, on the contrary, he blamed me for the superstitious value I set upon the verses on my vase; and observed that it would be the height of folly to lose a certain means of advancing my fortune, for the uncertain hope of magical protection. I could not bring myself to be of his opinion; I had not the courage to follow the advice he gave. The next day the lady returned, and my brother sold his vase to her for ten thousand pieces of gold. This money he laid out in the most advantageous manner, by purchasing a new stock of merchandise. I repented, when it was too late; but I believe it is part of the fatality attending certain persons, that they cannot decide rightly at the proper moment. When the opportunity has been lost, I have always regretted that I did not do exactly the contrary to what I had previously determined upon. Often, whilst I was hesitating, the favorable moment passed. Now this is what I call being unlucky. But to proceed with my story.

"The lady, who bought my brother Saladin's vase, was the favorite of the sultan, and all-powerful in the seraglio. Her dislike to me, in consequence of my opposition to her wishes, was so violent, that she refused to return to my brother's house while I remained there. He was unwilling to part with me; but I could not bear to be the ruin of so good a brother. Without telling him my design, I left his house, careless of what should become of me. Hunger, however, soon compelled me to think of some immediate mode of obtaining relief. I sat down upon a stone, before the door of a baker's shop; the smell of hot bread tempted me in, and with a feeble voice I demanded charity.

"The master baker gave me as much bread as I could eat, upon condition that I should change dresses with him, and carry the rolls for him through the city this day. To this I readily consented; but I had soon reason to repent of my compliance. Indeed, if my ill luck

had not, as usual, deprived me at this critical moment
of memory and judgment, I should never have complied
with the baker's treacherous proposal. For some time
before, the people of Constantinople had been much
dissatisfied with the weight and quality of the bread
furnished by the bakers. This species of discontent has
often been the sure forerunner of an insurrection; and,
in these disturbances, the master bakers frequently lose
their lives. All these circumstances I knew; but they
did not occur to my memory, when they might have been
useful.

"I changed dresses with the baker; but scarcely had
I proceeded through the adjoining streets with my rolls,
before the mob began to gather round me, with reproaches and execrations. The crowd pursued me even
to the gates of the grand seignior's palace; and the
grand vizier, alarmed at their violence, sent out an
order to have my head struck off; the usual remedy, in
such cases, being to strike off the baker's head.

"I now fell upon my knees, and protested I was not
the baker for whom they took me; that I had no connection with him; and that I had never furnished the
people of Constantinople with bread that was not weight.
I declared I had merely changed clothes with a master
baker, for this day; and that I should not have done so,
but for the evil destiny which governs all my actions.
Some of the mob exclaimed that I deserved to lose my
head for my folly; but others took pity on me, and
whilst the officer, who was sent to execute the vizier's
order, turned to speak to some of the noisy rioters, those
who were touched by my misfortune opened a passage
for me through the crowd, and, thus favored, I effected
my escape.

"I quitted Constantinople: my vase I had left in the

care of my brother. At some miles' distance from the
city, I overtook a party of soldiers. I joined them; and
learning that they were going to embark with the rest
of the grand seignior's army for Egypt, I resolved to
accompany them. If it be, thought I, the will of Mahomet that I should perish, the sooner I meet my fate the
better. The despondency into which I was sunk was
attended by so great a degree of indolence, that I scarcely
would take the necessary means to preserve my existence.
During our passage to Egypt, I sat all day long upon the
deck of the vessel, smoking my pipe; and I am convinced
that if a storm had risen, as I expected, I should not
have taken my pipe from my mouth, nor should I have
handled a rope, to save myself from destruction. Such
is the effect of that species of resignation or torpor,
whichever you please to call it, to which my strong belief in *fatality* had reduced my mind.

"We landed, however, safely, contrary to my melancholy forebodings. By a trifling accident, not worth
relating, I was detained longer than any of my companions in the vessel when we disembarked; and I did not
arrive at the camp till late at night. It was moonlight,
and I could see the whole scene distinctly. There was
a vast number of small tents scattered over a desert of
white sand; a few date trees were visible at a distance;
all was gloomy, and all still; no sound was to be heard
but that of the camels, feeding near the tents; and, as I
walked on, I met with no human creature.

"My pipe was now out, and I quickened my pace a
little towards a fire, which I saw near one of the tents.
As I proceeded, my eye was caught by something sparkling in the sand: it was a ring. I picked it up, and put
it on my finger, resolving to give it to the public crier
the next morning, who might find out its rightful owner:

but by ill luck, I put it on my little finger, for which it was much too large; and as I hastened towards the fire to light my pipe, I dropped the ring. I stooped to search for it amongst the provender on which a mule was feeding; and the cursed animal gave me so violent a kick on the head that I could not help roaring aloud.

"My cries awakened those who slept in the tent, near which the mule was feeding. Provoked at being disturbed, the soldiers were ready enough to think ill of me; and they took it for granted that I was a thief, who had stolen the ring I pretended to have just found. The ring was taken from me by force; and the next day I was bastinadoed for having found it: the officer persisting in the belief that stripes would make me confess where I had concealed certain other articles of value, which had lately been missed in the camp. All this was the consequence of my being in a hurry to light my pipe, and of my having put the ring on a finger that was too little for it; which no one but Murad the Unlucky would have done.

"When I was able to walk again after my wounds were healed, I went into one of the tents distinguished by a red flag, having been told that these were coffee-houses. Whilst I was drinking coffee, I heard a stranger near me complaining that he had not been able to recover a valuable ring he had lost; although he had caused his loss to be published for three days by the public crier, offering a reward of two hundred sequins to whoever should restore it. I guessed that this was the very ring which I had unfortunately found. I addressed myself to the stranger, and promised to point out to him the person who had forced it from me. The stranger recovered his ring; and, being convinced that I had acted honestly, he made me a present of two hundred sequins, as some amends for the punishment which I had unjustly suffered on his account.

"Now you would imagine that this purse of gold was advantageous to me: far the contrary; it was the cause of new misfortunes.

"One night, when I thought that the soldiers who were in the same tent with me were all fast asleep, I indulged myself in the pleasure of counting my treasure. The next day I was invited by my companions to drink sherbet with them. What they mixed with the sherbet which I drank, I know not; but I could not resist the drowsiness it brought on. I fell into a profound slumber; and, when I awoke, I found myself lying under a date tree, at some distance from the camp.

"The first thing I thought of, when I came to my recollection, was my purse of sequins. The purse I found still safe in my girdle; but, on opening it, I perceived that it was filled with pebbles, and not a single sequin was left. I had no doubt that I had been robbed by the soldiers with whom I had drunk sherbet; and I am certain that some of them must have been awake the night I counted my money; otherwise, as I had never trusted the secret of my riches to any one, they could not have suspected me of possessing any property; for, ever since I kept company with them, I had appeared to be in great indigence.

"I applied in vain to the superior officers for redress: the soldiers protested they were innocent; no positive proof appeared against them, and I gained nothing by my complaint but ridicule and ill will. I called myself, in the first transport of my grief, by that name which, since my arrival in Egypt, I had avoided to pronounce: I called myself Murad the Unlucky! The name and the story ran through the camp; and I was accosted afterwards, very frequently, by this appellation. Some, indeed, varied their wit by calling me Murad with the Purse of Pebbles.

"All that I had yet suffered is nothing compared to my succeeding misfortunes.

"It was the custom at this time, in the Turkish camp, for the soldiers to amuse themselves with firing at a mark. The superior officers remonstrated against this dangerous practice, but ineffectually. Sometimes a party of soldiers would stop firing for a few minutes, after a message was brought them from their commanders; and then they would begin again, in defiance of all orders. Such was the want of discipline in our army, that this disobedience went unpunished. In the mean time, the frequency of the danger made most men totally regardless of it. I have seen tents pierced with bullets, in which parties were quietly seated smoking their pipes, whilst those without were preparing to take fresh aim at the red flag on the top.

"This apathy proceeded, in some, from unconquerable indolence of body; in others, from the intoxication produced by the fumes of tobacco and of opium; but in most of my brother Turks it arose from the confidence which the belief in predestination inspired. When a bullet killed one of their companions, they only observed, scarcely taking the pipes from their mouths, ' Our hour is not yet come: it is not the will of Mahomet that we should fall.'

"I own that this rash security appeared to me, at first, surprising; but it soon ceased to strike me with wonder; and it even tended to confirm my favorite opinion, that some were born to good and some to evil fortune. I became almost as careless as my companions, from following the same course of reasoning. It is not, thought

I, in the power of human prudence to avert the stroke
of destiny. I shall perhaps die to-morrow; let me there-
for enjoy to-day.

"I now made it my study, every day, to procure as
much amusement as possible. My poverty, as you will
imagine, restricted me from indulgence and excess; but
I soon found means to spend what did not actually belong to me. There were certain Jews who were followers of the camp, and who, calculating on the probability
of victory for our troops, advanced money to the soldiers; for which they engaged to pay these usurers exor-
bitant interest. The Jew to whom I applied traded with
me also upon the belief that my brother Saladin, with
whose character and circumstances he was acquainted,
would pay my debts, if I should fall. With the money
I raised from the Jew I continually bought coffee and
opium, of which I grew immoderately fond. In the delirium it created, I forgot all my misfortunes, all fear of
the future.

"One day, when I had raised my spirits by an unusual quantity of opium, I was strolling through the camp,
sometimes singing, sometimes dancing, like a madman,
and repeating that I was not now Murad the Unlucky.
Whilst these words were on my lips, a friendly spectator,
who was in possession of his sober senses, caught me
by the arm, and attempted to drag me from the place
where I was exposing myself. 'Do you not see,' said
he, 'those soldiers, who are firing at a mark? I saw one
of them, just now, deliberately taking aim at your turban; and, observe, he is now reloading his piece.' My
ill luck prevailed even at this instant, the only instant
in my life when I defied its power. I struggled with my
adviser, repeating, 'I am not the wretch you take me
for; I am not Murad the Unlucky.' He fled from the

danger himself: I remained, and in a few seconds afterwards a ball reached me, and I fell senseless on the sand.

"The ball was cut out of my body by an awkward surgeon, who gave me ten times more pain than was necessary. He was particularly hurried, at this time, because the army had just received orders to march in a few hours, and all was confusion in the camp. My wound was excessively painful, and the fear of being left behind with those who were deemed incurable added to my torments. Perhaps, if I had kept myself quiet, I might have escaped some of the evils I afterwards endured; but, as I have repeatedly told you, gentlemen, it was my ill fortune never to be able to judge what was best to be done, till the time for prudence was past.

"During that day, when my fever was at the height, and when my orders were to keep my bed, contrary to my natural habits of indolence, I rose a hundred times, and went out of my tent in the very heat of the day, to satisfy my curiosity as to the number of the tents which had not been struck, and of the soldiers who had not yet marched. The orders to march were tardily obeyed, and many hours elapsed before our encampment was raised. Had I submitted to my surgeon's orders, I might have been in a state to accompany the most dilatory of the stragglers; I could have borne, perhaps, the slow motion of a litter, on which some of the sick were transported; but in the evening, when the surgeon came to dress my wounds, he found me in such a situation that it was scarcely possible to remove me.

"He desired a party of soldiers, who were left to bring up the rear, to call for me the next morning. They did so; but they wanted to put me upon the mule which I recollected, by a white streak on its back, to be the cursed animal that had kicked me whilst I was looking for the ring. I could not be prevailed upon to go upon this unlucky animal. I tried to persuade the soldiers to carry me, and they took me a little way; but, soon growing weary of their burden, they laid me down on the sand, pretending that they were going to fill a skin with water at a spring they had discovered, and bade me lie still, and wait for their return.

"I waited and waited, longing for the water to moisten my parched lips; but no water came, — no soldiers returned; and there I lay, for several hours, expecting every moment to breathe my last. I made no effort to move, for I was now convinced my hour was come, and that it was the will of Mahomet that I should perish in this miserable manner, and lie unburied like a dog; a death, thought I, worthy of Murad the Unlucky.

"My forebodings were not this time just; a detachment of English soldiers passed near the place where I lay: my groans were heard by them, and they humanely came to my assistance. They carried me with them, dressed my wound, and treated me with the utmost tenderness. Christians though they were, I must acknowledge that I had reason to love them better than any of the followers of Mahomet, my good brother only excepted.

"Under their care I recovered; but scarcely had I regained my strength before I fell into new disasters. It was hot weather, and my thirst was excessive. I went out with a party, in hopes of finding a spring of water. The English soldiers began to dig for a well, in a place pointed out to them by one of their men of science. I was not inclined to such hard labor, but preferred sauntering on in search of a spring. I saw at a distance something that looked like a pool of water; and I pointed it out to my companions. Their man of science warned me by his interpreter not to trust to this deceitful appearance; for that such were common in this country, and that, when I came close to the spot, I should find no water there. He added that it was at a greater distance than I imagined; and that I should, in all probability, be lost in the desert, if I attempted to follow this phantom.

"I was so unfortunate as not to attend to his advice: I set out in pursuit of this accursed delusion, which assuredly was the work of evil spirits, who clouded my reason, and allured me into their dominion. I went on, hour after hour, in expectation continually of reaching the object of my wishes; but it fled faster than I pursued, and I discovered at last that the Englishman, who had doubtless gained his information from the people of the country, was right; and that the shining appearance, which I had taken for water, was a mere deception.

"I was now exhausted with fatigue: I looked back in vain after the companions I had left; I could see neither men, animals, nor any trace of vegetation in the sandy desert. I had no resource but, weary as I was, to measure back my footsteps, which were imprinted in the sand.

"I slowly and sorrowfully traced them as my guides in this unknown land. Instead of yielding to my indolent inclinations, I ought, however, to have made the best of my way back, before the evening breeze sprung up. I felt the breeze rising, and, unconscious of my danger, I rejoiced, and opened my bosom to meet it; but what was my dismay when I saw that the wind swept before it all trace of my footsteps in the sand. I knew not which way to proceed; I was struck with despair, tore my garments, threw off my turban, and cried aloud;

but neither human voice nor echo answered me. The silence was dreadful. I had tasted no food for many hours, and I now became sick and faint. I recollected that I had put a supply of opium into the folds of my turban; but, alas! when I took my turban up, I found that the opium had fallen out. I searched for it in vain on the sand, where I had thrown the turban.

"I stretched myself out upon the ground, and yielded without further struggle to my evil destiny. What I suffered from thirst, hunger, and heat cannot be described! At last I fell into a sort of trance, during which images of various kinds seemed to flit before my eyes. How long I remained in this state I know not; but I remember that I was brought to my senses by a loud shout, which came from persons belonging to a caravan returning from Mecca. This was a shout of joy for their safe arrival at a certain spring, well known to them in this part of the desert.

" The spring was not a hundred yards from the spot where I lay; yet, such had been the fate of Murad the Unlucky, that he missed the reality, whilst he had been hours in pursuit of the phantom. Feeble and spiritless as I was, I sent forth as loud a cry as I could, in hopes of obtaining assistance; and I endeavored to crawl to the place from which the voices appeared to come. The caravan rested for a considerable time whilst the slaves filled the skins with water, and whilst the camels took in their supply. I worked myself on towards them; yet, notwithstanding my efforts, I was persuaded that, according to my usual ill fortune, I should never be able to make them hear my voice. I saw them mount their camels! I took off my turban, unrolled it, and waved it in the air. My signal was seen! The caravan came towards me!

"I had scarcely strength to speak: a slave gave me some water; and, after I had drunk, I explained to them who I was, and how I came into this situation.

"Whilst I was speaking, one of the travellers observed the purse which hung to my girdle: it was the same the merchant, for whom I recovered the ring, had given to me; I had carefully preserved it, because the initials of my benefactor's name, and a passage from the Koran, were worked upon it. When he gave it to me, he said that perhaps we should meet again in some other part of the world, and he should recognize me by this token. The person who now took notice of the purse was his brother; and when I related to him how I had obtained it, he had the goodness to take me under his protection. He was a merchant, who was now going with the caravan to Grand Cairo: he offered to take me with him, and I willingly accepted the proposal, promising to serve him as faithfully as any of his slaves. The caravan proceeded, and I was carried with it.

II

"The merchant, who was become my master, treated me with great kindness; but, on hearing me relate the whole series of my unfortunate adventures, he exacted a promise from me, that I would do nothing without first consulting him. 'Since you are so unlucky, Murad,' said he, 'that you always choose for the worst when you choose for yourself, you should trust entirely to the judgment of a wiser or a more fortunate friend.'

"I fared well in the service of this merchant, who was a man of mild disposition, and who was so rich that he could afford to be generous to all his dependents. It was my business to see his camels loaded and unloaded at proper places, to count his bales of merchandise, and to take care that they were not mixed with those of his companions. This I carefully did, till the day we arrived at Alexandria; when, unluckily, I neglected to count the bales, taking it for granted that they were all right, as I had found them so the preceding day. However, when we were to go on board the vessel that was to take us to Cairo, I perceived that three bales of cotton were missing.

"I ran to inform my master, who, though a good deal provoked at my negligence, did not reproach me as I deserved. The public crier was immediately sent round the city, to offer a reward for the recovery of the merchandise; and it was restored by one of the merchants' slaves, with whom we had traveled. The vessel was now under sail; my master and I and the bales of cotton were obliged to follow in a boat; and when we were taken on board, the captain declared he was so loaded that he could not tell where to stow the bales of cotton. After much difficulty, he consented to let them remain upon deck: and I promised my master to watch them night and day.

"We had a prosperous voyage, and were actually in sight of shore, which the captain said we could not fail to reach early the next morning. I stayed, as usual, this night upon deck; and solaced myself by smoking my pipe. Ever since I had indulged in this practice at the camp at El Arish, I could not exist without opium and tobacco. I suppose that my reason was this night a little clouded with the dose I took; but, towards midnight, I was sobered by terror. I started up from the deck on which I had stretched myself; my turban was in flames; the bale of cotton on which I had rested was all on fire. I awakened two sailors, who were fast asleep on deck. The consternation became general, and the confusion increased the danger. The captain and my master were the most active, and suffered the most in extinguishing the flames: my master was terribly scorched.

"For my part, I was not suffered to do anything; the captain ordered that I should be bound to the mast; and, when at last the flames were extinguished, the passengers, with on accord, besought him to keep me bound hand and foot, lest I should be the cause of some new disaster. All that had happened was, indeed, occasioned by my ill luck. I had laid my pipe down, when I was falling asleep, upon the bale of cotton that was beside me. The fire from my pipe fell out, and set the cotton in flames. Such was the mixture of rage and terror with which I had inspired the whole crew, that I am sure they would have set me ashore on a desert island, rather than have had me on board for a week longer. Even my humane master, I could perceive, was secretly impatient to get rid of Murad the Unlucky, and his evil fortune.

"You may believe that I was heartily glad when we landed, and when I was unbound. My master put a purse containing fifty sequins into my hand, and bade me farewell. 'Use this money prudently, Murad, if you can,' said he, 'and perhaps your fortune may change.' Of this I had little hopes, but determined to lay out my money as prudently as possible.

"As I was walking through the streets of Grand Cairo, considering how I should lay out my fifty sequins to the greatest advantage, I was stopped by one who called me by my name, and asked me if I could pretend to have forgotten his face. I looked steadily at him, and recollected to my sorrow that he was the Jew Rachub, from whom I had borrowed certain sums of money at

the camp at El Arish. What brought him to Grand
Cairo, except it was my evil destiny, I cannot tell. He
would not quit me; he would take no excuses; he said
he knew that I had deserted twice, once from the Turkish and once from the English army; that I was not
entitled to any pay; and that he could not imagine it
possible that my brother Saladin would own me, or pay
my debts.

"I replied, for I was vexed by the insolence of this
Jewish dog, that I was not, as he imagined, a beggar;
that I had the means of paying him my just debt, but
that I hoped he would not extort from me all that exor-
bitant interest which none but a Jew could exact. He
smiled, and answered that, if a Turk loved opium better
than money, this was no fault of his; that he had supplied me with what I loved best in the world; and that
I ought not to complain, when he expected I should return the favor.

"I will not weary you, gentlemen, with all the arguments that passed between me and Rachub. At last we
compromised matters; he would take nothing less than
the whole debt: but he let me have at a very cheap rate
a chest of second-hand clothes, by which he assured me
I might make my fortune. He brought them to Grand
Cairo, he said, for the purpose of selling them to slave-
merchants, who at this time of the year were in want of
them to supply their slaves; but he was in haste to get
home to his wife and family at Constantinople, and
therefore he was willing to make over to a friend the
profits of this speculation. I should have distrusted
Rachub's professions of friendship and especially of dis-
interestedness; but he took me with him to the khan,
where his goods were, and unlocked the chest of clothes
to show them to me. They were of the richest and finest

materials, and had been but little worn. I could not doubt the evidence of my senses; the bargain was concluded, and the Jew sent porters to my inn with the chest.

"The next day I repaired to the public market-place; and, when my business was known, I had choice of customers before night: my chest was empty, — and my purse was full. The profit I made upon the sale of these clothes was so considerable, that I could not help feeling astonishment at Rachub's having brought himself so readily to relinquish them.

"A few days after I had disposed of the contents of my chest, a Damascene merchant, who had bought two suits of apparel from me, told me, with a very melancholy face, that both the female slaves who had put on these clothes were sick. I could not conceive that the clothes were the cause of their sickness; but soon afterwards, as I was crossing the market, I was attacked by at least a dozen merchants, who made similar complaints. They insisted upon knowing how I came by the garments, and demanded whether I had worn any of them myself. This day I had for the first time indulged myself with wearing a pair of yellow slippers, the only finery I had reserved for myself out of all the tempting goods. Convinced by my wearing these slippers that I could have had no insidious designs, since I shared the danger, whatever it might be, the merchants were a little pacified; but what was my terror and remorse the next day, when one of them came to inform me that plague-boils had broken out under the arms of all the slaves who had worn this pestilential apparel! On looking carefully into the chest, we found the word Smyrna written, and half effaced, upon the lid. Now, the plague had for some time raged at Smyrna; and, as the mer-

chants suspected, these clothes had certainly belonged
to persons who had died of that distemper. This was the
reason why the Jew was willing to sell them to me so
cheap; and it was for this reason that he would not stay
at Grand Cairo himself to reap *the profits of his speculation*. Indeed, if I had paid attention to it at the proper
time, a slight circumstance might have revealed the
truth to me. Whilst I was bargaining with the Jew, before he opened the chest, he swallowed a large dram of
brandy, and stuffed his nostrils with sponge dipped in
vinegar: this he told me he did to prevent his perceiving
the smell of musk, which always threw him into convulsions.

"The horror I felt, when I discovered that I had
spread the infection of the plague, and that I had probably caught it myself, overpowered my senses; a cold
dew spread over all my limbs, and I fell upon the lid
of the fatal chest in a swoon. It is said that fear dis-
poses people to take the infection; however this may be,
I sickened that evening, and soon was in a raging fever.
It was worse for me whenever the delirium left me, and
I could reflect upon the miseries my ill fortune had
occasioned. In my first lucid interval, I looked round
and saw that I had been removed from the khan to a
wretched hut. An old woman, who was smoking her
pipe in the farthest corner of my room, informed me
that I had been sent out of the town of Grand Cairo by
order of the cadi, to whom the merchants had made their
complaint. The fatal chest was burned, and the house in
which I had lodged razed to the ground. 'And if it
had not been for me,' continued the old woman, 'you
would have been dead, probably, at this instant; but I
have made a vow to our great prophet, that I would
never neglect an opportunity of doing a good action:

therefore, when you were deserted by all the world, I took care of you. Here, too, is your purse, which I saved from the rabble; and, what is more difficult, from the officers of justice: I will account to you for every para that I have expended; and will moreover tell you the reason of my making such an extraordinary vow.

"As I believed that this benevolent old woman took great pleasure in talking, I made an inclination of my head to thank her for her promised history, and she proceeded; but I must confess I did not listen with all the attention her narrative doubtless deserved. Even curiosity, the strongest passion of us Turks, was dead within me. I have no recollection of the old woman's story. It is as much as I can do to finish my own.

"The weather became excessively hot; it was affirmed, by some of the physicians, that this heat would prove fatal to their patients; but, contrary to the prognostics of the physicians, it stopped the progress of the plague. I recovered, and found my purse much lightened by my illness. I divided the remainder of my money with my humane nurse, and sent her out into the city, to inquire how matters were going on.

"She brought me word that the fury of the plague had much abated; but that she had met several funerals, and that she had heard many of the merchants cursing the folly of Murad the Unlucky, who, as they said, had brought all this calamity upon the inhabitants of Cairo. Even fools, they say, learn by experience. I took care to burn the bed on which I had lain, and the clothes I had worn: I concealed my real name, which I knew would inspire detestation, and gained admittance, with a crowd of other poor wretches, into a lazaretto, where I performed quarantine, and offered up prayers daily for the sick.

"When I thought it was impossible I could spread the infection, I took my passage home. I was eager to get away from Grand Cairo, where I knew I was an object of execration. I had a strange fancy haunting my mind; I imagined that all my misfortunes, since I left Constantinople, had arisen from my neglect of the talisman upon the beautiful china vase. I dreamed three times, when I was recovering from the plague, that a genius appeared to me, and said, in a reproachful tone, 'Murad, where is the vase that was entrusted to thy care?'

"This dream operated strongly upon my imagination. As soon as we arrived at Constantinople, which we did, to my great surprise, without meeting with any untoward accidents, I went in search of my brother Saladin, to inquire for my vase. He no longer lived in the house in which I left him, and I began to be apprehensive that he was dead; but a porter, hearing my inquiries, exclaimed, 'Who is there in Constantinople that is ignorant of the dwelling of Saladin the Lucky? Come with me, and I will show it to you.'

"The mansion to which he conducted me looked so magnificent that I was almost afraid to enter lest there should be some mistake. But, whilst I was hesitating, the doors opened, and I heard my brother Saladin's voice. He saw me almost at the same instant that I fixed my eyes upon him, and immediately sprang forward to embrace me. He was the same good brother as ever, and I rejoiced in his prosperity with all my heart. 'Brother Saladin,' said I, 'can you now doubt that some men are born to be fortunate, and others to be unfortunate? How often you used to dispute this point with me!'

"'Let us not dispute it now in the public street,'

said he, smiling; 'but come in and refresh yourself, and we will consider the question afterwards at leisure.'

"'No, my dear brother,' said I, drawing back, 'you are too good: Murad the Unlucky shall not enter your house, lest he should draw down misfortunes upon you and yours. I come only to ask for my vase.'

"'It is safe,' cried he; 'come in, and you shall see it; but I will not give it up till I have you in my house. I have none of these superstitious fears: pardon me the expression, but I have none of these superstitious fears.'

"I yielded, entered his house, and was astonished at all I saw! My brother did not triumph in his prosperity; but, on the contrary, seemed intent only upon making me forget my misfortunes: he listened to the account of them with kindness, and obliged me by the recital of his history; which was, I must acknowledge, far less wonderful than my own. He seemed, by his own account, to have grown rich in the common course of things; or, rather, by his own prudence. I allowed for his prejudices, and, unwilling to dispute further with him, said, 'You must remain of your opinion, brother; and I of mine: you are Saladin the Lucky, and I Murad the Unlucky; and so we shall remain to the end of our lives.'

"I had not been in his house four days when an accident happened, which showed how much I was in the right. The favorite of the sultan, to whom he had formerly sold his china vase, though her charms were now somewhat faded by time, still retained her power, and her taste for magnificence. She commissioned my brother to bespeak for her, at Venice, the most splendid looking-glass that money could purchase. The mirror, after many delays and disappointments, at length arrived at my brother's house. He unpacked it, and sent to let the lady know it was in perfect safety. It was late in the evening, and she ordered it should remain where it was that night; and that it should be brought to the seraglio the next morning. It stood in a sort of ante-chamber to the room in which I slept; and with it were left some packages, containing glass chandeliers for an unfinished saloon in my brother's house. Saladin charged all his domestics to be vigilant this night, because he had money to a great amount by him, and there had been frequent robberies in our neighborhood. Hearing these orders, I resolved to be in readiness at a moment's warning. I laid my scimitar beside me upon a cushion; and left my door half open, that I might hear the slight-est noise in the antechamber or the great staircase. About midnight I was suddenly awakened by a noise in the antechamber. I started up, seized my scimitar, and the instant I got to the door, saw, by the light of the lamp which was burning in the room, a man standing opposite to me, with a drawn sword in his hand. I rushed forward, demanding what he wanted, and received no answer; but, seeing him aim at me with his scimitar, I gave him, as I thought, a deadly blow. At this instant, I heard a great crash; and the fragments of the looking-glass, which I had shivered, fell at my feet. At the same moment something black brushed by my shoulder: I pursued it, stumbled over the packages of glass, and rolled over them down the stairs.

"My brother came out of his room, to inquire the cause of all this disturbance; and when he saw the fine mirror broken, and me lying amongst the glass chande-liers at the bottom of the stairs, he could not forbear exclaiming, 'Well, brother! you are indeed Murad the Unlucky.'

"When the first emotion was over, he could not,

however, forbear laughing at my situation. With a degree of goodness, which made me a thousand times more sorry for the accident, he came downstairs to help me up, gave me his hand, and said, 'Forgive me, if I was angry with you at first. I am sure you did not mean to do me any injury; but tell me how all this has happened.'

"Whilst Saladin was speaking, I heard the same kind of noise which had alarmed me in the antechamber; but, on looking back, I saw only a black pigeon, which flew swiftly by me, unconscious of the mischief he had occasioned. This pigeon I had unluckily brought into the house the preceding day; and had been feeding and trying to tame it for my young nephews. I little thought it would be the cause of such disasters. My brother, though he endeavored to conceal his anxiety from me, was much disturbed at the idea of meeting the favorite's displeasure, who would certainly be grievously disappointed by the loss of her splendid looking-glass. I saw that I should inevitably be his ruin, if I continued in his house; and no persuasions could prevail upon me to prolong my stay. My generous brother, seeing me determined to go, said to me, 'A factor, whom I have employed for some years to sell merchandise for me, died a few days ago. Will you take his place? I am rich enough to bear any little mistakes you may fall into, from ignorance of business; and you will have a partner who is able and willing to assist you.'

"I was touched to the heart by this kindness, especially at such a time as this. He sent one of his slaves with me to the shop in which you now see me, gentlemen. The slave, by my brother's directions, brought with us my china vase, and delivered it safely to me, with this message: 'The scarlet dye that was found in this vase, and in its fellow, was the first cause of Saladin's making the fortune he now enjoys: he therefore does no more than justice, in sharing that fortune with his brother Murad.'

"I was now placed in as advantageous a situation as possible; but my mind was ill at ease, when I reflected that the broken mirror might be my brother's ruin. The lady by whom it had been bespoken was, I well knew, of a violent temper; and this disappointment was sufficient to provoke her to vengeance. My brother sent me word this morning, however, that, though her displeasure was excessive, it was in my power to prevent any ill consequences that might ensue. 'In my power!' I exclaimed; 'then, indeed, I am happy! Tell my brother there is nothing I will not do to show him my gratitude, and to save him from the consequences of my folly.'

"The slave who was sent by my brother seemed unwilling to name what was required of me, saying that his master was afraid I should not like to grant the request. I urged him to speak freely, and he then told me the favorite declared nothing would make her amends for the loss of the mirror but the fellow vase to that which she had bought from Saladin. It was impossible for me to hesitate; gratitude for my brother's generous kindness overcame my superstitious obstinacy; and I sent him word I would carry the vase to him myself.

"I took it down this evening from the shelf on which it stood; it was covered with dust, and I washed it, but unluckily, in endeavoring to clean the inside from the remains of the scarlet powder, I poured hot water into it and immediately I heard a simmering noise, and my vase, in a few instants, burst asunder with a loud explosion. These fragments, alas! are all that remain. The

measure of my misfortunes is now completed! Can you
wonder, gentlemen, that I bewail my evil destiny? Am
I not justly called Murad the Unlucky? Here end all
my hopes in this world! Better would it have been if
I had died long ago! Better that I had never been born!
Nothing I ever have done or attempted has prospered.
Murad the Unlucky is my name, and ill fate has marked
me for her own."

III

The lamentations of Murad were interrupted by the
entrance of Saladin. Having waited in vain for some
hours, he now came to see if any disaster had happened
to his brother Murad. He was surprised at the sight
of the two pretended merchants, and could not refrain
from exclamations on beholding the broken vase. However, with his usual equanimity and good nature, he
began to console Murad; and, taking up the fragments,
examined them carefully, one by one joined them together again, found that none of the edges of the china
were damaged, and declared he could have it mended so
as to look as well as ever.

Murad recovered his spirits upon this. "Brother,"
said he, "I comfort myself for being Murad the Unlucky, when I reflect that you are Saladin the Lucky.
See, gentlemen," continued he, turning to the pretended merchants, "scarcely has this most fortunate of
men been five minutes in company before he gives a
happy turn to affairs. His presence inspires joy: I observe your countenances, which had been saddened by
my dismal history, have brightened up since he has
made his appearance. Brother, I wish you would make
these gentlemen some amends for the time they have
wasted in listening to my catalogue of misfortunes, by

relating your history, which, I am sure, they will find rather more exhilarating."

Saladin consented, on condition that the strangers would accompany him home, and partake of a social banquet. They at first repeated the former excuse of their being obliged to return to their inn; but at length the sultan's curiosity prevailed, and he and his vizier went home with Saladin the Lucky, who, after supper, related his history in the following manner: —

"My being called Saladin the Lucky first inspired me with confidence in myself; though I own that I cannot remember any extraordinary instances of good luck in my childhood. An old nurse of my mother's, indeed, repeated to me, twenty times a day, that nothing I undertook could fail to succeed, because I was Saladin the Lucky. I became presumptuous and rash; and my nurse's prognostics might have effectually prevented their accomplishment, had I not, when I was about fifteen, been roused to reflection during a long confinement, which was the consequence of my youthful conceit and imprudence.

"At this time there was at the Porte a Frenchman, an ingenious engineer, who was employed and favored by the sultan, to the great astonishment of many of my prejudiced countrymen. On the grand seignior's birthday he exhibited some extraordinarily fine fireworks; and I, with numbers of the inhabitants of Constantinople, crowded to see them. I happened to stand near the place where the Frenchman was stationed; the crowd pressed upon him, and I amongst the rest; he begged we would, for our own sakes, keep at a greater distance, and warned us that we might be much hurt by the combustibles which he was using. I, relying upon my good fortune, disregarded all these cautions; and the conse-

quence was, that as I touched some of the materials
prepared for the fireworks, they exploded, dashed me
upon the ground with great violence, and I was terribly
burnt.

"This accident, gentlemen, I consider as one of the
most fortunate circumstances of my life; for it checked
and corrected the presumption of my temper. During
the time I was confined to my bed, the French gentleman came frequently to see me. He was a very sensible
man; and the conversations he had with me enlarged
my mind, and cured me of many foolish prejudices,
especially of that which I had been taught to entertain,
concerning the predominance of what is called luck, or
fortune, in human affairs. 'Though you are called Saladin the Lucky,' said he, 'you find that your neglect of
prudence has nearly brought you to the grave even in
the bloom of youth. Take my advice, and henceforward
trust more to prudence than to fortune. Let the multitude, if they will, call you Saladin the Lucky; but call
yourself, and make yourself, Saladin the Prudent.'

"These words left an indelible impression on my
mind, and gave a new turn to my thoughts and character. My brother, Murad, had doubtless told you that
our difference of opinion, on the subject of predestination, produced between us frequent arguments; but we
could never convince one another, and we each have
acted, through life, in consequence of our different beliefs. To this I attribute my success and his misfortunes.

"The first rise of my fortune, as you have probably
heard from Murad, was owing to the scarlet dye, which
I brought to perfection with infinite difficulty. The
powder, it is true, was accidentally found by me in our
china vases; but there it might have remained to this
instant, useless, if I had not taken the pains to make it

useful. I grant that we can only partially foresee and command events; yet on the use we make of our own powers, I think, depends our destiny. But, gentlemen, you would rather hear my adventures, perhaps, than my reflections; and I am truly concerned, for your sakes, that I have no wonderful events to relate. I am sorry I cannot tell you of my having been lost in a sandy desert. I have never had the plague, nor even been shipwrecked: I have been all my life an inhabitant of Constantinople, and have passed my time in a very quiet and uniform manner.

"The money I received from the sultan's favorite for my china vase, as my brother may have told you, enabled me to trade on a more extensive scale. I went on steadily with my business; and made it my whole study to please my employers, by all fair and honorable means. This industry and civility succeeded beyond my expectations: in a few years, I was rich for a man in my way of business.

"I will not proceed to trouble you with the journal of a petty merchant's life; I pass on to the incident which made a considerable change in my affairs.

"A terrible fire broke out near the walls of the grand seignior's seraglio: as you are strangers, gentlemen, you may not have heard of this event, though it produced so great a sensation in Constantinople. The vizier's superb palace was utterly consumed; and the melted lead poured down from the roof of the mosque of St. Sophia. Various were the opinions formed by my neighbors respecting the cause of the conflagration. Some supposed it to be a punishment for the sultan's having neglected, one Friday, to appear at the mosque of St. Sophia; others considered it as a warning sent by Mahomet, to dissuade the Porte from persisting in a war in which we were just engaged. The generality, however, of the coffee-house politicians contented themselves with observing that it was the will of Mahomet that the palace should be consumed. Satisfied by this supposition, they took no precaution to prevent similar accidents in their own houses. Never were fires so common in the city as at this period; scarcely a night passed without our being wakened by the cry of fire.

"These frequent fires were rendered still more dreadful by villains, who were continually on the watch to increase the confusion by which they profited, and to pillage the houses of the sufferers. It was discovered that these incendiaries frequently skulked, towards evening, in the neighborhood of the bezestein, where the richest merchants store their goods; some of these wretches were detected in throwing *coundaks*, or matches, into the windows; and if these combustibles remained a sufficient time, they could not fail to set the house on fire.

"Notwithstanding all these circumstances, many even of those who had property to preserve continued to repeat, 'It is the will of Mahomet,' and consequently to neglect all means of preservation. I, on the contrary, recollecting the lesson I had learned from the sensible foreigner, neither suffered my spirits to sink with superstitious fears of ill luck, nor did I trust presumptuously to my good fortune. I took every possible means to secure myself. I never went to bed without having seen that all the lights and fires in the house were extinguished, and that I had a supply of water in the cistern. I had likewise learned from my Frenchman that wet mortar was the most effectual thing for stopping the progress of flames: I therefore had a quantity of mortar made up in one of my outhouses, which I could use at a moment's warning. These precautions were all useful to me: my own house, indeed, was never actually on fire, but the houses of my next-door neighbors were no less than five times in flames, in the course of one winter. By my exertions, or rather by my precautions, they suffered but little damage; and all my neighbors looked upon me as their deliverer and friend: they loaded me with presents, and offered more, indeed, than I would accept. All repeated that I was Saladin the Lucky. This compliment I disclaimed, feeling more ambitious of being called Saladin the Prudent. It is thus that what we call modesty is often only a more refined species of pride. But to proceed with my story.

"One night I had been later than usual at supper, at a friend's house: none but the watch were in the streets, and even they, I believe, were asleep.

"As I passed one of the conduits, which convey water to the city, I heard a trickling noise; and, upon examination, I found that the cock of the water-spout was half turned, so that the water was running out. I turned it back to its proper place, thought it had been left unturned by accident, and walked on; but I had not proceeded far before I came to another spout and another, which were in the same condition. I was convinced that this could not be the effect merely of accident, and suspected that some ill-intentioned persons designed to let out and waste the water of the city, that there might be none to extinguish any fire that should break out in the course of the night.

"I stood still for a few moments, to consider how it would be most prudent to act. It would be impossible for me to run to all parts of the city, that I might stop the pipes that were running to waste. I first thought of wakening the watch and the firemen, who were most of them slumbering at their stations; but I reflected that they were perhaps not to be trusted, and that they were in a confederacy with the incendiaries; otherwise, they would certainly, before this hour, have observed and stopped the running of the sewers in their neighborhood. I determined to waken a rich merchant, called Damat Zade, who lived near me, and who had a number of slaves whom he could send to different parts of the city, to prevent mischief, and give notice to the inhabitants of their danger.

"He was a very sensible, active man, and one that would easily be wakened: he was not, like some Turks, an hour in recovering their lethargic senses. He was quick in decision and action; and his slaves resembled their master. He dispatched a messenger immediately to the grand vizier, that the sultan's safety might be secured; and sent others to the magistrates, in each quarter of Constantinople. The large drums in the janissary aga's tower beat to rouse the inhabitants; and scarcely had this been heard to beat half an hour before the fire broke out in the lower apartment of Damat Zade's house, owing to a *coundak*, which had been left behind one of the doors.

"The wretches who had prepared the mischief came to enjoy it, and to pillage; but they were disappointed. Astonished to find themselves taken into custody, they could not comprehend how their designs had been frustrated. By timely exertions, the fire in my friend's house was extinguished; and though fires broke out, during the night, in many parts of the city, but little damage was sustained, because there was time for precautions; and by the stopping of the spouts, sufficient water was preserved. People were awakened, and warned of the danger, and they consequently escaped unhurt.

"The next day, as soon as I made my appearance at

the bezestein, the merchants crowded round, called me
their benefactor, and the preserver of their lives and
fortunes.   Damat Zade, the merchant whom I had
awakened the preceding night, presented to me a heavy
purse of gold, and put upon my finger a diamond ring
of considerable value; each of the merchants followed
his example, in making me rich presents: the magistrates also sent me tokens of their approbation; and the
grand vizier sent me a diamond of the first water, with
a line written by his own hand: 'To the man who has
saved Constantinople.' Excuse me, gentlemen, for the
vanity I seem to show in mentioning these circumstances.
You desired to hear my history, and I cannot therefore omit the principal circumstance of my life. In the
course of four-and-twenty hours, I found myself raised,
by the munificent gratitude of the inhabitants of this
city, to a state of affluence far beyond what I had ever
dreamed of attaining.

"I now took a house suited to my circumstances, and
bought a few slaves. As I was carrying my slaves home,
I was met by a Jew, who stopped me, saying, in his language, 'My lord, I see, has been purchasing slaves: I
could clothe them cheaply.' There was something mysterious in the manner of this Jew, and I did not like his
countenance; but I considered that I ought not to be
governed by caprice in my dealings, and that, if this
man could really clothe my slaves more cheaply than
another, I ought not to neglect his offer merely because
I took a dislike to the cut of his beard, the turn of his
eye, or the tone of his voice. I therefore bade the Jew
follow me home, saying that I would consider of his
proposal.

"When we came to talk over the matter, I was surprised to find him so reasonable in his demands. On one

point, indeed, he appeared unwilling to comply. I required not only to see the clothes I was offered, but also to know how they came into his possession. On this subject he equivocated; I therefore suspected there must be something wrong. I reflected what it could be, and judged that the goods had been stolen, or that they had been the apparel of persons who had died of some contagious distemper. The Jew showed me a chest, from which he said I might choose whatever suited me best. I observed that, as he was going to unlock the chest, he stuffed his nose with some aromatic herbs. He told me that he did so to prevent his smelling the musk with which the chest was perfumed: musk, he said, had an extraordinary effect upon his nerves. I begged to have some of the herbs which he used himself; declaring that musk was likewise offensive to me.

"The Jew, either struck by his own conscience, or observing my suspicions, turned as pale as death. He pretended he had not the right key, and could not unlock the chest; said he must go in search of it, and that he would call on me again.

"After he had left me, I examined some writing upon the lid of the chest, that had been nearly effaced. I made out the word Smyrna, and this was sufficient to confirm all my suspicions. The Jew returned no more: he sent some porters to carry away the chest, and I heard nothing of him for some time, till one day, when I was at the house of Damat Zade, I saw a glimpse of the Jew passing hastily through one of the courts, as if he wished to avoid me. 'My friend,' said I to Damat Zade, 'do not attribute my question to impertinent curiosity, or to a desire to intermeddle with your affairs, if I venture to ask the nature of your business with the Jew, who has just now crossed your court.'

"'He has engaged to supply me with clothing for my slaves,' replied my friend, 'cheaper than I can purchase it elsewhere. I have a design to surprise my daughter, Fatima, on her birthday, with an entertainment in the pavilion in the garden; and all her female slaves shall appear in new dresses on the occasion.'

"I interrupted my friend, to tell him what I suspected relative to this Jew and his chest of clothes. It is certain that the infection of the plague can be communicated by clothes, not only after months but after years have elapsed. The merchant resolved to have nothing more to do with this wretch, who could thus hazard the lives of thousands of his fellow creatures for a few pieces of gold: we sent notice of the circumstance to the cadi, but the cadi was slow in his operations; and before he could take the Jew into custody, the cunning fellow had effected his escape. When his house was searched, he and his chest had disappeared: we discovered that he sailed for Egypt, and rejoiced that we had driven him from Constantinople.

"My friend, Damat Zade, expressed the warmest gratitude to me. 'You formerly saved my fortune: you have now saved my life; and a life yet dearer than my own, that of my daughter Fatima.'

"At the sound of that name I could not, I believe, avoid showing some emotion. I had accidentally seen this lady, and I had been captivated by her beauty, and by the sweetness of her countenance; but as I knew she was destined to be the wife of another, I suppressed my feeling, and determined to banish the recollection of the fair Fatima forever from my imagination. Her father, however, at this instant, threw into my way a temptation which it required all my fortitude to resist. 'Saladin,' continued he, 'it is but just that you, who have saved our lives, should share our festivity. Come here on the birthday of my Fatima: I will place you in a balcony, which overlooks the garden, and you shall see the whole spectacle. We shall have a *feast of tulips*, in imitation of that which, as you know, is held in the grand seignior's gardens. I assure you, the sight will be worth seeing; and besides, you will have a chance of beholding my Fatima, for a moment, without her veil.'

"'That,' interrupted I, 'is the thing I most wish to avoid. I dare not indulge myself in a pleasure which might cost me the happiness of my life. I will conceal nothing from you, who treat me with so much confidence. I have already beheld the charming countenance of your Fatima, but I know that she is destined to be the wife of a happier man.'

"Damat Zade seemed much pleased by the frankness with which I explained myself; but he would not give up the idea of my sitting with him, in the balcony, on the day of the feast of tulips, and I, on my part, could not consent to expose myself to another view of the charming Fatima. My friend used every argument, or rather every sort of persuasion, he could imagine to prevail upon me: he then tried to laugh me out of my resolution; and, when all failed, he said, in a voice of anger, 'Go, then, Saladin; I am sure you are deceiving me: you have a passion for some other woman, and you would conceal it from me, and persuade me you refuse the favor I offer you from prudence, when, in fact, it is from indifference and contempt. Why could you not speak the truth of your heart to me with that frankness with which one friend should treat another?'

"Astonished at this unexpected charge, and at the anger which flashed from the eyes of Damat Zade, who till this moment had always appeared to me a man of a mild and reasonable temper, I was for an instant tempted to fly into a passion and leave him: but friends, once lost, are not easily regained. This consideration had power sufficient to make me command my temper. 'My friend,' replied I, 'we will talk over this affair to-morrow: you are now angry, and cannot do me justice; but to-morrow you will be cool: you will then be convinced that I have not deceived you; and that I have no design but to secure my own happiness by the most prudent means in my power, by avoiding the sight of the dangerous Fatima. I have no passion for any other woman.'

"'Then,' said my friend, embracing me, and quitting the tone of anger which he had assumed only to try my resolution to the utmost, — 'then, Saladin, Fatima, is yours.'

"I scarcely dared to believe my senses! I could not express my joy! 'Yes, my friend,' continued the merchant, 'I have tried your prudence to the utmost; it has been victorious, and I resign my Fatima to you, certain that you will make her happy. It is true, I had a greater alliance in view for her: the Pacha of Maksoud has demanded her from me; but I have found, upon private inquiry, he is addicted to the intemperate use of opium: and my daughter shall never be the wife of one who is a violent madman one half the day, and a melancholy idiot during the remainder. I have nothing to apprehend from the pacha's resentment, because I have powerful friends with the grand vizier who will oblige him to listen to reason, and to submit quietly to a disappointment he so justly merits. And now, Saladin, have you any objection to seeing the feast of tulips?'

"I replied only by falling at the merchant's feet, and embracing his knees. The feast of tulips came, and on that day I was married to the charming Fatima! The

charming Fatima I continue still to think her, though
she has now been my wife some years. She is the joy
and pride of my heart; and, from our mutual affection, I
have experienced more felicity than from all the other
circumstances of my life, which are called so fortunate.
Her father gave me the house in which I now live, and
joined his possessions to ours; so that I have more
wealth even than I desire. My riches, however, give
me continually the means of relieving the wants of
others; and therefore I cannot affect to despise them. I
must persuade my brother Murad to share them with
me, and to forget his misfortunes: I shall then think
myself completely happy. As to the sultana's looking-
glass, and your broken vase, my dear brother," continued Saladin, "we must think of some means —"

"Think no more of the sultana's looking-glass, or of
the broken vase," exclaimed the sultan, throwing aside
his merchant's habit, and showing beneath it his own
imperial vest. "Saladin, I rejoice to have heard, from
your own lips, the history of your life. I acknowledge,
vizier, I have been in the wrong, in our argument," continued the sultan, turning to his vizier. "I acknowledge
that the histories of Saladin the Lucky and Murad the
Unlucky favor your opinion, that prudence has more
influence than chance in human affairs. The success and
happiness of Saladin seem to me to have arisen from his
prudence: by that prudence, Constantinople has been
saved from flames, and from the plague. Had Murad
possessed his brother's discretion, he would not have
been on the point of losing his head, for selling rolls
which he did not bake; he would not have been kicked
by a mule, or bastinadoed for finding a ring; he would
not have been robbed by one party of soldiers, or shot
by another; he would not have been lost in a desert, or

cheated by a Jew; he would not have set a ship on fire; nor would he have caught the plague, and spread it through Grand Cairo; he would not have run my sultana's looking-glass through the body, instead of a robber; he would not have believed that the fate of his life depended on certain verses on a china vase; nor would he, at last, have broken this precious talisman, by washing it with hot water. Henceforward, let Murad the Unlucky be named Murad the Imprudent: let Saladin preserve the surname he merits, and be henceforth called Saladin the Prudent."

So spake the sultan, who, unlike the generality of monarchs, could bear to find himself in the wrong; and could discover his vizier to be in the right, without cutting off his head. History further informs us that the sultan offered to make Saladin a pacha, and to commit to him the government of a province; but Saladin the Prudent declined this honor, saying he had no ambition, was perfectly happy in his present situation, and that, when this was the case, it would be folly to change, because no one can be more than happy. What further adventures befell Murad the Imprudent are not recorded; it is known only that he became a daily visitor to the *Teriaky;* and that he died a martyr to the immoderate use of opium.

ESTHER[1]

THE story of Esther presents an excellent illustration of the "dramatic plot" type of narrative structure.[2] The first characteristic of this type is found in the fact that it must represent a struggle between two antagonistic forces, — usually one representing Good, and the other Evil: in this case, between Mordecai, a son of the Chosen Race, and Haman, one of its heathen persecutors.

A second characteristic consists in the logical nature of the action. Each episode is an *event*, in that it "issues from" some antecedent cause. Typical drama presupposes some Controlling Power working out its own definite purposes; it may be Fate, it may be Divine Purpose. In the case of *Esther*, the reader is constantly aware of the fact that Mordecai and Esther are but instruments in the hands of Jehovah, carrying into operation his will with reference to the Chosen People; Haman and his cause are foredoomed to failure, as prophetically realized by Zeresh.

In the ordering of the structure, the dramatic type of plot is also unique. It consists of two distinct phases, — the Rise and the Fall, — leading respectively to and from a medial Climax, or Moment of Greatest Suspense. The Rise is marked by a Preliminary Exposition for the enlightenment of the reader as to the facts to be elaborated; a Moment of Exciting Force wherein the two rival forces are thrown into active antagonism; and finally of the successive episodes that lead up to the Climax, where the relative fortunes of the rival forces become reversed, apparent success yielding to failure, and *vice versa*. In the Fall, which leads from the Climax down to the final Catastrophe, one usually finds several episodes, or "scenes," among them one known as the Moment of Final

[1] From the Book of Esther, in the Old Testament. The ordering of the text is, in general, that of the Authorized Version, with the omission of certain verses not essential to the narrative structure.

[2] For a full discussion of this type and a complete analysis of the Esther narrative see *Rhetorical Principles of Narration*, pp. 205-19.

Suspense, at which point, for a moment, impending disaster seems about to be checked, but in reality rendering the inevitable catastrophe all the more forceful and impressive. The *Esther* narrative presents a suggestion of this Final Suspense at the banquet scene when Haman throws himself on the queen's mercy, but, with the sudden advent of the angry king, his fate is sealed and "they covered his face."

The Bible story has here been ordered so as to bring out the various stages of the dramatic structure.

I

PRELIMINARY EXPOSITION

(1) *The Feast of Ahasuerus to his princes and servants at Shushan* — Now it came to pass in the days of Ahasuerus, (this is Ahasuerus which reigned from India even unto Ethiopia, over an hundred and seven and twenty provinces) that in those days, when the king Ahasuerus sat on the throne of his kingdom, which was in Shushan the palace, in the third year of his reign, he made a feast unto all his princes and his servants; the power of Persia and Media, the nobles and princes of the provinces, being before him: when he shewed the riches of his glorious kingdom and the honour of his excellent majesty many days, even an hundred and fourscore days. And when these days were fulfilled, the king made a feast unto all the people that were present in Shushan the palace, both great and small, seven days, in the court of the garden of the king's palace; there were hangings of white cloth, of green, and of blue, fastened with cords of fine linen and purple to silver rings and pillars of marble: the couches were of gold and silver, upon a pavement of red, and white, and yellow, and black marble. And they gave them drink in vessels of gold, (the vessels being diverse one from another,) and

royal wine in abundance, according to the bounty of
the king. And the drinking was according to the law;
none could compel; for so the king had appointed to all
the officers of his house, that they should do according
to every man's pleasure. Also Vashti the queen made
a feast for the women in the royal house which belonged
to king Ahasuerus.

On the seventh day, when the heart of the king was
merry with wine, he commanded to Mehuman, Biztha,
Harbona, Bigtha, and Abagtha, Zethar, and Carcas, the
seven chamberlains that ministered in the presence of
Ahasuerus the king, to bring Vashti the queen before
the king with the crown royal, to shew the peoples and
the princes her beauty: for she was fair to look on.
But the queen Vashti refused to come at the king's commandment by the chamberlains: therefore was the king
very wroth, and his anger burned in him.

Then said the king to the wise men, which knew the
times: "What shall we do unto the queen Vashti according to law, because she hath not done the bidding of the
king Ahasuerus by the chamberlains?"

And Memucan answered before the king and the
princes: "Vashti the queen hath not done wrong to the
king only, but also to all the princes, and to all the peoples that are in all the provinces of the king Ahasuerus.
For this deed of the queen shall come abroad unto all
women, to make their husbands contemptible in their
eyes, when it shall be reported, 'The king Ahasuerus
commanded Vashti the queen to be brought in before
him, but she came not.' And this day shall the princesses of Persia and Media which have heard of the deed
of the queen say the like unto all the king's princes.
So shall there arise much contempt and wrath. If it
please the king, let there go forth a royal command-

ment from him, and let it be written among the laws of the Persians and the Medes, that it be not altered, that Vashti come no more before king Ahasuerus; and let the king give her royal state unto another that is better than she. And when the king's decree which he shall make shall be published throughout all his kingdom, (for it is great,) all the wives shall give to their husbands honour, both to great and small."

And the saying pleased the king and the princes; and the king did according to the word of Memucan: for he sent letters into all the king's provinces, into every province according to the writing thereof, and to every people after their language, that every man should bear rule in his own house, and should publish it according to the language of the people.

(2) *The preparations for the appointment of Vashti's successor* — After these things, when the wrath of king Ahasuerus was pacified, he remembered Vashti, and what she had done, and what was decreed against her. Then said the king's servants that ministered unto him, "Let there be fair young virgins sought for the king: and let the king appoint officers in all the provinces of his kingdom, that they may gather together all the fair young virgins unto Shushan the palace, to the house of the women, unto the custody of Hegai, the king's chamberlain, keeper of the women; and let their things for purification be given them: and let the maiden which pleaseth the king be queen instead of Vashti. And the thing pleased the king; and he did so.

(3) *The Introduction of Mordecai and Esther* — There was a certain Jew in Shushan the palace, whose name was Mordecai, the son of Jair, the son of Shimei, the son of Kish, a Benjaminite; who had been carried away from Jerusalem with the captives which had

been carried away with Jeconiah king of Judah, whom Nebuchadnezzar the king of Babylon had carried away. And he brought up Hadassah, that is, Esther, his uncle's daughter: for she had neither father nor mother, and the maiden was fair and beautiful; and when her father and mother were dead, Mordecai took her for his own daughter.

(4) *Esther's year of preparation in the house of Hegai* — So it came to pass, when the king's commandment and his decree was heard, and when many maidens were gathered together unto Shushan the palace, to the custody of Hegai, that Esther was taken into the king's house, to the custody of Hegai, keeper of the women. And the maiden pleased him, and she obtained kindness of him; and he speedily gave her her things for purification, with her portions, and the seven maidens, which were meet to be given her, out of the king's house: and he removed her and her maidens to the best place of the house of the women. Esther had not shewed her people nor her kindred: for Mordecai had charged her that she should not shew it. And Mordecai walked every day before the court of the women's house, to know how Esther did, and what should become of her.

Now when the turn of every maiden was come to go in to king Ahasuerus, after that it had been done to her according to the law for the women, twelve months, then in this wise came the maiden unto the king; whatsoever she desired was given her to go with her out of the house of the women unto the king's house. In the evening she went, and on the morrow she returned into the second house of the women, to the custody of Shaashgaz, the king's chamberlain, which kept the concubines: she came in unto the king no more, except the king delighted in her, and that she were called by name.

(5) *Her coronation* — Now when the turn of Esther, the daughter of Abihail, the uncle of Mordecai, who had taken her for his daughter, was come to go in unto the king, she required nothing but what Hegai the king's chamberlain, the keeper of the women, appointed. And Esther obtained favour in the sight of all them that looked upon her. So Esther was taken unto king Ahasuerus into his house royal in the tenth month, which is the month Tebeth, in the seventh year of his reign. And the king loved Esther above all the women, and she obtained grace and favour in his sight more than all the virgins; so that he set the royal crown upon her head, and made her queen instead of Vashti. Then the king made a great feast unto all his princes and his servants, even Esther's feast; and he made a release to the provinces, and gave gifts, according to the bounty of the king.

(6) *The conspiracy of Bigthan and Teresh; Mordecai's service to the king* — And when the virgins were gathered together the second time, then Mordecai sat in the king's gate. Esther had not yet shewed her kindred nor her people; as Mordecai had charged her: for Esther did the commandmant of Mordecai, like as when she was brought up with him. In those days, while Mordecai sat in the king's gate, two of the king's chamberlains, Bigthan and Teresh, of those which kept the door, were wroth, and sought to lay hands on the king Ahasuerus. And the thing was known to Mordecai, who shewed it unto Esther the queen; and Esther told the king thereof in Mordecai's name. And when inquisition was made of the matter, and it was found to be so, they were both hanged on a tree: and it was written in the book of the chronicles before the king.

II

EXCITING FORCE

After these things did king Ahasuerus promote Haman, the son of Hammedatha the Agagite, and advanced him and his seat above all the princes that were with him. And all the king's servants, that were in the king's gate, bowed down, and did reverence to Haman; for the king had so commanded concerning him. But Mordecai bowed not down, nor did him reverence.

Then the king's servants, that were in the king's gate, said unto Mordecai: "Why trangressest thou the king's commandment?"

Now it came to pass, when they spake daily unto him, and he hearkened not unto them, that they told Haman, to see whether Mordecai's matters would stand: for he had told them that he was a Jew. And when Haman saw that Mordecai bowed not down, nor did him reverence, then was Haman full of wrath. But he thought scorn to lay hands on Mordecai alone; for they had shewed him the people of Mordecai: wherefore Haman sought to destroy all the Jews that were throughout the whole kingdom of Ahasuerus, even the people of Mordecai.

III

RISING ACTION

(1) *Haman's plan of revenge* — In the first month, which is the month Nisan, in the twelfth year of king Ahasuerus, they cast Pur, that is, the lot, before Haman from day to day, and from month to month, to the twelfth month, which is the month Adar.

And Haman said unto king Ahasuerus: "There is a certain people scattered abroad and dispersed among the peoples in all the provinces of thy kingdom; and their laws are diverse from those of every people; neither keep they the king's laws: therefore it is not for the king's profit to suffer them. If it please the king, let it be written that they be destroyed: and I will pay ten thousand talents of silver into the hands of those that have charge of the king's business, to bring it into the king's treasuries."

And the king took his ring from his hand, and gave it unto Haman, the son of Hammedatha the Agagite, the Jews' enemy.

And the king said unto Haman: "The silver is given to thee, the people also, to do with them as it seemeth good to thee."

Then were the king's scribes called in the first month, on the thirteenth day thereof, and there was written according to all that Haman commanded unto the king's satraps, and to the governors that were over every province, and to the princes of every people; to every province according to the writing thereof, and to every people after their language: in the name of king Ahasuerus was it written, and it was sealed with the king's ring. And letters were sent by posts into all the king's provinces, to destroy, to slay, and to cause to perish, all Jews, both young and old, little children and women, in one day, even upon the thirteenth day of the twelfth month, which is the month Adar, and to take the spoil of them for a prey. A copy of the writing, that the decree should be given out in every province, was published unto all the peoples, that they should be ready against that day. The posts went forth in haste by the king's commandment, and the decree was given out in Shushan the palace. And the king and Haman sat down to drink; but the city of Shushan was perplexed.

(2) *The responsibility imposed upon Esther by Mordecai* — Now when Mordecai knew all that was done, Mordecai rent his clothes, and put on sackcloth with ashes, and went out into the midst of the city, and cried with a loud and bitter cry: and he came even before the king's gate: for none might enter within the king's gate clothed with sackcloth. And in every province whithersoever the king's commandment and his decree came, there was great mourning among the Jews, and fasting, and wailing; and many lay in sackcloth and ashes.

And Esther's maidens and her chamberlains came and told it her; and the queen was exceedingly grieved: and she sent raiment to clothe Mordecai, and to take his sackcloth from off him: but he received it not. Then called Esther for Hathach, one of the king's chamberlains, whom he had appointed to attend upon her, and charged him to go to Mordecai, to know what this was, and why it was. So Hathach went forth to Mordecai unto the broad place of the city, which was before the king's gate. And Mordecai told him of all that had happened unto him, and the exact sum of the money that Haman had promised to pay to the king's treasuries for the Jews, to destroy them. And he gave him the copy of the writing of the decree that was given out in Shushan to destroy them, to shew it unto Esther, and to declare it unto her; and to charge her that she should go in unto the king, to make supplication unto him, and to make request before him, for her people. And Hathach came and told Esther the words of Mordecai.

Then Esther spake unto Hathach, and gave him a

message unto Mordecai, saying: "All the king's servants, and the people of the king's provinces, do know, that whosoever, whether man or woman, shall come unto the king into the inner court, who is not called, there is one law for him, that he be put to death, except such to whom the king shall hold out the golden sceptre, that he may live: but I have not been called to come in unto the king these thirty days."

And they told to Mordecai Esther's words.

Then Mordecai bade them return answer unto Esther: "Think not with thyself that thou shalt escape in the king's house, more than all the Jews. For if thou altogether holdest thy peace at this time, then shall relief and deliverance arise to the Jews from another place, but thou and thy father's house shall perish. And who knoweth whether thou art not come to the kingdom for such a time as this?"

Then Esther bade them return answer to Mordecai: "Go, gather together all the Jews that are present in Shushan, and fast ye for me, and neither eat nor drink three days, night or day: I also and my maidens will fast in like manner; and so will I go in unto the king, which is not according to the law: and if I perish, I perish."

So Mordecai went his way, and did according to all that Esther had commanded him.

(3) *Esther's audience with the king; her banquet to the king and to Haman* — Now it came to pass on the third day, that Esther put on her royal apparel, and stood in the inner court of the king's house, over against the king's house: and the king sat upon his royal throne in the royal house, over against the entrance of the house. And it was so, when the king saw Esther the queen standing in the court, that she obtained favour in his

sight: and the king held out to Esther the golden sceptre
that was in his hand. So Esther drew near, and touched
the top of the sceptre.

Then said the king unto her: "What wilt thou, queen
Esther? and what is thy request? it shall be given thee
even to the half of the kingdom."

And Esther said: "If it seem good unto the king, let
the king and Haman come this day unto the banquet
that I have prepared for him."

Then the king said: "Cause Haman to make haste,
that it may be done as Esther hath said."

So the king and Haman came to the banquet that
Esther had prepared.

And the king said unto Esther at the banquet of wine:
"What is thy petition? and it shall be granted thee:
and what is thy request? even to the half of the kingdom
it shall be performed."

Then answered Esther, and said: "My petition and
my request is, if I have found favour in the sight of the
king, and if it please the king to grant my petition, and
to perform my request, let the king and Haman come
to the banquet that I shall prepare for them, and I
will do to-morrow as the king hath said."

(4) *Haman's confidence and pride* — Then went
Haman forth that day joyful and glad of heart: but
when Haman saw Mordecai in the king's gate, that he
stood not up nor moved for him, he was filled with wrath
against Mordecai. Nevertheless Haman refrained himself, and went home; and he sent and fetched his friends
and Zeresh his wife. And Haman recounted unto them
the glory of his riches, and the multitude of his children,
and all the things wherein the king had promoted him,
and how he had advanced him above the princes and
servants of the king.

Haman said moreover: "Yea, Esther the queen did let no man come in with the king unto the banquet that she had prepared but myself; and to-morrow also am I invited by her together with the king. Yet all this availeth me nothing, so long as I see Mordecai the Jew sitting at the King's gate."

Then said Zeresh his wife and all his friends unto him: "Let a gallows be made of fifty cubits high, and in the morning speak thou unto the king that Mordecai may be hanged thereon; then go thou in merrily with the king in to the banquet."

And the thing pleased Haman; and he caused the gallows to be made.

(5) *The king reminded of Mordecai's service* — On that night could not the king sleep; and he commanded to bring the book of records of the chronicles, and they were read before the king. And it was found written that Mordecai had told of Bigthana and Teresh, two of the king's chamberlains, of those that kept the door, who had sought to lay hands on the king Ahasuerus.

And the king said: "What honour and dignity hath been done to Mordecai for this?"

Then said the king's servants that ministered unto him: "There is nothing done for him."

And the king said: "Who is in the court?"

Now Haman was come into the outward court of the king's house, to speak unto the king to hang Mordecai on the gallows that he had prepared for him.

And the king's servants said unto him: "Behold, Haman standeth in the court."

And the king said: "Let him come in."

So Haman came in.

IV

THE CLIMAX

And the king said unto him: "What shall be done unto the man whom the king delighteth to honor?"

Now Haman said in his heart: "To whom would the king delight to do honor more than to myself?" And Haman said unto the king: "For the man whom the king delighteth to honor, let royal apparel be brought which the king useth to wear, and the horse that the king rideth upon, and on the head of which a crown royal is set: and let the apparel and the horse be delivered to the hand of one of the king's most noble princes, that they may array the man withal whom the king delighteth to honor, and cause him to ride on horseback through the streets of the city, and proclaim before him: 'Thus shall it be done to the man whom the king delighteth to honor.'"

Then the king said to Haman: "Make haste, and take the apparel and the horse, as thou hast said, and do even so to Mordecai the Jew, that sitteth at the king's gate: let nothing fail of all that thou hast spoken."

V

THE FALLING ACTION

(1) *The fall of Haman's pride* — Then took Haman the apparel and the horse, and arrayed Mordecai, and caused him to ride through the streets of the city, and proclaimed before him: "Thus shall it be done unto the man whom the king delighteth to honor." And Mordecai came again unto the king's gate.

But Haman hasted to his house, mourning and having his head covered. And Haman recounted unto Zeresh his wife and all his friends everything that had befallen him.

Then said his wise men and Zeresh his wife unto him: "If Mordecai, before whom thou hast begun to fall, be of the seed of the Jews, thou shalt not prevail against him, but shalt surely fall before him."

While they were yet talking with him, came the king's chamberlains, and hasted to bring Haman unto the banquet that Esther had prepared.

(2) *The banquet of wine* — So the king and Haman came to banquet with Esther the queen.

And the king said again unto Esther on the second day at the banquet of wine: "What is thy petition, queen Esther? and it shall be granted thee: and what is thy request? even to the half of the kingdom it shall be performed."

Then Esther the queen answered and said: "If I have found favor in thy sight, O king, and if it please the king, let my life be given me at my petition, and my people at my request: for we are sold, I and my people, to be destroyed, to be slain, and to perish. But if we had been sold for bondmen and bondwomen, I had held my peace, although the adversary could not have compensated for the king's damage."

Then spake the king Ahasuerus and said unto Esther the queen: "Who is he, that durst presume in his heart to do so?"

And Esther said: "An adversary and an enemy, even this wicked Haman."

Then Haman was afraid before the king and the queen. And the king arose in his wrath from the banquet of wine and went into the palace garden: and

Haman stood up to make request for his life to Esther the queen: for he saw that there was evil determined against him by the king.

VI

THE CATASTROPHE

Then the king returned out of the palace garden into the place of the banquet of wine; and Haman was fallen upon the couch whereon Esther was.

Then said the king: "Will he even force the queen before me in the house?"

As the word went out of the king's mouth, they covered Haman's face.

Then said Harbonah, one of the chamberlains that were before the king: "Behold, also, the gallows fifty cubits high, which Haman hath made for Mordecai, who spake good for the king, standeth in the house of Haman."

And the king said: "Hang him thereon."

So they hanged Haman on the gallows that he had prepared for Mordecai. Then was the king's wrath pacified.

THE BLACK POODLE[1]

BY FRANK ANSTEY

THE dramatic structure illustrated in *Esther* is too limited in the scope of its subject-matter and too elaborate in form for general use in narrative prose composition. A more common ordering of plot details is found in what has been called the "method of story." In this the climax, instead of standing midway between the beginning and the end, stands at the end and is a combination of climax and catastrophe. Narrative of this type presents the prefatory exposition, the exciting force, and a rising action of several episodes leading to the climax-catastrophe. This, in turn, is followed by a more or less fully elaborated post-exposition, or adjustment of characters and action as seen under the new conditions established by the course of events developed in the course of the narrative. Of this "method of story" *The Black Poodle* offers illustration, as will be seen from the following analysis: —[2]

1. PRELIMINARY EXPOSITION.
    - *a.* Motive of the story.
    - *b.* Setting: Wistaria Villa.
    - *c.* *Dramatis personæ:* the Weatherheads.
    - *d.* Antecedent action.
2. INTRODUCTORY ACTION.
    - *a.* At Shuturgarden.
        - Introduction of Bingo.
        - Incipient love for Lilian.
        - Bingo's hostility.
    - *b.* At Wistaria Villa.
        - Feline amenities.
3. MOMENT OF EXCITING FORCE.
    - Bingo's death.
4. RISING ACTION OF COMPLICATION.
    - Complication 1. In the garden at Wistaria Villa.
        - With the Colonel.

[1] By permission of Longmans, Green & Co.
[2] *Rhetorical Principles of Narration*, pp. 222-24.

Bingo's burial.
Visions.
Complication 2. At Shuturgarden: one evening later.
Family desolation.
Weatherhead's encouragement.
Lilian's incredulity.
Complication 3. At Shuturgarden: Sunday evening.
The declaration.
Lilian's condition.
Weatherhead's resolution.
Complication 4.
   a. At Blagg's.
The discovery and the purchase.
   b. At Wistaria Villa.
The restoration.
The dinner.
Bingo's accomplishments.
Complication 5. At Wistaria Villa.
The strolling Frenchman.
"Azor"!
Compounding a felony.
The collar.
5. CLIMAX.
Revelation and desperation.
6. CONCLUSION.
The tablet.

The course of the story might be diagrammatically presented as in the following figure:—

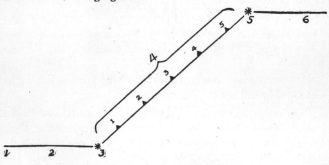

I HAVE set myself the task of relating in the course of this story, without suppressing or altering a single detail, the most painful and humiliating episode in my life.

I do this, not because it will give me the least pleasure, but simply because it affords me an opportunity of extenuating myself, which has hitherto been wholly denied to me.

As a general rule, I am quite aware that to publish a lengthy explanation of one's conduct in any questionable transaction is not the best means of recovering a lost reputation; but in my own case there is one to whom I shall nevermore be permitted to justify myself by word of mouth — even if I found myself able to attempt it. And as she could not possibly think worse of me than she does at present, I write this, knowing it can do me no harm, and faintly hoping that it may come to her notice and suggest a doubt whether I am quite so unscrupulous a villian, so consummate a hypocrite, as I have been forced to appear in her eyes.

The bare chance of such a result makes me perfectly indifferent to all else; I cheerfully expose to the derision of the whole reading world the story of my weakness and my shame, since by doing so I may possibly rehabilitate myself somewhat in the good opinion of one person.

Having said so much, I will begin my confession without further delay.

My name is Algernon Weatherhead, and I may add that I am in one of the government departments, that I am an only son, and live at home with my mother.

We had had a house at Hammersmith until just before the period covered by this history, when, our lease expiring, my mother decided that my health required country air at the close of the day, and so we took a "desirable villa residence" on one of the many new building estates which have lately sprung up in such profusion in the home counties.

We have called it "Wistaria Villa." It is a pretty little place, the last of a row of detached villas, each with its tiny rustic carriage-gate and gravel sweep in front, and lawn enough for a tennis-court behind, which lines the road leading over the hill to the railway-station.

I could certainly have wished that our landlord, shortly after giving us the agreement, could have found some other place to hang himself in than one of our attics, for the consequence was that a housemaid left us in violent hysterics about every two months, having learned the tragedy from the tradespeople, and naturally "seen a somethink" immediately afterward.

Still it is a pleasant house, and I can now almost forgive the landlord for what I shall always consider an act of gross selfishness on his part.

In the country, even so near town, a next-door neighbor is something more than a mere numeral; he is a possible acquaintance, who will at least consider a newcomer as worth the experiment of a call. I soon knew that "Shuturgarden," the next house to our own, was occupied by a Colonel Currie, a retired Indian officer; and often, as across the low boundary wall I caught a glimpse of a graceful girlish figure flitting about among the rosebushes in the neighboring garden, I would lose myself in pleasant anticipations of a time not far distant when the wall which separated us would be (metaphorically) leveled.

I remember — ah, how vividly! — the thrill of excitement with which I heard from my mother, on returning from town one evening, that the Curries had called, and seemed disposed to be all that was neighborly and kind.

I remember, too, the Sunday afternoon on which I returned their call — alone, as my mother had already done so during the week. I was standing on the steps of the colonel's villa, waiting for the door to open, when I was startled by a furious snarling and yapping behind, and, looking round, discovered a large poodle in the act of making for my legs.

He was a coal-black poodle, with half of his right ear gone, and absurd little thick mustaches at the end of his nose; he was shaved in the sham-lion fashion, which is considered, for some mysterious reason, to improve a poodle, but the barber had left sundry little tufts of hair, which studded his haunches capriciously.

I could not help being reminded, as I looked at him, of another black poodle, which Faust entertained for a short time with unhappy results, and I thought that a very moderate degree of incantation would be enough to bring the fiend out of this brute.

He made me intensely uncomfortable, for I am of a slightly nervous temperament, with a constitutional horror of dogs, and a liability to attacks of diffidence on performing the ordinary social rites under the most favorable conditions, and certainly the consciousness that a strange and apparently savage dog was engaged in worrying the heels of my boots was the reverse of reassuring.

The Currie family received me with all possible kindness. "So charmed to make your acquaintance, Mr. Weatherhead," said Mrs. Currie, as I shook hands. "I see," she added, pleasantly, "you've brought the doggie in with you." As a matter of fact, I had brought the doggie in at the ends of my coat-tails; but it was evidently no unusual occurrence for visitors to appear in this undignified manner, for she detached him quite as a matter of course, and as soon as I was sufficiently collected we fell into conversation.

I discovered that the colonel and his wife were childless, and the slender willowy figure I had seen across the garden wall was that of Lilian Roseblade, their niece and adopted daughter. She came into the room shortly afterward, and I felt, as I went through the form of an introduction, that her sweet, fresh face, shaded by soft masses of dusky-brown hair, more than justified all the dreamy hopes and fancies with which I had looked forward to that moment.

She talked to me in a pretty, confidential, appealing way, which I have heard her dearest friends censure as childish and affected; but I thought then that her manner had an indescribable charm and fascination about it, and the memory of it makes my heart ache now with a pang that is not all pain.

Even before the colonel made his appearance I had begun to see that my enemy, the poodle, occupied an exceptional position in that household. It was abundantly clear by the time I took my leave.

He seemed to be the center of their domestic system, and even lovely Lilian revolved contentedly around him as a kind of satellite; he could do no wrong in his owner's eyes, his prejudices (and he was a narrow-minded animal) were rigorously respected, and all domestic arrangements were made with a primary view to his convenience.

I may be wrong, but I cannot think that it is wise to put any poodle upon such a pedestal as that. How this one in particular, as ordinary a quadruped as ever breathed, had contrived to impose thus upon his infatuated proprietors, I never could understand, but so it was; he even engrossed the chief part of the conversation, which after any lull seemed to veer round to him by a sort of natural law.

I had to endure a long biographical sketch of him, — what a society paper would call an "anecdotal photo," — and each fresh anecdote seemed to me to exhibit the depraved malignity of the beast in a more glaring light, and render the doting admiration of the family more astounding than ever.

"Did you tell Mr. Weatherhead, Lily, about Bingo" (Bingo was the poodle's preposterous name) "and Tacks? No? Oh, I *must* tell him that; it'll make him laugh. Tacks is our gardener down in the village (d'ye know Tacks?). Well, Tacks was up here the other day, nailing up some trellis-work at the top of a ladder, and all the time there was Master Bingo sitting quietly at the foot of it looking on; wouldn't leave it on any account. Tacks said he was quite company for him. Well, at last, when Tacks had finished and was coming down, what do you think that rascal there did? Just sneaked quietly up behind and nipped him in both calves and ran off. Been looking out for that the whole time! Ha! ha! — deep that, eh?"

I agreed, with an inward shudder, that it was very deep, thinking privately that, if this was a specimen of Bingo's usual treatment of the natives, it would be odd if he did not find himself deeper still before — probably *just* before — he died.

"Poor, faithful old doggie!" murmured Mrs. Currie; "he thought Tacks was a nasty burglar, didn't he? He wasn't going to see master robbed, was he?"

"Capital house-dog, sir," struck in the Colonel. "Gad, I shall never forget how he made poor Heavisides run for it the other day! Ever met Heavisides of the Bombay Fusileers? Well, Heavisides was staying here, and the dog met him one morning as he was coming down from the bathroom. Did n't recognize him in 'pajamas' and a dressing-gown, of course, and made at him. He kept poor old Heavisides outside the landing window on the top of the cistern for a quarter of an hour, till I had to come and raise the siege!"

Such were the stories of that abandoned dog's blunderheaded ferocity to which I was forced to listen, while all the time the brute sat opposite me on the hearthrug, blinking at me from under his shaggy mane with his evil, bleared eyes, and deliberating where he would have me when I rose to go.

This was the beginning of an intimacy which soon displaced all ceremony. It was very pleasant to go in there after dinner, even to sit with the colonel over his claret, and hear more stories about Bingo; for afterward I could go into the pretty drawing-room and take my tea from Lilian's hands, and listen while she played Schubert to us in the summer twilight.

The poodle was always in the way, to be sure, but even his ugly black head seemed to lose some of its ugliness and ferocity when Lilian laid her pretty hand on it.

On the whole, I think that the Currie family were well disposed toward me, the colonel considering me as a harmless specimen of the average eligible young man, — which I certainly was, — and Mrs. Currie showing me favor for my mother's sake, for whom she had taken a strong liking.

As for Lilian, I believed I saw that she soon suspected the state of my feelings toward her, and was not displeased by it. I looked forward with some hopefulness to a day when I could declare myself with no fear of a repulse.

But it was a serious obstacle in my path that I could

not secure Bingo's good opinion on any terms. The family would often lament this pathetically themselves. "You see," Mrs. Currie would observe in apology, "Bingo is a dog that does not attach himself easily to strangers" — though, for that matter, I thought he was unpleasantly ready to attach himself to *me*.

I did try hard to conciliate him. I brought him propitiatory buns, which was weak and ineffectual, as he ate them with avidity, and hated me as bitterly as ever; for he had conceived from the first a profound contempt for me, and a distrust which no blandishments of mine could remove. Looking back now, I am inclined to think it was a prophetic instinct that warned him of what was to come upon him through my instrumentality.

Only his approbation was wanting to establish for me a firm footing with the Curries, and perhaps determine Lilian's wavering heart in my direction; but, though I wooed that inflexible poodle with an assiduity I blush to remember, he remained obstinately firm.

Still, day by day Lilian's treatment of me was more encouraging; day by day I gained in the esteem of her uncle and aunt; I began to hope that soon I should be able to disregard canine influence altogether.

Now there was one inconvenience about our villa (besides its flavor of suicide) which it is necessary to mention here. By common consent all the cats of the neighborhood had selected our garden for their evening reunions. I fancy that a tortoise-shell kitchen cat of ours must have been a sort of leader of local feline society — I know she was "at home," with music and recitations, on most evenings.

My poor mother found this interfere with her after-dinner nap, and no wonder; for if a cohort of ghosts had been "shrieking and squealing," as Calpurnia puts it, in our back garden, or it had been fitted up as a *crèche* for a nursery of goblin infants in the agonies of teething, the noise could not possibly have been more unearthly.

We sought for some means of getting rid of the nuisance: there was poison, of course; but we thought it would have an invidious appearance, and even lead to legal difficulties, if each dawn were to discover an assortment of cats expiring in hideous convulsions in various parts of the same garden.

Firearms too were open to objection, and would scarcely assist my mother's slumbers; so for some time we were at a loss for a remedy. At last, one day, walking down the Strand, I chanced to see (in an evil hour) what struck me as the very thing: it was an air-gun of superior construction, displayed in a gunsmith's window. I went in at once, purchased it, and took it home in triumph; it would be noiseless, and would reduce the local average of cats without scandal, — one or two examples, — and feline fashion would soon migrate to a more secluded spot.

I lost no time in putting this to the proof. That same evening I lay in wait after dusk at the study window, protecting my mother's repose. As soon as I heard the long-drawn wail, the preliminary sputter, and the wild stampede that followed, I let fly in the direction of the sound. I suppose I must have something of the national sporting instinct in me, for my blood was tingling with excitement; but the feline constitution assimilates lead without serious inconvenience, and I began to fear that no trophy would remain to bear witness to my marksmanship.

But all at once I made out a dark, indistinct form slinking in from behind the bushes. I waited till it crossed the belt of light which streamed from the back kitchen below me, and then I took careful aim and pulled the trigger.

This time at least I had not failed; there was a smothered yell, a rustle, and then silence again. I ran out with the calm pride of a successful revenge to bring in the body of my victim, and I found underneath a laurel no predatory tom-cat, but (as the discerning reader will no doubt have foreseen long since) the quivering carcass of the colonel's black poodle!

I intend to set down here the exact unvarnished truth, and I confess that at first, when I knew what I had done, I was *not* sorry. I was quite innocent of any intention of doing it, but I felt no regret. I even laughed — madman that I was — at the thought that there was the end of Bingo, at all events; that impediment was removed; my weary task of conciliation was over for ever!

But soon the reaction came; I realized the tremendous nature of my deed, and shuddered. I had done that which might banish me from Lilian's side for ever! All unwittingly I had slaughtered a kind of sacred beast, the animal around which the Currie household had wreathed their choicest affections! How was I to break it to them? Should I send Bingo in, with a card tied to his neck and my regrets and compliments? That was too much like a present of game. Ought I not to carry him in myself? I would wreathe him in the best crape, I would put on black for him; the Curries would hardly consider a taper and a white sheet, or sackcloth and ashes, an excessive form of atonement, but I could not grovel to quite such an abject extent.

I wondered what the colonel would say. Simple and hearty, as a general rule, he had a hot temper on occasions, and it made me ill as I thought, would he and, worse still, would *Lilian* believe it was really an accident?

They knew what an interest I had in silencing the deceased poodle — would they believe the simple truth?

I vowed that they *should* believe me. My genuine remorse and the absence of all concealment on my part would speak powerfully for me. I would choose a favorable time for my confession; that very evening I would tell all.

Still I shrank from the duty before me, and, as I knelt down sorrowfully by the dead form and respectfully composed his stiffening limbs, I thought that it was unjust of fate to place a well-meaning man, whose nerves were not of iron, in such a position.

Then, to my horror, I heard a well-known ringing tramp on the road outside, and smelled the peculiar fragrance of a Burmese cheroot. It was the colonel himself, who had been taking out the doomed Bingo for his usual evening run.

I don't know how it was, exactly, but a sudden panic came over me. I held my breath, and tried to crouch down unseen behind the laurels; but he had seen me, and came over at once to speak to me across the hedge.

He stood there, not two yards from his favorite's body! Fortunately it was unusually dark that evening.

"Ha, there you are, eh?" he began, heartily; "don't rise, my boy, don't rise."

I was trying to put myself in front of the poodle, and did not rise — at least, only my hair did.

"You're out late, ain't you?" he went on; "laying out your garden, hey?"

I could not tell him that I was laying out his poodle! My voice shook as, with a guilty confusion that was veiled by the dusk, I said it was a fine evening — which it was not.

"Cloudy, sir," said the colonel, "cloudy; rain before

morning, I think. By the way, have you seen anything of my Bingo in here?"

This was the turning-point. What I *ought* to have done was to say mournfully, "Yes, I'm sorry to say I've had a most unfortunate accident with him. Here he is; the fact is, I'm afraid I've *shot* him!"

But I couldn't. I could have told him at my own time, in a prepared form of words — but not then. I felt I must use all my wits to gain time, and fence with the questions.

"Why," I said, with a leaden airiness, "he hasn't given you the slip, has he?"

"Never did such a thing in his life!" said the colonel, warmly; "he rushed off after a rat or a frog or something a few minutes ago, and as I stopped to light another cheroot I lost sight of him. I thought I saw him slip in under your gate, but I've been calling him from the front there and he won't come out."

No, and he never *would* come out any more. But the colonel must not be told that just yet. I temporized again: "If," I said, unsteadily — "if he had slipped in under the gate I should have seen him. Perhaps he took it into his head to run home?"

"Oh, I shall find him on the doorstep, I expect, the knowing old scamp! Why, what d'ye think was the last thing he did now?"

I could have given him the very latest intelligence, but I dared not. However, it was altogether too ghastly to kneel there and laugh at anecdotes of Bingo told across Bingo's dead body; I could not stand that! "Listen," I said, suddenly, "wasn't that his bark? There, again; it seems to come from the front of your house, don't you think?"

"Well," said the colonel, "I'll go and fasten him up

before he's off again. How your teeth are chattering! You've caught a chill, man; go indoors at once, and, if you feel equal to it, look in half an hour later, about grog-time, and I'll tell you all about it. Compliments to your mother. Don't forget — about grog-time!"

I had got rid of him at last, and I wiped my forehead, gasping with relief. I would go round in half an hour, and then I should be prepared to make my melancholy announcement. For, even then, I never thought of any other course, until suddenly it flashed upon me with terrible clearness that my miserable shuffling by the hedge had made it impossible to tell the truth! I had not told a direct lie, to be sure, but then I had given the colonel the impression that I had denied having seen the dog. Many people can appease their consciences by reflecting that, whatever may be the effect their words produce, they did contrive to steer clear of a downright lie. I never quite knew where the distinction lay morally, but there *is* that feeling — I have it myself.

Unfortunately, prevarication has this drawback: that, if ever the truth comes to light, the prevaricator is in just the same case as if he had lied to the most shameless extent, and for a man to point out that the words he used contained no absolute falsehood will seldom restore confidence.

I might, of course, still tell the colonel of my misfortune, and leave him to infer that it had happened after our interview; but the poodle was fast becoming cold and stiff, and they would most probably suspect the real time of the occurrence.

And then Lilian would hear that I had told a string of falsehoods to her uncle over the dead body of their idolized Bingo — an act, no doubt, of abominable desecration, of unspeakable profanity, in her eyes.

If it would have been difficult before to prevail on her to accept a blood-stained hand, it would be impossible after that. No, I had burned my ships, I was cut off for ever from the straightforward course; that one moment of indecision had decided my conduct in spite of me; I must go on with it now, and keep up the deception at all hazards.

It was bitter. I had always tried to preserve as many of the moral principles which had been instilled into me as can be conveniently retained in this grasping world, and it had been my pride that, roughly speaking, I had never been guilty of an unmistakable falsehood.

But henceforth, if I meant to win Lilian, that boast must be relinquished for ever. I should have to lie now with all my might, without limit or scruple, to dissemble incessantly, and "wear a mask," as the poet Bunn beautifully expressed it long ago, "over my hollow heart." I felt all this keenly; I did not think it was right, but what was I to do?

After thinking all this out very carefully, I decided that my only course was to bury the poor animal where he fell, and say nothing about it. With some vague idea of precaution, I first took off the silver collar he wore, and then hastily interred him with a garden-trowel, and succeeded in removing all traces of the disaster.

I fancy I felt a certain relief in the knowledge that there would now be no necessity to tell my pitiful story and risk the loss of my neighbors' esteem.

By and by, I thought, I would plant a rose-tree over his remains, and some day, as Lilian and I, in the noon-tide of our domestic bliss, stood before it admiring its creamy luxuriance, I might (perhaps) find courage to confess that the tree owed some of that luxuriance to the long-lost Bingo.

There was a touch of poetry in this idea that lightened my gloom for the moment.

I need scarcely say that I did not go round to Shutur-garden that evening. I was not hardened enough for that yet; my manner might betray me, and so I very prudently stayed at home.

But that night my sleep was broken by frightful dreams. I was perpetually trying to bury a great, gaunt poodle, which would persist in rising up through the damp mould as fast as I covered him up. . . . Lilian and I were engaged, and we were in church together on Sunday, and the poodle, resisting all attempts to eject him, forbade our banns with sepulchral barks. . . . It was our wedding-day, and at the critical moment the poodle leaped between us and swallowed the ring. . . . Or we were at the wedding-breakfast, and Bingo, a grisly black skeleton with flaming eyes, sat on the cake and would not allow Lilian to cut it. Even the rose-tree fancy was reproduced in a distorted form — the tree grew, and every blossom contained a miniature Bingo, which barked; and as I woke I was desperately trying to persuade the colonel that they were ordinary dog-roses.

I went up to the office next day with my gloomy secret gnawing my bosom, and, whatever I did, the spec-ter of the murdered poodle rose before me. For two days after that I dared not go near the Curries, until at last one evening after dinner I forced myself to call, feeling that it was really not safe to keep away any longer.

My conscience smote me as I went in. I put on an unconscious, easy manner, which was such a dismal failure that it was lucky for me that they were too much engrossed to notice it.

I never before saw a family so stricken down by a domestic misfortune as the group I found in the drawing-room, making a dejected pretense of reading or working. We talked at first — and hollow talk it was — on indifferent subjects, till I could bear it no longer, and plunged boldly into danger.

"I don't see the dog," I began. "I suppose you — you found him all right the other evening, colonel?" I wondered, as I spoke, whether they would not notice the break of my voice, but they did not.

"Why, the fact is," said the colonel, heavily, gnawing his gray mustache, "we've not heard anything of him since; he's — he's run off!"

"Gone, Mr. Weatherhead; gone without a word!" said Mrs. Currie, plaintively, as if she thought the dog might at least have left an address.

"I wouldn't have believed it of him," said the colonel; "it has completely knocked me over. Haven't been so cut up for years — the ungrateful rascal!"

"O uncle!" pleaded Lilian, "don't talk like that; perhaps Bingo couldn't help it — perhaps some one has s-s-shot him!"

"Shot!" cried the colonel, angrily. "By heaven! if I thought there was a villain on earth capable of shooting that poor, inoffensive dog, I'd — Why *should* they shoot him, Lilian? Tell me that! I — I hope you won't let me hear you talk like that again. *You* don't think he's shot, eh, Weatherhead?"

I said — Heaven forgive me! — that I thought it highly improbable.

"He's not dead!" cried Mrs. Currie. "If he were dead I should know it somehow — I'm sure I should! But I'm certain he's alive. Only last night I had such a beautiful dream about him. I thought he came back to us, Mr. Weatherhead, driving up in a hansom-cab, and he was just the same as ever — only he wore blue spectacles, and the shaved part of him was painted a bright red. And I woke up with the joy — so, you know, it's sure to come true!"

It will be easily understood what torture conversations like these were to me, and how I hated myself as I sympathized and spoke encouraging words concerning the dog's recovery, when I knew all the time he was lying hid under my garden mould. But I took it as a part of my punishment, and bore it all uncomplainingly; practice even made me an adept in the art of consolation — I believe I really was a great comfort to them.

I had hoped that they would soon get over the first bitterness of their loss, and that Bingo would be first replaced and then forgotten in the usual way; but there seemed no signs of this coming to pass.

The poor colonel was too plainly fretting himself ill about it; he went pottering about forlornly, advertising, searching, and seeing people, but all, of course, to no purpose; and it told upon him. He was more like a man whose only son and heir had been stolen than an Anglo-Indian officer who had lost a poodle. I had to affect the liveliest interest in all his inquiries and expeditions, and to listen to and echo the most extravagant eulogies of the departed; and the wear and tear of so much duplicity made me at last almost as ill as the colonel himself.

I could not help seeing that Lilian was not nearly so much impressed by my elaborate concern as her relatives, and sometimes I detected an incredulous look in her frank brown eyes that made me very uneasy. Little by little, a rift widened between us, until at last in despair I determined to know the worst before the time came when it would be hopeless to speak at all. I chose a Sunday evening as we were walking across the green from church in the golden dusk, and then I ventured to speak to her of my love. She heard me to the end, and was evidently very much agitated. At last she murmured that it could not be, unless — no, it never could be now.

"Unless what?" I asked. "Lilian — Miss Rose-blade, something has come between us lately; you will tell me what that something is, won't you?"

"Do you want to know *really?*" she said, looking up at me through her tears. "Then I'll tell you; it — it's Bingo!"

I started back overwhelmed. Did she know all? If not, how much did she suspect? I must find out that at once! "What about Bingo?" I managed to pronounce, with a dry tongue.

"You never l-loved him when he was here," she sobbed; "you know you did n't!"

I was relieved to find it was no worse than this.

"No," I said, candidly; "I did not love Bingo. Bingo did n't love *me*, Lilian; he was alway looking out for a chance of nipping me somewhere. Surely you won't quarrel with me for that!"

"Not for that," she said; "only, why do you pretend to be so fond of him now, and so anxious to get him back again? Uncle John believes you, but *I* don't. I can see quite well that you would n't be glad to find him. You could find him easily if you wanted to!"

"What do you mean, Lilian?" I said, hoarsely. "*How* could I find him?" Again I feared the worst.

"You're in a government office," cried Lilian, "and if you only chose, you could easily g-get g-government to find Bingo! What's the use of government if it can't do that? Mr. Travers would have found him long ago if I'd asked him!"

Lilian had never been so childishly unreasonable as

this before, and yet I loved her more madly than ever; but I did not like this allusion to Travers, a rising barrister, who lived with his sister in a pretty cottage near the station, and had shown symptoms of being attracted by Lilian.

He was away on circuit just then, luckily; but, at least, even he would have found it a hard task to find Bingo — there was comfort in that.

"You know that isn't just, Lilian," I observed; "but only tell me what you want me to do."

"Bub — bub — bring back Bingo!" she said.

"Bring back Bingo!" I cried, in horror. "But suppose I *can't* — suppose he's out of the country, or — dead, what then, Lilian?"

"I can't help it," she said, "but I don't believe he *is* out of the country or dead. And while I see you pretending to uncle that you cared awfully about him, and going on doing nothing at all, it makes me think you're not quite — quite *sincere!* And I couldn't possibly marry any one while I thought that of him. And I shall always have that feeling unless you find Bingo!"

It was of no use to argue with her; I knew Lilian by that time. With her pretty, caressing manner she united a latent obstinacy which it was hopeless to attempt to shake. I feared, too, that she was not quite certain as yet whether she cared for me or not, and that this condition of hers was an expedient to gain time.

I left her with a heavy heart. Unless I proved my worth by bringing back Bingo within a very short time Travers would probably have everything his own way. And Bingo was dead!

However, I took heart. I thought that perhaps if I could succeed by my earnest efforts in persuading Lilian that I really was doing all in my power to recover the poodle, she might relent in time, and dispense with his actual production.

So, partly with this object, and partly to appease the remorse which now revived and stung me deeper than before, I undertook long and weary pilgrimages after office hours. I spent many pounds in advertisements; I interviewed dogs of every size, color, and breed, and of course I took care to keep Lilian informed of each successive failure. But still her heart was not touched; she was firm. If I went on like that, she told me, I was certain to find Bingo one day; then, but not before, would her doubts be set at rest.

I was walking one day through the somewhat squalid district which lies between Bow Street and High Holborn, when I saw, in a small theatrical costumer's window, a hand-bill stating that a black poodle had "followed a gentleman" on a certain date, and if not claimed and the finder remunerated before a stated time would be sold to pay expenses.

I went in and got a copy of the bill to show Lilian, and, although by that time I scarcely dared to look a poodle in the face, I thought I would go to the address given and see the animal, simply to be able to tell Lilian that I had done so.

The gentleman whom the dog had very unaccountably followed was a certain Mr. William Blagg, who kept a little shop near Endell Street, and called himself a bird-fancier, though I should scarcely have credited him with the necessary imagination. He was an evil-browed ruffian in a fur cap, with a broad broken nose and little shifty red eyes; and after I had told him what I wanted he took me through a horrible little den, stacked with piles of wooden, wire, and wicker prisons, each quivering with restless, twittering life, and then out into a back yard, in which were two or three rotten old kennels and tubs. "That there's him," he said, jerking his thumb to the farthest tub; "follered me all the way 'ome from Kinsington Gardings, *he* did. Kim out, will yer?"

And out of the tub there crawled slowly, with a snuffling whimper and a rattling of its chain, the identical dog I had slain a few evenings before!

At least, so I thought for a moment, and felt as if I had seen a specter; the resemblance was so exact — in size, in every detail, even to the little clumps of hair about the hind parts, even to the lop of half an ear, this dog might have been the *Doppelgänger* of the deceased Bingo. I suppose, after all, one black poodle is very like any other black poodle of the same size, but the likeness startled me.

I think it was then that the idea occurred to me that here was a miraculous chance of securing the sweetest girl in the whole world, and at the same time atoning for my wrong by bringing back gladness with me to Shuturgarden. It only needed a little boldness; one last deception, and I could embrace truthfulness once more.

Almost unconsciously, when my guide turned round and asked, "Is that there dawg yourn?" I said hurriedly, "Yes, yes; that's the dog I want; that — that's Bingo!"

"He don't seem to be a-puttin' of 'isself out about seein' you again," observed Mr. Blagg, as the poodle studied me with a calm interest.

"Oh, he's not exactly *my* dog, you see," I said; "he belongs to a friend of mine!"

He gave me a quick, furtive glance. "Then maybe you're mistook about him," he said, "and I can't run no risks. I was a-goin' down in the country this 'ere werry evenin' to see a party as lives at Wistaria Willa; he's been a-hadwertisin' about a black poodle, *he* has!"

"But look here," I said; "that's *me*."

He gave me a curious leer. "No offense, you know, guv'nor," he said, "but I should wish for some evidence as to that afore I part with a vallyable dawg like this 'ere!"

"Well," I said, "here's one of my cards; will that do for you?"

He took it and spelled it out with a pretense of great caution; but I saw well enough that the old scoundrel suspected that if I had lost a dog at all it was not this particular dog. "Ah," he said, as he put it in his pocket, "if I part with him to you I must be cleared of all risks. I can't afford to get into trouble about no mistakes. Unless you likes to leave him for a day or two you must pay accordin', you see."

I wanted to get the hateful business over as soon as possible. I did not care what I paid — Lilian was worth all the expense! I said I had no doubt myself as to the real ownership of the animal, but I would give him any sum in reason, and would remove the dog at once.

And so we settled it. I paid him an extortionate sum, and came away with a duplicate poodle, a canine counterfeit, which I hoped to pass off at Shuturgarden as the long-lost Bingo.

I know it was wrong, — it even came unpleasantly near dog-stealing, — but I was a desperate man. I saw Lilian gradually slipping away from me, I knew that nothing short of this could ever recall her, I was sorely tempted, I had gone far on the same road already; it was the old story of being hung for a sheep. And so I fell.

Surely some who read this will be generous enough to consider the peculiar state of the case, and mingle a little pity with their contempt.

I was dining in town that evening, and took my purchase home by a late train; his demeanor was grave and intensely respectable; he was not the animal to commit himself by any flagrant indiscretion; he was gentle and tractable, too, and in all respects an agreeable contrast in character to the original. Still, it may have been the after-dinner workings of conscience, but I could not help fancying that I saw a certain look in the creature's eyes, as if he were aware that he was required to connive at a fraud, and rather resented it.

If he would only be good enough to back me up! Fortunately, however, he was such a perfect facsimile of the outward Bingo that the risk of detection was really inconsiderable.

When I got him home I put Bingo's silver collar round his neck, congratulating myself on my forethought in preserving it, and took him in to see my mother. She accepted him as what he seemed without the slightest misgiving; but this, though it encouraged me to go on, was not decisive — the spurious poodle would have to encounter the scrutiny of those who knew every tuft on the genuine animal's body!

Nothing would have induced me to undergo such an ordeal as that of personally restoring him to the Curries. We gave him supper, and tied him up on the lawn, where he howled dolefully all night and buried bones.

The next morning I wrote a note to Mrs. Currie, expressing my pleasure at being able to restore the lost one, and another to Lilian, containing only the words, "Will you believe *now* that I am sincere?" Then I tied both round the poodle's neck, and dropped him over the wall into the colonel's garden just before I started to catch my train to town.

I had an anxious walk home from the station that evening; I went round by the longer way, trembling the whole time lest I should meet any of the Currie household, to which I felt myself entirely unequal just then. I could not rest until I knew whether my fraud had succeeded, or if the poodle to which I had entrusted my fate had basely betrayed me; but my suspense was happily ended as soon as I entered my mother's room. "You can't think how delighted those poor Curries were to see Bingo again," she said at once; "and they said such charming things about you, Algy, — Lilian particularly: quite affected she seemed, poor child! And they wanted you to go round and dine there and be thanked to-night, but at last I persuaded them to come to us instead. And they're going to bring the dog to make friends. Oh, and I met Frank Travers; he's back from circuit again now, so I asked him in, too, to meet them!"

I drew a deep breath of relief. I had played a desperate game, but I had won! I could have wished, to be sure, that my mother had not thought of bringing in Travers on that of all evenings, but I hoped that I could defy him after this.

The colonel and his people were the first to arrive, he and his wife being so effusively grateful that they made me very uncomfortable indeed; Lilian met me with downcast eyes and the faintest possible blush, but she said nothing just then. Five minutes afterward, when she and I were alone together in the conservatory, where I had brought her on pretense of showing a new begonia, she laid her hand on my sleeve and whispered, almost shyly, "Mr. Weatherhead — Algernon! Can you ever forgive me for being so cruel and unjust to you?" And I replied that, upon the whole, I could.

We were not in that conservatory long, but before we left it beautiful Lilian Roseblade had consented to make my life happy. When we reëntered the drawing-room we found Frank Travers, who had been told the story of the recovery; and I observed his jaw fall as he glanced at our faces, and noted the triumphant smile which I have no doubt mine wore, and the tender, dreamy look in Lilian's soft eyes. Poor Travers! I was sorry for him, although I was not fond of him. Travers was a good type of the rising young common-law barrister, tall, not bad-looking, with keen dark eyes, black whiskers, and the mobile forensic mouth which can express every shade of feeling, from deferential assent to cynical incredulity; possessed, too, of an endless flow of conversation that was decidedly agreeable, if a trifle too laboriously so, he had been a dangerous rival. But all that was over now; he saw it himself at once, and during dinner sank into dismal silence, gazing pathetically at Lilian, and sighing almost obtrusively between the courses. His stream of small talk seemed to have been cut off at the main.

"You've done a kind thing, Weatherhead," said the colonel. "I can't tell you all that dog is to me, and how I missed the poor beast. I'd quite given up all hope of ever seeing him again, and all the time there was Weatherhead, Mr. Travers, quietly searching all London till he found him! I shan't forget it. It shows a really kind feeling."

I saw by Travers's face that he was telling himself he would have found fifty Bingos in half the time — if he had only thought of it; he smiled a melancholy assent to all the colonel said, and then began to study me with an obviously depreciatory air.

"You can't think," I heard Mrs. Currie telling my

mother, "how really *touching* it was to see poor dear Bingo's emotion at seeing all the old familiar objects again! He went up and sniffed at them all in turn, quite plainly recognizing everything. And he was quite put out to find that we had moved his favorite ottoman out of the drawing-room. But he *is* so penitent, too, and so ashamed of having run away; he hardly dares to come when John calls him, and he kept under a chair in the hall all the morning; he would n't come in here, either, so we had to leave him in your garden."

"He's been sadly out of spirits all day," said Lilian; "he has n't bitten one of the tradespeople."

"Oh, *he's* all right, the rascal!" said the colonel, cheerily. "He'll be after the cats again as well as ever in a day or two."

"Ah, those cats!" said my poor innocent mother. "Algy, you have n't tried the air-gun on them again lately, have you? They're worse than ever."

I troubled the colonel to pass the claret. Travers laughed for the first time. "That's a good idea," he said, in that carrying "bar-mess" voice of his; "an air-gun for cats, ha, ha! Make good bags, eh, Weatherhead?" I said that I did, *very* good bags, and felt I was getting painfully red in the face.

"Oh, Algy is an excellent shot — quite a sportsman," said my mother. "I remember, oh, long ago, when we lived at Hammersmith, he had a pistol, and he used to strew crumbs in the garden for the sparrows, and shoot at them out of the pantry window; he frequently hit one."

"Well," said the colonel, not much impressed by these sporting reminiscences, "don't go rolling over our Bingo by mistake, you know, Weatherhead, my boy. Not but what you've a sort of right after this —

only don't. I would n't go through it all twice for anything."

"If you really won't take any more wine," I said,
hurriedly, addressing the colonel and Travers, "suppose we all go out and have our coffee on the lawn? It
— it will be cooler there." For it was getting very hot
indoors, I thought.

I left Travers to amuse the ladies — he could do no
more harm now; and, taking the colonel aside, I seized
the opportunity, as we strolled up and down the garden
path, to ask his consent to Lilian's engagement to me.
He gave it cordially. "There's not a man in England,"
he said, "that I'd sooner see her married to after to-day.
You're a quiet, steady young fellow, and you've a good
kind heart. As for the money, that's neither here nor
there; Lilian won't come to you without a penny, you
know. But, really, my boy, you can hardly believe what
it is to my poor wife and me to see that dog. Why,
bless my soul, look at him now! What's the matter
with him, eh?"

To my unutterable horror, I saw that that miserable
poodle, after begging unnoticed at the tea-table for some
time, had retired to an open space before it, where he
was now industriously standing on his head.

We gathered round and examined the animal curiously,
as he continued to balance himself gravely in his abnor-
mal position. "Good gracious, John," cried Mrs. Currie,
"I never saw Bingo do such a thing before in his life!"

"Very odd," said the colonel, putting up his glasses;
"never learned that from *me*."

"I tell you what I fancy it is," I suggested, wildly.
"You see, he was always a sensitive, excitable animal,
and perhaps the — the sudden joy of his return has gone
to his head — *upset* him, you know."

They seemed disposed to accept this solution, and, indeed, I believe they would have credited Bingo with every conceivable degree of sensibility; but I felt myself that if this unhappy animal had many more of these accomplishments I was undone, for the original Bingo had never been a dog of parts.

"It's very odd," said Travers, reflectively, as the dog recovered his proper level, "but I always thought that it was half the *right* ear that Bingo had lost."

"So it is, is n't it?" said the colonel. "Left, eh? Well, I thought myself it was the right."

My heart almost stopped with terror; I had altogether forgotten that. I hastened to set the point at rest. "Oh, it *was* the left," I said, positively; "I know it because I remember so particularly thinking how odd it was that it *should* be the left ear, and not the right!" I told myself this should be positively my last lie.

"*Why* odd?" asked Frank Travers, with his most offensive Socratic manner.

"My dear fellow, I can't tell you," I said, impatiently; "everything seems odd when you come to think at all about it."

"Algernon," said Lilian, later on, "will you tell Aunt Mary and Mr. Travers and — and me how it was you came to find Bingo? Mr. Travers is quite anxious to hear all about it."

I could not very well refuse; I sat down and told the story, all my own way. I painted Blagg perhaps rather bigger and blacker than life, and described an exciting scene, in which I recognized Bingo by his collar in the streets, and claimed and bore him off then and there in spite of all opposition.

I had the inexpressible pleasure of seeing Travers grinding his teeth with envy as I went on, and feeling

Lilian's soft, slender hand glide silently into mine as I told my tale in the twilight.

All at once, just as I reached the climax, we heard the poodle barking furiously at the hedge which separated my garden from the road.

"There's a foreign-looking man staring over the hedge," said Lilian; "Bingo always *did* hate foreigners."

There certainly was a swarthy man there, and, though I had no reason for it then, somehow my heart died within me at the sight of him.

"Don't be alarmed, sir," cried the colonel; "the dog won't bite you — unless there's a hole in the hedge anywhere."

The stranger took off his small straw hat with a sweep. "Ah, I am not afraid," he said, and his accent proclaimed him a Frenchman; "he is not enrage at me. May I ask, is it pairmeet to speak viz Misterre Vezzered?"

I felt I must deal with this person alone, for I feared the worst; and, asking them to excuse me, I went to the hedge and faced the Frenchman with the frightful calm of despair. He was a short, stout little man, with blue cheeks, sparkling black eyes, and a vivacious walnut-colored countenance; he wore a short black alpaca coat, and a large white cravat, with an immense oval malachite brooch in the center of it, which I mention because I found myself staring mechanically at it during the interview.

"My name is Weatherhead," I began, with the bearing of a detected pickpocket. "Can I be of any service to you?"

"Of a great service," he said, emphatically; "you can restore to me ze poodle vich I see zere!"

Nemesis had called at last in the shape of a rival

claimant. I staggered for an instant; then I said, "Oh, I think you are under a mistake; that dog is not mine."

"I know it," he said; "zere 'as been leetle mistake, so if ze dog is not to you, you give him back to me, *hein?*"

"I tell you," I said, "that poodle belongs to the gentleman over there." And I pointed to the colonel, seeing that it was best now to bring him into the affair without delay.

"You are wrong," he said, doggedly; "ze poodle is my poodle! And I was direct to you — it is your name on ze carte!" And he presented me with that fatal card which I had been foolish enough to give to Blagg as a proof of my identity. I saw it all now; the old villain had betrayed me, and to earn a double reward had put the real owner on my track.

I decided to call the colonel at once, and attempt to brazen it out with the help of his sincere belief in the dog.

"Eh, what's that; what's it all about?" said the colonel, bustling up, followed at intervals by the others.

The Frenchman raised his hat again. "I do not vant to make a trouble," he began, "but zere is leetle mistake. My word of honor, sare, I see my own poodle in your garden. Ven I appeal to zis gentilman to restore 'im he reffer me to you."

"You must allow me to know my own dog, sir," said the colonel. "Why, I've had him from a pup. Bingo old boy, you know your master, don't you?"

But the brute ignored him altogether, and began to leap wildly at the hedge in frantic efforts to join the Frenchman. It needed no Solomon to decide *his* ownership!

"I tell you, you 'ave got ze wrong poodle — it is my

own dog, my Azor! He remember me well, you see? I lose him, it is three, four days. . . . I see a nottice zat he is found, and ven I go to ze address zey tell me, 'Oh, he is reclaim, he is gone viz a strangaire who has advertise.' Zey show me ze placard; I follow 'ere, and ven I arrive I see my poodle in ze garden before me!"

"But look here," said the colonel, impatiently; "it's all very well to say that, but how can you prove it? I give you *my* word that the dog belongs to *me!* You must prove your claim, eh, Travers?"

"Yes," said Travers, judicially; "mere assertion is no proof; it's oath against oath at present."

"Attend an instant; your poodle, was he 'ighly train, had he some talents — a dog viz tricks, eh?"

"No, he's not," said the colonel; "I don't like to see dogs taught to play the fool; there's none of that nonsense about *him*, sir!"

"Ah, remark him well, then. *Azor, mon chou, danse donc un peu!*"

And, on the foreigner's whistling a lively air, that infernal poodle rose on his hind legs and danced solemnly about half way round the garden! We inside followed his movements with dismay.

"Why, dash it all!" cried the disgusted colonel, "he's dancing along like a d—d mountebank! But it's my Bingo, for all that!"

"You are not convince? You shall see more. *Azor, ici! Pour Beesmarck, Azor!*" (The poodle barked ferociously.) "*Pour Gambetta!*" (He wagged his tail and began to leap with joy.) "*Meurs pour la patrie!*" And the too accomplished animal rolled over as if killed in battle!

"Where could Bingo have picked up so much French?" cried Lilian incredulously.

"Or so much French history?" added that serpent, Travers.

"Shall I command 'im to jomp, or reverse 'imself?" inquired the obliging Frenchman.

"We've seen that, thank you," said the colonel, gloomily. "Upon my word, I don't know what to think. It can't be that that's not my Bingo after all — I'll never believe it!"

I tried a last desperate stroke. "Will you come round to the front?" I said to the Frenchman. "I'll let you in, and we can discuss the matter quietly." Then, as we walked back together, I asked him eagerly what he would take to abandon his claims and let the colonel think the poodle was his after all.

He was furious — he considered himself insulted; with great emotion he informed me that the dog was the pride of his life (it seems to be the mission of black poodles to serve as domestic comforts of this priceless kind!), that he would not part with him for twice his weight in gold.

"Figure," he began, as we joined the others, "zat zis gentilman 'ere 'as offer me money for ze dog! He agrees zat it is to me, you see? Ver' well, zen, zere is no more to be said!"

"Why, Weatherhead, have *you* lost faith too, then?" said the colonel.

I saw that it was no good; all I wanted now was to get out of it creditably and get rid of the Frenchman. "I'm sorry to say," I replied, "that I'm afraid I've been deceived by the extraordinary likeness. I don't think, on reflection, that that *is* Bingo!"

"What do you think, Travers?" asked the colonel.

"Well, since you ask me," said Travers, with quite unnecessary dryness, "I never did think so."

"Nor I," said the colonel; "I thought from the first that was never my Bingo. Why, Bingo would make two of that beast!"

And Lilian and her aunt both protested that they had had their doubts from the first.

"Zen you pairmeet zat I remove 'im?" said the Frenchman.

"Certainly," said the colonel; and, after some apologies on our part for the mistake, he went off in triumph, with the detestable poodle frisking after him.

When he had gone the colonel laid his hand kindly on my shoulder. "Don't look so cut up about it, my boy," he said; "you did your best — there was a sort of likeness to any one who did n't know Bingo as we did."

Just then the Frenchman again appeared at the hedge. "A thousand pardons," he said, "but I find zis upon my dog; it is not to me. Suffer me to restore it viz many compliments."

It was Bingo's collar. Travers took it from his hand and brought it to us.

"This was on the dog when you stopped that fellow, did n't you say?" he asked me.

One more lie — and I was so weary of falsehood! Y-yes," I said, reluctantly; "that was so."

"Very extraordinary," said Travers; "that's the wrong poodle beyond a doubt, but when he's found he's wearing the right dog's collar! Now, how do you account for that?"

"My good fellow," I said, impatiently, "I'm not in the witness-box. I *can't* account for it. It— it's a mere coincidence!"

"But look here, my *dear* Weatherhead," argued Travers (whether in good faith or not I never could quite make out), "don't you see what a tremendously important link it is? Here's a dog who (as I understand the facts) had a silver collar, with his name engraved on it, round his neck at the time he was lost. Here's that identical collar turning up soon afterward round the neck of a totally different dog! We must follow this up; we must get at the bottom of it somehow! With a clue like this, we're sure to find out either the dog himself, or what's become of him! Just try to recollect exactly what happened, there's a good fellow. This is just the sort of thing I like!"

It was the sort of thing I did not enjoy at all. "You must excuse me to-night, Travers," I said, uncomfortably; "you see, just now it's rather a sore subject for me, and I'm not feeling very well!" I was grateful just then for a reassuring glance of pity and confidence from Lilian's sweet eyes, which revived my drooping spirits for the moment.

"Yes, we'll go into it to-morrow, Travers," said the colonel; "and then — hullo, there's that confounded Frenchman *again!*"

It was indeed; he came prancing back delicately, with a malicious enjoyment on his wrinkled face. "Once more I return to apologize," he said. "My poodle 'as permit 'imself ze grave indiscretion to make a very big 'ole at ze bottom of ze garden!"

I assured him that it was of no consequence.

"Perhaps," he replied, looking steadily at me through his keen, half-shut eyes, "you vill not say zat ven you regard ze 'ole. And you others, I spik to you: somtimes von loses a somzing vich is qvite near all ze time. It is ver' droll, eh? my vord, ha, ha, ha!" And he ambled off, with an aggressively fiendish laugh that chilled my blood.

"What the deuce did he mean by that, eh?" said the colonel, blankly.

"Don't know," said Travers; "suppose we go and in-spect the hole?"

But before that I had contrived to draw near it my-self, in deadly fear lest the Frenchman's last words had contained some innuendo which I had not understood.

It was light enough still for me to see something, at the unexpected horror of which I very nearly fainted.

That thrice accursed poodle which I had been insane enough to attempt to foist upon the colonel must, it seems, have buried his supper the night before very near the spot in which I had laid Bingo, and in his attempts to exhume his bone had brought the remains of my vic-tim to the surface!

There the corpse lay, on the very top of the excava-tions. Time had not, of course, improved its appearance, which was ghastly in the extreme, but still plainly re-cognizable by the eye of affection.

"It's a very ordinary hole," I gasped, putting my-self before it and trying to turn them back. "Nothing in it — nothing at all!"

"Except one Algernon Weatherhead, Esq., eh?" whispered Travers, jocosely, in my ear.

"No; but," persisted the colonel, advancing, "look here! Has the dog damaged any of your shrubs?"

"No, no!" I cried, piteously; "quite the reverse. Let's all go indoors now; it's getting so cold!"

"See, there *is* a shrub or something uprooted," said the colonel, still coming nearer that fatal hole. "Why, hullo, look there! What's that?"

Lilian, who was by his side, gave a slight scream. "Uncle," she cried, "it looks like — like *Bingo!*"

The colonel turned suddenly upon me. "Do you

hear?" he demanded, in a choked voice. "You hear what she says? Can't you speak out? Is that our Bingo?"

I gave it up at last; I only longed to be allowed to crawl away under something! "Yes," I said, in a dull whisper, as I sat down heavily on a garden seat, "yes . . . that's Bingo . . . misfortune . . . shoot him . . . quite an accident!"

There was a terrible explosion after that; they saw at last how I had deceived them, and put the very worst construction upon everything. Even now I writhe impotently at times, and my cheeks smart and tingle with humiliation, as I recall that scene — the colonel's very plain speaking, Lilian's passionate reproaches and contempt, and her aunt's speechless prostration of disappointment.

I made no attempt to defend myself; I was not, perhaps, the complete villain they deemed me, but I felt dully that no doubt it all served me perfectly right.

Still I do not think I am under any obligation to put their remarks down in black and white here.

Travers had vanished at the first opportunity — whether out of delicacy, or the fear of breaking out into unseasonable mirth, I cannot say; and shortly afterward the others came to where I sat silent with bowed head, and bade me a stern and final farewell.

And then, as the last gleam of Lilian's white dress vanished down the garden path, I laid my head down on the table among the coffee-cups, and cried like a beaten child.

I got leave as soon as I could, and went abroad. The morning after my return I noticed, while shaving, that there was a small square marble tablet placed against the wall of the colonel's garden. I got my opera-glass and read — and pleasant reading it was — the following inscription: —

IN AFFECTIONATE MEMORY

OF

BINGO

SECRETLY AND CRUELLY PUT TO DEATH,

IN COLD BLOOD,

BY A

NEIGHBOR AND FRIEND.

JUNE, 1881

If this explanation of mine ever reaches my neighbors' eyes, I humbly hope they will have the humanity either to take away or tone down that tablet. They cannot conceive what I suffer when curious visitors insist, as they do every day, on spelling out the words from our windows, and asking me countless questions about them!

Sometimes I meet the Curries about the village, and as they pass me with averted heads I feel myself growing crimson. Travers is almost always with Lilian now. He has given her a dog, — a fox-terrier, — and they take ostentatiously elaborate precautions to keep it out of my garden.

I should like to assure them here that they need not be under any alarm. I have shot one dog.

THE THREE STRANGERS[1]

BY THOMAS HARDY

The Three Strangers is an additional example of the plot structure already illustrated in *The Black Poodle* — the "method of story." The narrative also approaches the type of "hoax-plot" exemplified in *Marjorie Daw*, but it is by no means so clearly typical. One does not feel that the purpose of the author is to hoodwink the reader: the hints as to the identity of at least two of the three strangers are sufficiently broad to dispel doubt.

But the ultimate value of the story depends in considerable degree on the descriptive portions. Like all of Mr. Hardy's work, *The Three Strangers* shows a wonderful power in the handling of nature. Many of his scenes are based on actual originals, which the traveler may easily verify. Higher Crowstairs, for example, may be found to-day on the slopes above Cerne Abbas, on a deserted coach-road over the heath to Dorchester, — or "Casterbridge," as it is called in the story. But the vividness of the scenes as portrayed is not merely a matter of guide-book exactness, of expository description presented for the purposes of identification: the writer gives actual life to his pictures as a result of his own keen observation of nature and his instinctive appreciation of the power of language. Of the first, the reader will find exemplification in the opening paragraphs descriptive of the heath and the storm. And the connotativeness, the condensed suggestiveness of the writer's diction, is constantly present. The following paragraph is a good instance, and, if one re-reads it, one becomes conscious of the new values that are constantly making themselves felt: —

"But Elijah and the boy, in the excitement of their position, quite forgot the injunction. Moreover, Oliver Giles, a man of seventeen, one of the dancers, who was enamored of his partner, a fair girl of thirty-three rolling years, had recklessly

[1] From *Wessex Tales*. Published by Harper & Brothers.

handed a new crown-piece to the musicians as a bribe to keep going as long as they had muscle and wind. Mrs. Fennel, seeing the steam begin to generate on the countenances of her guests, crossed over and touched the fiddler's elbow and put her hand on the serpent's mouth. But they took no notice, and fearing she might lose her character of genial hostess if she were to interfere too markedly, she retired and sat down helpless. And so the dance whizzed on with cumulative fury, the performers moving in their planet-like courses, direct and retrograde, from apogee to perigee, till the hand of the well-kicked clock at the bottom of the room had traveled over the circumference of an hour."

AMONG the few features of agricultural England which retain an appearance but little modified by the lapse of centuries may be reckoned the high, grassy, and furzy downs, coombs, or ewe-leases, as they are indifferently called, that fill a large area of certain counties in the south and southwest. If any mark of human occupation is met with hereon it usually takes the form of the solitary cottage of some shepherd.

Fifty years ago such a lonely cottage stood on such a down, and may possibly be standing there now. In spite of its loneliness, however, the spot, by actual measurement, was not more than five miles from a county town. Yet what of that? Five miles of irregular upland, during the long, inimical seasons, with their sleets, snows, rains, and mists, afford withdrawing space enough to isolate a Timon or a Nebuchadnezzar; much less, in fair weather, to please that less repellent tribe, the poets, philosophers, artists, and others who "conceive and meditate of pleasant things."

Some old earthern camp or barrow, some clump of trees, at least some starved fragment of ancient hedge, is usually taken advantage of in the erection of these forlorn dwellings; but in the present case such a kind of shelter had been disregarded. Higher Crowstairs, as the house was called, stood quite detached and undefended. The only reason for its precise situation seemed to be the crossing of two footpaths at right angles hard by, which may have crossed there and thus for a good five hundred years. The house was thus exposed to the elements on all sides. But, though the wind up here blew unmistakably when it did blow, and the rain hit hard whenever it fell, the various weathers of the winter season were not quite so formidable on the coomb as they were imagined to be by dwellers on low ground. The raw rimes were not so pernicious as in the hollows, and the frosts were scarcely so severe. When the shepherd and his family who tenanted the house were pitied for their sufferings from the exposure, they said that upon the whole they were less inconvenienced by "wuzzes and flames" (hoarses and phlegms) than when they had lived by the stream of a snug neighboring valley.

The night of March 28, 182–, was precisely one of the nights that were wont to call forth these expressions of commiseration. The level rainstorm smote walls, slopes, and hedges like the clothyard shafts of Senlac and Crécy. Such sheep and outdoor animals as had no shelter stood with their buttocks to the wind, while the tails of little birds trying to roost on some scraggy thorn were blown inside out like umbrellas. The gable end of the cottage was stained with wet, and the eavesdroppings flapped against the wall. Yet never was commiseration for the shepherd more misplaced. For that cheerful rustic was entertaining a large party in glorification of the christening of his second girl.

The guests had arrived before the rain began to fall, and they were all now assembled in the chief or living room of the dwelling. A glance into the apartment at eight o'clock on this eventful evening would have resulted in the opinion that it was as cozy and comfortable a nook as could be wished for in boisterous weather. The calling of its inhabitant was proclaimed by a number of highly polished sheep-crooks without stems, that were hung ornamentally over the fireplace, the curl of each shining crook varying from the antiquated type engraved in the patriarchal pictures of old family Bibles to the most approved fashion of the last local sheep fair. The room was lighted by half a dozen candles, having wicks only a trifle smaller than the grease which enveloped them, in candlesticks that were never used but at high-days, holy days, and family feasts. The lights were scattered about the room, two of them standing on the chimney-piece. This position of candles was in itself significant. Candles on the chimney-piece always meant a party.

On the hearth, in front of a back brand to give substance, blazed a fire of thorns, that crackled "like the laughter of the fool."

Nineteen persons were gathered here. Of these, five women, wearing gowns of various bright hues, sat in chairs along the wall; girls shy and not shy filled the window-bench; four men, including Charley Jake, the hedge-carpenter, Elijah New, the parish clerk, and John Pitcher, a neighboring dairyman, the shepherd's father-in-law, lolled in the settle; a young man and maid, who were blushing over tentative *pourparlers* on a life-companionship, sat beneath the corner cupboard; and an elderly engaged man of fifty or upward moved restlessly about from spots where his betrothed was not to the spot where she was. Enjoyment was pretty general, and so much the more prevailed in being unhampered by conventional restrictions. Absolute confidence in one another's good opinion begat perfect ease, while the finishing stroke of manner, amounting to a truly princely serenity, was lent to the majority by the absence of any expression or trait denoting that they wished to get on in the world, enlarge their minds, or do any eclipsing thing whatever, which nowadays so generally nips the bloom, and bonhomie of all except the two extremes of the social scale.

Shepherd Fennel had married well, his wife being a dairyman's daughter from the valley below, who brought fifty guineas in her pocket — and kept them there till they should be required for ministering to the needs of a coming family. This frugal woman had been somewhat exercised as to the character that should be given to the gathering. A sit-still party had its advantages; but an undisturbed position of ease in chairs and settles was apt to lead on the men to such an unconscionable deal of toping that they would sometimes fairly drink the house dry. A dancing-party was the alternative; but this, while avoiding the foregoing objection on the score of good drink, had a counterbalancing disadvantage in the matter of good victuals, the ravenous appetites engendered by the exercise causing immense havoc in the buttery. Shepherdess Fennel fell back upon the intermediate plan of mingling short dances with short periods of talk and singing, so as to hinder any ungovernable rage in either. But this scheme was entirely confined to her own gentle mind; the shepherd himself was in the mood to exhibit the most reckless phases of hospitality.

The fiddler was a boy of those parts, about twelve years of age, who had a wonderful dexterity in jigs and reels, though his fingers were so small and short as to necessitate a constant shifting for the high notes, from

which he scrambled back to the first position with
sounds not of unmixed purity of tone. At seven the shrill
"tweedledee" of this youngster had begun, accompanied by a booming ground bass from Elijah New, the
parish clerk, who had thoughtfully brought with him
his favorite musical instrument, the serpent. Dancing
was instantaneous, Mrs. Fennel privately enjoining the
players on no account to let the dance exceed the length
of a quarter of an hour.

But Elijah and the boy, in the excitement of their
position, quite forgot the injunction. Moreover, Oliver
Giles, a man of seventeen, one of the dancers, who was
enamoured of his partner, a fair girl of thirty-three
rolling years, had recklessly handed a new crown-piece
to the musicians as a bribe to keep going as long as they
had muscle and wind. Mrs. Fennel, seeing the steam
begin to generate on the countenances of her guests,
crossed over and touched the fiddler's elbow and put
her hand on the serpent's mouth. But they took no
notice, and, fearing she might lose her character of genial
hostess if she were to interfere too markedly, she retired
and sat down helpless. And so the dance whizzed on
with cumulative fury, the performers moving in their
planet-like courses, direct and retrograde, from apogee
to perigee, till the hand of the well-kicked clock at the
bottom of the room had traveled over the circumference of an hour.

While these cheerful events were in course of enact-
ment within Fennel's pastoral dwelling, an incident
having considerable bearing on the party had occurred
in the gloomy night without. Mrs. Fennel's concern
about the growing fierceness of the dance corresponded
in point of time with the ascent of a human figure to the
solitary hill of Higher Crowstairs from the direction of

the distant town. This personage strode on through the rain without a pause, following the little worn path which, farther on in its course, skirted the shepherd's cottage.

It was nearly the time of full moon, and on this account, though the sky was lined with a uniform sheet of dripping cloud, ordinary objects out of doors were readily visible. The sad, wan light revealed the lonely pedestrian to be a man of supple frame; his gait suggested that he had somewhat passed the period of perfect and instinctive agility, though not so far as to be otherwise than rapid of motion when occasion required. In point of fact, he might have been about forty years of age. He appeared tall; but a recruiting sergeant, or other person accustomed to the judging of men's heights by the eye, would have discerned that his was chiefly owing to his gauntness, and that he was not more than five feet eight or nine.

Notwithstanding the regularity of his tread, there was caution in it, as in that of one who mentally feels his way; and, in despite the fact that it was not a black coat nor a dark garment of any sort that he wore, there was something about him which suggested that he naturally belonged to the black-coated tribes of men. His clothes were of fustian and his boots hobnailed, yet in his progress he showed not the mud-accustomed bearing of hobnailed and fustianed peasantry.

By the time that he had arrived abreast of the shepherd's premises, the rain came down, or rather came along, with yet more determined violence. The outskirts of the little homestead partially broke the force of wind and rain, and this induced him to stand still. The most salient of the shepherd's domestic erections was an empty sty at the forward corner of his hedgeless garden, for in these latitudes the principle of masking the homelier features of your establishment by a conventional frontage was unknown. The traveler's eye was attracted to this small building by the pallid shine of the wet slates that covered it. He turned aside, and, finding it empty, stood under the pent-roof for shelter.

While he stood, the boom of the serpent within and the lesser strains of the fiddler reached the spot, as an accompaniment to the surging hiss of the flying rain on the sod, its louder beating on the cabbage-leaves of the garden, on the eight or ten beehives just discernible by the path, and its dripping from the eaves into a row of buckets and pans that had been placed under the walls of the cottage; for at Higher Crowstairs, as at all such elevated domiciles, the grand difficulty of housekeeping was an insufficiency of water, and a casual rainfall was utilized by turning out as catchers every utensil that the house contained. Some queer stories might be told of the contrivances for economy in suds and dishwaters that are absolutely necessitated in upland habitations during the droughts of summer. But at this season there were no such exigencies; a mere acceptance of what the skies bestowed was sufficient for an abundant store.

At last the notes of the serpent ceased and the house was silent. This cessation of activity aroused the solitary pedestrian from the reverie into which he had lapsed, and, emerging from the shed, with an apparently new intention, he walked up the path to the house door. Arrived here, his first act was to kneel down on a large stone beside the row of vessels and to drink a copious draught from one of them. Having quenched his thirst, he rose and lifted his hand to knock, but paused with his eye upon the panel. Since the dark surface of the wood revealed absolutely nothing, it was evident that he must be mentally looking through the door, as if he wished to measure thereby all the possibilities that a house of this sort might include, and how they might bear upon the question of his entry.

In his indecision he turned and surveyed the scene around. Not a soul was anywhere visible. The garden path stretched downward from his feet, gleaming like the track of a snail; the roof of the little well (mostly dry), the well-cover, the top rail of the garden gate, were varnished with the same dull liquid glaze; while, far away in the vale, a faint whiteness of more than usual extent showed that the rivers were high in the meads. Beyond all this winked a few bleared lamplights through the beating drops, lights that denoted the situation of the county town from which he had appeared to come. The absence of all notes of life in that direction seemed to clinch his intentions, and he knocked at the door.

Within a desultory chat had taken the place of movement and musical sound. The hedge-carpenter was suggesting a song to the company, which nobody just then was inclined to undertake, so that the knock afforded a not unwelcome diversion.

"Walk in!" said the shepherd, promptly.

The latch clicked upward, and out of the night our pedestrian appeared upon the doormat. The shepherd arose, snuffed two of the nearest candles, and turned to look at him.

Their light disclosed that the stranger was dark in complexion and not unprepossessing as to feature. His hat, which for a moment he did not remove, hung low over his eyes, without concealing that they were large, open, and determined, moving with a flash rather than a glance round the room. He seemed pleased with the survey, and, baring his shaggy head, said, in a rich, deep voice, "The rain is so heavy, friends, that I ask leave to come in and rest awhile."

"To be sure, stranger," said the shepherd. "And, faith, you've been lucky in choosing your time, for we are having a bit of a fling for a glad cause — though, to be sure, a man could hardly wish that glad cause to happen more than once a year."

"Nor less," spoke up a woman; "for 't is best to get your family over and done with as soon as you can, so as to be all the earlier out of the fag o't."

"And what may be this glad cause?" asked the stranger.

"A birth and christening," said the shepherd.

The stranger hoped his host might not be made unhappy either by too many or too few of such episodes, and, being invited by a gesture to a pull at the mug, he readily acquiesced. His manner, which before entering had been so dubious, was now altogether that of a careless and candid man.

"Late to be traipsing athwart this coomb — hey?" said the engaged man of fifty.

"Late it is, master, as you say. I'll take a seat in the chimney-corner if you have nothing to urge against it, ma'am, for I am a little moist on the side that was next the rain."

Mrs. Shepherd Fennel assented, and made room for the self-invited comer, who, having got completely inside the chimney-corner, stretched out his legs and his arms with the expansiveness of a person quite at home.

"Yes, I am rather thin in the vamp," he said, freely, seeing that the eyes of the shepherd's wife fell upon his boots, "and I am not well fitted, either. I have had some rough times lately, and have been forced to pick up what

I can get in the way of wearing; but I must find a suit better fit for working-days when I reach home."

"One of hereabouts?" she inquired.

"Not quite that — farther up the country."

"I thought so. And so am I; and by your tongue you come from my neighborhood."

"But you would hardly have heard of me," he said quickly. "My time would be long before yours, ma'am, you see."

This testimony to the youthfulness of his hostess had the effect of stopping her cross-examination.

"There is only one thing more wanted to make me happy," continued the newcomer; "and that is a little 'baccy, which I am sorry to say I am out of."

"I'll fill your pipe," said the shepherd.

"I must ask you to lend me a pipe likewise."

"A smoker, and no pipe about ye?"

"I have dropped it somewhere on the road."

The shepherd filled and handed him a new clay pipe, saying as he did so, "Hand me your 'baccy-box; I'll fill that too, now I am about it."

The man went through the movement of searching his pockets.

"Lost that, too?" said the entertainer, with some surprise.

"I am afraid so," said the man, with some confusion. "Give it to me in a screw of paper." Lighting his pipe at the candle with a suction that drew the whole flame into the bowl, he resettled himself in the corner, and bent his looks upon the faint steam from his damp legs as if he wished to say no more.

Meanwhile the general body of guests had been taking little notice of this visitor by reason of an absorbing discussion in which they were engaged with the band

about a tune for the next dance. The matter being settled, they were about to stand up, when an interruption
came in the shape of another knock at the door.

At sound of the same the man in the chimney-corner
took up the poker and began stirring the fire as if doing
it thoroughly were the one aim of his existence, and a
second time the shepherd said, "Walk in!" In a moment another man stood upon the straw-woven doormat. He, too, was a stranger.

This individual was one of a type radically different
from the first. There was more of the commonplace in
his manner, and a certain jovial cosmopolitanism sat
upon his features. He was several years older than the
first arrival, his hair being slightly frosted, his eyebrows
bristly, and his whiskers cut back from his cheeks. His
face was rather full and flabby, and yet it was not altogether a face without power. A few grog-blossoms
marked the neighborhood of his nose. He flung back
his long drab greatcoat, revealing that beneath it he
wore a suit of cinder-gray shade throughout, large,
heavy seals, of some metal or other that would take a
polish, dangling from his fob as his only personal orna-
ment. Shaking the water-drops from his low-crowned,
glazed hat, he said, "I must ask for a few minutes'
shelter, comrades, or I shall be wetted to my skin before
I get to Casterbridge."

"Make yerself at home, master," said the shepherd,
perhaps a trifle less heartily than on the first occasion.
Not that Fennel had the least tinge of niggardliness in
his composition, but the room was far from large, spare
chairs were not numerous, and damp companions were
not altogether comfortable at close quarters for the
women and girls in their bright-colored gowns.

However, the second comer, after taking off his greatcoat and hanging his hat on a nail in one of the ceiling beams as if he had been specially invited to put it there, advanced, and sat down at the table. This had been pushed so closely into the chimney-corner, to give all available room to the dancers, that its inner edge grazed the elbow of the man who had ensconced himself by the fire, and thus the two strangers were brought into close companionship. They nodded to each other by way of breaking the ice of unacquaintance, and the first stranger handed his neighbor the large mug — a huge vessel of brown ware, having its upper edge worn away, like a threshold, by the rub of whole genealogies of thirsty lips that had gone the way of all flesh, and bearing the following inscription burned upon its rotund side in yellow letters: —

THERE IS NO FUN

UNTILL I CUM.

The other man, nothing loath, raised the mug to his lips, and drank on and on and on, till a curious blueness overspread the countenance of the shepherd's wife, who had regarded with no little surprise the first stranger's free offer to the second of what did not belong to him to dispense.

"I knew it!" said the toper to the shepherd, with much satisfaction. "When I walked up your garden afore coming in, and saw the hives all of a row, I said to myself, 'Where there's bees there's honey, and where there's honey there's mead.' But mead of such a truly comfortable sort as this I really did n't expect to meet in my older days." He took yet another pull at the mug, till it assumed an ominous horizontality.

"Glad you enjoy it!" said the shepherd, warmly.

"It is goodish mead," assented Mrs. Fennel, with an

absence of enthusiasm which seemed to say that it was possible to buy praise for one's cellar at too heavy a price. "It is trouble enough to make — and really I hardly think we shall make any more. For honey sells well, and we can make shift with a drop o' small mead and metheglin for common use from the comb-washings."

"Oh, but you'll never have the heart!" reproachfully cried the stranger in cinder gray, after taking up the mug a third time and setting it down empty. "I love mead, when 't is old like this, as I love to go to church o' Sundays or to relieve the needy any day of the week."

"Ha, ha, ha!" said the man in the chimney-corner, who, in spite of the taciturnity induced by the pipe of tobacco, could not or would not refrain from this slight testimony to his comrade's humor.

Now the old mead of those days, brewed of the purest first-year or maiden honey, four pounds to the gallon, — with its due complement of whites of eggs, cinnamon, ginger, cloves, mace, rosemary, yeast, and processes of working, bottling, and cellaring, — tasted remarkably strong; but it did not taste so strong as it actually was. Hence, presently the stranger in cinder gray at the table, moved by its creeping influence, unbuttoned his waistcoat, threw himself back in his chair, spread his legs, and made his presence felt in various ways.

"Well, well, as I say," he resumed, "I am going to Casterbridge, and to Casterbridge I must go. I should have been almost there by this time; but the rain drove me in to ye, and I'm not sorry for it."

"You don't live in Casterbridge?" said the shepherd.

"Not as yet, though I shortly mean to move there."

"Going to set up in trade, perhaps?"

"No, no," said the shepherd's wife; "it is easy to see

that the gentleman is rich and don't want to work at anything."

The cinder-gray stranger paused, as if to consider whether he would accept that definition of himself. He presently rejected it by answering, "Rich is not quite the word for me, dame. I do work, and I must work. And even if I only get to Casterbridge by midnight I must begin work there at eight to-morrow morning. Yes, het or wet, blow or snow, famine or sword, my day's work to-morrow must be done."

"Poor man! Then, in spite o' seeming, you be worse off than we?" replied the shepherd's wife.

"'T is the nature of my trade, men and maidens. 'T is the nature of my trade more than my poverty. But really and truly, I must up and off, or I shan't get a lodging in the town." However, the speaker did not move, and directly added, "There's time for one more draught of friendship before I go, and I'd perform it at once if the mug were not dry."

"Here's a mug o' small," said Mrs. Fennel. "Small, we call it, though, to be sure, 't is only the first wash o' the combs."

"No," said the stranger, disdainfully; "I won't spoil your first kindness by partaking o' your second."

"Certainly not," broke in Fennel. "We don't increase and multiply every day, and I'll fill the mug again." He went away to the dark place under the stairs where the barrel stood. The shepherdess followed him.

"Why should you do this?" she said, reproachfully, as soon as they were alone. "He's emptied it once, though it held enough for ten people; and now he's not contented wi' the small, but must needs call for more o' the strong! And a stranger unbeknown to any of us! For my part, I don't like the look o' the man at all."

"But he's in the house, my honey, and 't is a wet night, and a christening. Daze it, what's a cup of mead more or less? There 'll be plenty more next bee-burning."

"Very well — this time, then," she answered, looking wistfully at the barrel. "But what is the man's calling, and where is he one of, that he should come in and join us like this?"

"I don't know. I'll ask him again."

The catastrophe of having the mug drained dry at one pull by the stranger in cinder gray was effectually guarded against this time by Mrs. Fennel. She poured out his allowance in a small cup, keeping the large one at a discreet distance from him. When he had tossed off his portion the shepherd renewed his inquiry about the stranger's occupation.

The latter did not immediately reply, and the man in the chimney-corner, with sudden demonstrativeness, said, "Anybody may know my trade — I'm a wheel-wright."

"A very good trade for these parts," said the shepherd.

"And anybody may know mine — if they've the sense to find it out," said the stranger in cinder gray.

"You may generally tell what a man is by his claws," observed the hedge-carpenter, looking at his hands. "My fingers be as full of thorns as an old pincushion is of pins."

The hands of the man in the chimney-corner instinctively sought the shade, and he gazed into the fire as he resumed his pipe. The man at the table took up the hedge-carpenter's remark, and added smartly, "True; but the oddity of my trade is that, instead of setting a mark upon me, it sets a mark upon my customers."

No observation being offered by anybody in elucidation of this enigma, the shepherd's wife once more called for a song. The same obstacles presented themselves as at the former time: one had no voice, another had forgotten the first verse. The stranger at the table, whose soul had now risen to a good working temperature, relieved the difficulty by exclaiming that, to start the company, he would sing himself. Thrusting one thumb into the armhole of his waistcoat, he waved the other hand in the air, and, with an extemporizing gaze at the shining sheep-crooks above the mantlepiece, began: —

> "Oh, my trade it is the rarest one,
> Simple shepherds all,
> My trade is a sight to see;
> For my customers I tie, and take them up on high,
> And waft 'em to a far countree."

The room was silent when he had finished the verse, with one exception, that of the man in the chimney-corner, who, at the singer's word, "Chorus!" joined him in a deep bass voice of musical relish: —

> "And waft 'em to a far countree."

Oliver Giles, John Pitcher, the dairyman, the parish clerk, the engaged man of fifty, the row of young women against the wall, seemed lost in thought not of the gayest kind. The shepherd looked meditatively on the ground; the shepherdess gazed keenly at the singer, and with some suspicion; she was doubting whether this stranger was merely singing an old song from recollection, or composing one there and then for the occasion. All were as perplexed at the obscure revelation as the guests at Belshazzar's feast, except the man in the chimney-corner, who quietly said, "Second verse, stranger," and smoked on.

The singer thoroughly moistened himself from his lips inward, and went on with the next stanza, as requested:—

"My tools are but common ones,
            Simple shepherds all,
    My tools are no sight to see:
A little hempen string, and a post whereon to swing,
    Are implements enough for me."

Shepherd Fennel glanced round. There was no longer
any doubt that the stranger was answering his question
rhythmically. The guests one and all started back with
suppressed exclamations. The young woman engaged
to the man of fifty fainted halfway, and would have proceeded, but, finding him wanting in alacrity for catch-
ing her, she sat down trembling.

"Oh, he's the —" whispered the people in the background, mentioning the name of an ominous public
officer. "He's come to do it. 'T is to be at Casterbridge
jail to-morrow — the man for sheep-stealing — the
poor clock-maker we heard of, who used to live away
at Anglebury and had no work to do — Timothy Som-
mers, whose family were a-starving, and so he went out
of Anglebury by the highroad, and took a sheep in open
daylight, defying the farmer and the farmer's wife and
the farmer's man and every man Jack among 'em. He"
(and they nodded toward the stranger of the terrible
trade) "is come from up the country to do it because
there's not enough to do in his county town, and he's
got the place here, now our own county man's dead;
he's going to live in the same cottage under the prison
wall."

The stranger in cinder gray took no notice of this whispered string of observations, but again wetted his lips.
Seeing that his friend in the chimney-corner was the
only one who reciprocated his joviality in any way, he
held out his cup toward that appreciative comrade,
who also held out his own. They clinked together, the
eyes of the rest of the room hanging upon the singer's

actions. He parted his lips for the third verse, but at that moment another knock was audible upon the door. This time the knock was faint and hesitating.

The company seemed scared; the shepherd looked with consternation toward the entrance, and it was with some effort that he resisted his alarmed wife's deprecatory glance, and uttered for the third time the welcoming words, "Walk in!"

The door was gently opened, and another man stood upon the mat. He, like those who had preceded him, was a stranger. This time it was a short, small personage, of fair complexion, and dressed in a decent suit of dark clothes.

"Can you tell me the way to —" he began; when, gazing round the room to observe the nature of the company among whom he had fallen, his eyes lighted on the stranger in cinder gray. It was just at the instant when the latter, who had thrown his mind into his song with such a will that he scarcely heeded the interruption, silenced all whispers and inquiries by bursting into his third verse: —

> "To-morrow is my working-day,
> > Simple shepherds all,
> To-morrow is a working-day for me;
> For the farmer's sheep is slain, and the lad who did it ta'en,
> And on his soul may God ha' merc-y!"

The stranger in the chimney-corner, waving cups with the singer so heartily that his mead splashed over on the hearth, repeated in his bass voice as before: —

> "And on his soul may God ha' merc-y!"

All this time the third stranger had been standing in the doorway. Finding now that he did not come forward or go on speaking, the guests particularly regarded him. They noticed, to their surprise, that he stood before them the picture of abject terror — his knees trembling, his hand shaking so violently that the door-latch, by which he supported himself, rattled audibly; his white lips were parted, and his eyes fixed on the merry officer of justice in the middle of the room. A moment more, and he had turned, closed the door, and fled.

"What a man can it be?" said the shepherd.

The rest, between the awfulness of their late discovery and the odd conduct of this third visitor, looked as if they knew not what to think, and said nothing. Instinctively they withdrew farther and farther from the grim gentleman in their midst, whom some of them seemed to take for the Prince of Darkness himself, till they formed a remote circle, an empty space of floor being left between them and him —

"Circulus, cujus centrum diabolus."

The room was so silent — though there were more than twenty people in it — that nothing could be heard but the patter of the rain against the window-shutters, accompanied by the occasional hiss of a stray drop that fell down the chimney into the fire, and the steady puffing of the man in the corner, who had now resumed his long pipe of clay.

The stillness was unexpectedly broken. The distant sound of a gun reverberated through the air, apparently from the direction of the county town.

"Be jiggered!" cried the stranger who had sung the song, jumping up.

"What does that mean?" asked several.

"A prisoner escaped from the jail — that's what it means."

All listened. The sound was repeated, and none of

them spoke but the man in the chimney-corner, who said quietly, "I've often been told that in this county they fire a gun at such times, but I never heard it till now."

"I wonder if it is *my* man?" murmured the personage in cinder gray.

"Surely it is!" said the shepherd, involuntarily. "And surely we've seen him! That little man who looked in at the door by now, and quivered like a leaf when he seed ye and heard your song."

"His teeth chattered, and the breath went out of his body," said the dairyman.

"And his heart seemed to sink within him like a stone," said Oliver Giles.

"And he bolted as if he'd been shot at," said the hedge-carpenter.

"True — his teeth chattered, and his heart seemed to sink, and he bolted as if he'd been shot at," slowly summed up the man in the chimney-corner.

"I didn't notice it," remarked the grim songster.

"We were all a-wondering what made him run off in such a fright," faltered one of the women against the wall, "and now 't is explained."

The firing of the alarm-gun went on at intervals, low and sullenly, and their suspicions became a certainty. The sinister gentleman in cinder gray roused himself. "Is there a constable here?" he asked, in thick tones. "If so, let him step forward."

The engaged man of fifty stepped quavering out of the corner, his betrothed beginning to sob on the back of the chair.

"You are a sworn constable?"

"I be, sir."

"Then pursue the criminal at once, with assistance, and bring him back here. He can't have gone far."

"I will, sir, I will — when I've got my staff. I'll go home and get it, and come sharp here, and start in a body."

"Staff! never mind your staff — the man'll be gone!"

"But I can't do nothing without my staff — can I, William, and John, and Charles Jake? No; for there's the king's royal crown a-painted on en in yaller and gold, and the lion and the unicorn, so as when I raise en up and hit my prisoner 't is made a lawful blow thereby. I would n't 'tempt to take up a man without my staff — no, not I. If I had n't the law to gie me courage, why, instead o' my taking him up, he might take up me!"

"Now, I'm a king's man myself, and can give you authority enough for this," said the formidable person in cinder gray. "Now, then, all of ye, be ready. Have ye any lanterns?"

"Yes; have ye any lanterns? I demand it," said the constable.

"And the rest of you able-bodied —"

"Able-bodied men — yes — the rest of ye," said the constable.

"Have you some good stout staves and pitchforks —"

"Staves and pitchforks — in the name o' the law. And take 'em in yer hands and go in quest, and do as we in authority tell ye."

Thus aroused, the men prepared to give chase. The evidence was, indeed, though circumstantial, so convincing that but little argument was needed to show the shepherd's guests that, after what they had seen, it would look very much like connivance if they did not instantly pursue the unhappy third stranger, who could not as yet have gone more than a few hundred yards over such uneven country.

A shepherd is always well provided with lanterns; and, lighting these hastily, and with hurdle-staves in their hands, they poured out of the door, taking a direction along the crest of the hill, away from the town, the rain having fortunately a little abated.

Disturbed by the noise, or possibly by unpleasant dreams of her baptism, the child who had been christened began to cry heart-brokenly in the room overhead. These notes of grief came down through the chinks of the floor to the ears of the women below, who jumped up, one by one, and seemed glad of the excuse to ascend and comfort the baby; for the incidents of the last half-hour greatly oppressed them. Thus in the space of two or three minutes the room on the ground floor was deserted quite.

But it was not for long. Hardly had the sound of footsteps died away when a man returned round the corner of the house from the direction the pursuers had taken. Peeping in at the door, and seeing nobody there, he entered leisurely. It was the stranger of the chimney-corner, who had gone out with the rest. The motive of his return was shown by his helping himself to a cut piece of skimmer-cake that lay on a ledge beside where he had sat, and which he had apparently forgotten to take with him. He also poured out half a cup more mead from the quantity that remained, ravenously eating and drinking these as he stood. He had not finished when another figure came in just as quietly — the stranger in cinder gray.

"Oh, you here?" said the latter, smiling. "I thought you had gone to help in the capture." And this speaker also revealed the object of his return by looking solicitously round for the fascinating mug of old mead.

"And I thought you had gone," said the other, continuing his skimmer-cake with some effort.

"Well, on second thoughts, I felt there were enough without me," said the first, confidentially, "and such a night as it is, too. Besides, 't is the business o' the Government to take care of its criminals, not mine."

"True, so it is; and I felt as you did — that there were enough without me."

"I don't want to break my limbs running over the humps and hollows of this wild country."

"Nor I, either, between you and me."

"These shepherd people are used to it — simple-minded souls, you know, stirred up to anything in a moment. They'll have him ready for me before the morning, and no trouble to me at all."

"They'll have him, and we shall have saved ourselves all labor in the matter."

"True, true. Well, my way is to Casterbridge, and 't is as much as my legs will do to take me that far. Going the same way?"

"No, I'm sorry to say. I have to get home over there" (he nodded indefinitely to the right), "and I feel as you do — that it is quite enough for my legs to do before bedtime."

The other had by this time finished the mead in the mug, after which, shaking hands at the door and wishing each other well, they went their several ways.

In the mean time the company of pursuers had reached the end of the hog's-back elevation which dominated this part of the coomb. They had decided on no particular plan of action, and, finding that the man of the baleful trade was no longer in their company, they seemed quite unable to form any such plan now. They descended in all directions down the hill, and straightway several of the parties fell into the snare set by nature for all misguided midnight ramblers over the lower cretaceous formation. The "lynchets," or flint slopes, which belted the escarpment at intervals of a dozen yards, took the less cautious ones unawares, and, losing their footing on the rubbly steep, they slid sharply downward, the lanterns rolling from their hands to the bottom, and there lying on their sides till the horn was scorched through.

When they had again gathered themselves together, the shepherd, as the man who knew the country best, took the lead, and guided them round these treacherous inclines. The lanterns, which seemed rather to dazzle their eyes and warn the fugitive than to assist them in the exploration, were extinguished, due silence was observed, and in this more rational order they plunged into the vale. It was a grassy, briery, moist channel, affording some shelter to any person who had sought it; but the party perambulated it in vain, and ascended on the other side. Here they wandered apart, and after an interval closed together again to report progress. At the second time of closing in they found themselves near a lonely oak, the single tree on this part of the upland, probably sown there by a passing bird some hundred years before; and here, standing a little to one side of the the trunk, as motionless as the trunk itself, appeared the man they were in quest of, his outline being well defined against the sky beyond. The band noiselessly drew up and faced him.

"Your money or your life!" said the constable, sternly, to the still figure.

"No, no," whispered John Pitcher. "'T is n't our side ought to say that. That's the doctrine of vagabonds like him, and we be on the side of the law."

"Well, well," replied the constable, impatiently, "I must say something, must n't I? And if you had all

the weight o' this undertaking upon your mind, perhaps you'd say the wrong thing, too. Prisoner at the
bar, surrender, in the name of the Fath — the Crown,
I mane!"

The man under the tree seemed now to notice them for
the first time, and, giving them no opportunity whatever for exhibiting their courage, he strolled slowly
toward them. He was, indeed, the little man, the third
stranger, but his trepidation had in a great measure
gone.

"Well, travelers," he said, "did I hear ye speak to
me?"

"You did; you've got to come and be our prisoner
at once," said the constable. "We arrest ye on the charge
of not biding in Casterbridge jail in a decent, proper
manner, to be hung to-morrow morning. Neighbors,
do your duty, and seize the culpet!"

On hearing the charge, the man seemed enlightened,
and, saying not another word, resigned himself with
preternatural civility to the search-party, who, with
their staves in their hands, surrounded him on all sides,
and marched him back toward the shepherd's cottage.

It was eleven o'clock by the time they arrived. The
light shining from the open door, a sound of men's
voices within, proclaimed to them, as they approached
the house, that some new events had arisen in their
absence. On entering they discovered the shepherd's
living-room to be invaded by two officers from Casterbridge jail and a well-known magistrate who lived at
the nearest county-seat, intelligence of the escape having become generally circulated.

"Gentlemen," said the constable, "I have brought
back your man — not without risk and danger, but
every one must do his duty. He is inside this circle of

able-bodied persons, who have lent me useful aid, considering their ignorance of crown work. Men, bring forward your prisoner." And the third stranger was led to the light.

"Who is this?" said one of the officials.

"The man," said the constable.

"Certainly not," said the other turnkey, and the first corroborated his statement.

"But how can it be otherwise?" asked the constable. "Or why was he so terrified at sight of the singing instrument of the law?" Here he related the strange behavior of the third stranger on entering the house.

"Can't understand it," said the officer, coolly. "All I know is that it is not the condemned man. He's quite a different character from this one; a gauntish fellow, with dark hair and eyes, rather good-looking, and with a musical bass voice that, if you heard it once, you'd never mistake as long as you lived."

"Why, souls, 't was the man in the chimney-corner!"

"Hey — what?" said the magistrate, coming forward after inquiring particulars from the shepherd in the background. "Have n't you got the man, after all?"

"Well, sir," said the constable, "he's the man we were in search of, that's true; and yet he's not the man we were in search of. For the man we were in search of was not the man we wanted, sir, if you understand my everyday way; for 't was the man in the chimney-corner."

"A pretty kettle of fish altogether!" said the magistrate. "You had better start for the other man at once."

The prisoner now spoke for the first time. The mention of the man in the chimney-corner seemed to have moved him as nothing else could do. "Sir," he said, stepping forward to the magistrate, "take no more trouble about me. The time is come when I may as well speak. I have done nothing; my crime is that the condemned man is my brother. Early this afternoon I left home at Anglebury to tramp it all the way to Caster-bridge jail to bid him farewell. I was benighted, and called here to rest and ask the way. When I opened the door I saw before me the very man, my brother, that I thought to see in the condemned cell at Casterbridge. He was in this chimney-corner; and, jammed close to him, so that he could not have got out if he had tried, was the executioner who'd come to take his life, singing a song about it, and not knowing that it was his victim who was close by, joining in to save appearances. My brother looked a glance of agony at me, and I knew he meant, 'Don't reveal what you see; my life depends on it.' I was so terror-struck that I could hardly stand, and, not knowing what I did, I turned and hurried away."

The narrator's manner and tone had the stamp of truth, and his story made a great impression on all around.

"And do you know where your brother is at the present time?" asked the magistrate.

"I do not. I have never seen him since I closed this door."

"I can testify to that, for we've been between ye ever since," said the constable.

"Where does he think to fly to? What is his occupation?"

"He's a watch- and clock-maker, sir."

"'A said 'a was a wheelwright — a wicked rogue," said the constable.

"The wheels o' clocks and watches he meant, no doubt," said Shepherd Fennel. "I thought his hands were palish for 's trade."

"Well, it appears to me that nothing can be gained by retaining this poor man in custody," said the magistrate; "your business lies with the other unquestionably."

And so the little man was released offhand; but he looked nothing the less sad on that account, it being beyond the power of magistrate or constable to rase out the written troubles in his brain, for they concerned another, whom he regarded with more solicitude than himself. When this was done, and the man had gone his way, the night was found to be so far advanced that it was deemed useless to renew the search before the next morning.

Next day, accordingly, the quest for the clever sheep-stealer became general and keen — to all appearance, at least. But the intended punishment was cruelly disproportioned to the transgression, and the sympathy of a great many country folk in that district was strongly on the side of the fugitive. Moreover, his marvelous coolness and daring under the unprecedented circumstances of the shepherd's party won their admiration. So that it may be questioned if all those who ostensibly made themselves so busy in exploring woods and fields and lanes were quite so thorough when it came to the private examination of their own lofts and outhouses. Stories were afloat of a mysterious figure being occasionally seen in some old overgrown trackway or other remote from turnpike roads; but when a search was instituted in any of these suspected quarters nobody was found. Thus the days and weeks passed without tidings.

In brief, the bass-voiced man of the chimney-corner was never recaptured. Some said that he went across the sea, others that he did not, but buried himself in the depths of a populous city. At any rate, the gentle-

man in cinder gray never did his morning's work at
Casterbridge, nor met anywhere at all for business purposes the comrade with whom he had passed an hour of
relaxation in the lonely house on the coomb.

The grass has long been green on the graves of Shepherd Fennel and his frugal wife; the guests who made
up the christening-party have mainly followed their en-
tertainers to the tomb; the baby in whose honour they
all had met is a matron in the sear and yellow leaf; but
the arrival of the three strangers at the shepherd's
that night, and the details connected therewith, is a
story as well known as ever in the country about Higher
Crowstairs.

MARJORIE DAW[1]

BY THOMAS BAILEY ALDRICH

Marjorie Daw is the classic example of the "hoax-plot" type of narrative, in which the successive details lead the reader into deeper and deeper misconception as to what the *dénouement* is to be, and, at the very end, explode a climax entirely unforeseen. Structurally this type of plot differs from that of the two preceding narratives in that it contains no post-exposition. Like *The Black Poodle* and *The Three Strangers*, it presents preliminary exposition, — in this case, the events that give origin to the correspondence between Edward Delaney and his friend John Flemming, — the broken leg and the consequent change of summer plans. Then follows the "exciting force," which sets the machinery in motion, — the innocent suggestion of Dr. Dillon that Delaney provide some form of amusement for the invalid in order to prevent his becoming a victim of nerves. The various stages of the rising action are recorded in the series of letters that pass between the friends, constantly increasing in emotional tension until the climax suddenly is revealed in the closing words.

Narratives of this type may be graphically represented thus: —

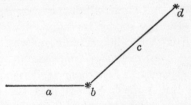

where *a* indicates the preliminary action; *b*, the moment of exciting force; *c*, the rising action of increasing tension; and

[1] From Aldrich's *Complete Works*. Published by Houghton Mifflin Company.

d, the terminal climax. The difference between this type and that of *The Black Poodle* will appear from a diagram of the latter: —

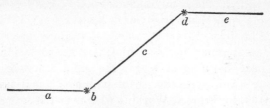

in which the climax is followed by a more or less extended conclusion, (*e*), wherein justice is distributed and stray plot strands are suitably caught up. An extended instance of this process may be found at the close of *The Marble Faun, A Tale of Two Cities*, or *The Newcomes*.

I

DR. DILLON TO EDWARD DELANEY, ESQ., AT THE PINES, NEAR RYE, N.H.

August 8, 187–.

MY DEAR SIR: I am happy to assure you that your anxiety is without reason. Flemming will be confined to the sofa for three or four weeks, and will have to be careful at first how he uses his leg. A fracture of this kind is always a tedious affair. Fortunately, the bone was very skillfully set by the surgeon who chanced to be in the drug-store where Flemming was brought after his fall, and I apprehend no permanent inconvenience from the accident. *Flemming is doing perfectly well physically;* but I must confess that the irritable and morbid state of mind into which he has fallen causes me a great deal of uneasiness. He is the last man in the world who ought to break his leg. You know how impetuous our friend is ordinarily, what a soul of restless-

ness and energy, never content unless he is rushing at
some object, like a sportive bull at a red shawl; but amiable withal. He is no longer amiable. His temper has
become something frightful. Miss Fanny Flemming
came up from Newport, where the family are staying
for the summer, to nurse him; but he packed her off
the next morning in tears. He has a complete set of
Balzac's works, twenty-seven volumes, piled up near
his sofa, to throw at Watkins whenever that exemplary
serving-man appears with his meals. Yesterday I very
innocently brought Flemming a small basket of lemons.
You know it was a strip of lemon-peel on the curbstone
that caused our friend's mischance. Well, he no sooner
set his eyes upon these lemons than he fell into such a
rage as I cannot adequately describe. This is only one of
his moods and the least distressing. At other times he
sits with bowed head regarding his splintered limb,
silent, sullen, despairing. When this fit is on him — and
it sometimes lasts all day — nothing can distract his melancholy. He refuses to eat, does not even read the newspapers; books, except as projectiles for Watkins, have
no charms for him. His state is truly pitiable.

Now, if he were a poor man, with a family depending
on his daily labor, this irritability and despondency
would be natural enough. But in a young fellow of
twenty-four, with plenty of money and seemingly not
a care in the world, the thing is monstrous. If he con-
tinues to give way to his vagaries in this manner, he will
end in bringing on an inflammation of the fibula. It was
the fibula he broke. I am at my wits' end to know what
to prescribe for him. I have anæsthetics and lotions, to
make people sleep and to soothe pain; but I've no medicine that will make a man have a little common sense.
That is beyond my skill, but maybe it is not beyond

yours. You are Flemming's intimate friend, his *fidus Achates*. Write to him, write to him frequently, distract his mind, cheer him up, and prevent him from becoming a confirmed case of melancholia. Perhaps he has some important plans disarranged by his present confinement. If he has, you will know, and will know how to advise him judiciously. I trust your father finds the change beneficial? I am, my dear sir, with great respect, etc.

II

EDWARD DELANEY TO JOHN FLEMMING, WEST
38TH STREET, NEW YORK

August 9, —.

MY DEAR JACK: I had a line from Dillon this morning, and was rejoiced to learn that your hurt is not so bad as reported. Like a certain personage, you are not so black and blue as you are painted. Dillon will put you on your pins again in two or three weeks, if you will only have patience and follow his counsels. Did you get my note of last Wednesday? I was greatly troubled when I heard of the accident.

I can imagine how tranquil and saintly you are with your leg in a trough! It is deuced awkward, to be sure, just as we had promised ourselves a glorious month together at the seaside; but we must make the best of it. It is unfortunate too, that my father's health renders it impossible for me to leave him. I think he has much improved; the sea air is his native element; but he still needs my arm to lean upon in his walks, and requires some one more careful than a servant to look after him. I cannot come to you, dear Jack, but I have hours of unemployed time on hand, and I will write you a whole post-office full of letters if that will divert you. Heaven

knows, I have n't anything to write about. It is n't as
if we were living at one of the beach houses; then I could
do you some character studies, and fill your imagination
with groups of sea-goddesses, with their (or somebody
else's) raven and blond manes hanging down their
shoulders. You should have Aphrodite in morning
wrapper, in evening costume, and in her prettiest bath-
ing-suit. But we are far from all that here. We have
rooms in a farmhouse, on a cross-road, two miles from
the hotels, and lead the quietest of lives.

I wish I were a novelist. This old house, with its
sanded floors and high wainscots, and its narrow windows looking out upon a cluster of pines that turn themselves into Æolian harps every time the wind blows,
would be the place in which to write a summer romance.
It should be a story with the odors of the forest and the
breath of the sea in it. It should be a novel like one of
that Russian fellow's, — what's his name? — Tourgué-
nieff, Turguenef, Turgenif, Toorguniff, Turgénjew, —
nobody knows how to spell him. Yet I wonder if even
a Liza or an Alexandra Paulovna could stir the heart of
a man who has constant twinges in his leg. I wonder
if one of our own Yankee girls of the best type, haughty
and *spirituelle*, would be of any comfort to you in your
present deplorable condition. If I thought so, I would
hasten down to the Surf House and catch one for you;
or, better still, I would find you one over the way.

Picture to yourself a large white house just across the
road, nearly opposite our cottage. It is not a house, but
a mansion, built, perhaps, in the colonial period, with
rambling extensions, and gambrel roof, and a wide piazza
on three sides, — a self-possessed, high-bred piece of
architecture, with its nose in the air. It stands back
from the road, and has an obsequious retinue of fringed

elms and oaks and weeping willows. Sometimes in the morning, and oftener in the afternoon, when the sun has withdrawn from that part of the mansion, a young woman appears on the piazza with some mysterious Penelope web of embroidery in her hand, or a book. There is a hammock over there, — of pineapple fiber, it looks from here. A hammock is very becoming when one is eighteen, and has golden hair, and dark eyes, and an emerald-colored illusion dress looped up after the fashion of a Dresden china shepherdess, and is *chaussée* like a belle of the time of Louis Quatorze. All this splendor goes into that hammock, and sways there like a pond-lily in the golden afternoon. The window of my bedroom looks down on that piazza, — and so do I.

But enough of this nonsense, which ill becomes a sedate young attorney taking his vacation with an invalid father. Drop me a line, dear Jack, and tell me how you really are. State your case. Write me a long, quiet letter. If you are violent or abusive, I'll take the law to you.

III

John Flemming to Edward Delaney

August 11, —.

Your letter, dear Ned, was a godsend. Fancy what a fix I am in, — I, who never had a day's sickness since I was born. My left leg weighs three tons. It is embalmed in spices and smothered in layers of fine linen, like a mummy. I can't move. I have n't moved for five thousand years. I'm of the time of Pharaoh.

I lie from morning till night on a lounge, staring into the hot street. Everybody is out of town enjoying himself. The brownstone-front houses across the street resemble a row of particularly ugly coffins set up on end. A green mould is settling on the names of the deceased, carved on the silver doorplates. Sardonic spiders have sewed up the keyholes. All is silence and dust and desolation. — I interrupt this a moment, to take a shy at Watkins with the second volume of César Birotteau. Missed him! I think I could bring him down with a copy of Sainte-Beuve or the Dictionnaire Universel, if I had it. These small Balzac books somehow don't quite fit my hand; but I shall fetch him yet. I've an idea Watkins is tapping the old gentleman's Château Yquem. Duplicate key of the wine-cellar. Hibernian swarries in the front basement. Young Cheops upstairs, snug in his cerements. Watkins glides into my chamber, with that colorless, hypocritical face of his drawn out long like an accordion; but I know he grins all the way downstairs, and is glad I have broken my leg. Was not my evil star in the very zenith when I ran up to town to attend that dinner at Delmonico's? I did n't come up altogether for that. It was partly to buy Frank Livingstone's roan mare Margot. And now I shall not be able to sit in the saddle these two months. I'll send the mare down to you at The Pines, — is that the name of the place?

Old Dillon fancies that I have something on my mind. He drives me wild with lemons. Lemons for a mind diseased! Nosense. I am only as restless as the devil under this confinement, — a thing I'm not used to. Take a man who has never had so much as a headache or a toothache in his life, strap one of his legs in a section of water-spout, keep him in a room in the city for weeks, with the hot weather turned on, and then expect him to smile and purr and be happy! It is preposterous. I can't be cheerful or calm.

Your letter is the first consoling thing I have had

since my disaster, ten days ago. It really cheered me up
for half an hour. Send me a screed, Ned, as often as you
can, if you love me. Anything will do. Write me more
about that little girl in the hammock. That was very
pretty, all that about the Dresden china shepherdess and
the pond-lily; the imagery a little mixed, perhaps, but
very pretty. I did n't suppose you had so much sentimental furniture in your upper story. It shows how one
may be familiar for years with the reception-room of his
neighbor, and never suspect what is directly under his
mansard. I supposed your loft stuffed with dry legal
parchments, mortgages, and affidavits; you take down
a package of manuscripts, and lo! there are lyrics and
sonnets and canzonettas. You really have a graphic descriptive touch, Edward Delaney, and I suspect you of
anonymous love-tales in the magazines.

I shall be a bear until I hear from you again. Tell me
all about your pretty *inconnue* across the road. What
is her name? Who is she? Who's her father? Where's
her mother? Who's her lover? You cannot imagine how
this will occupy me. The more trifling the better. My
imprisonment has weakened me intellectually to such
a degree that I find your epistolary gifts quite considerable. I am passing into my second childhood. In a week
or two I shall take to India-rubber rings and prongs of
coral. A silver cup, with an appropriate inscription,
would be a delicate attention on your part. In the mean
time, write!

IV

Edward Delaney to John Flemming

August 12, —.

The sick pasha shall be amused. *Bismillah!* he wills
it so. If the story-teller becomes prolix and tedious, —

the bowstring and the sack, and two Nubians to drop
him into the Piscataqua! But, truly, Jack, I have a
hard task. There is literally nothing here, — except the
little girl over the way. She is swinging in the hammock at this moment. It is to me compensation for
many of the ills of life to see her now and then put out
a small kid boot, which fits like a glove, and set herself
going. Who is she, and what is her name? Her name is
Daw. Only daughter of Mr. Richard W. Daw, ex-colonel
and banker. Mother dead. One brother at Harvard,
elder brother killed at the battle of Fair Oaks, nine years
ago. Old, rich family, the Daws. This is the homestead,
where father and daughter pass eight months of the
twelve; the rest of the year in Baltimore and Washington. The New England winter too many for the old
gentleman. The daughter is called Marjorie, — Marjorie Daw. Sounds odd at first, does n't it? But after
you say it over to yourself half a dozen times, you like
it. There's a pleasing quaintness to it, something prim
and violet-like. Must be a nice sort of girl to be called
Marjorie Daw.

I had mine host of The Pines in the witness-box last
night, and drew the foregoing testimony from him. He
has charge of Mr. Daw's vegetable-garden, and has
known the family these thirty years. Of course I shall
make the acquaintance of my neighbors before many
days. It will be next to impossible for me not to meet
Mr. Daw or Miss Daw in some of my walks. The young
lady has a favorite path to the sea-beach. I shall inter-
cept her some morning, and touch my hat to her. Then
the princess will bend her fair head to me with courteous
surprise not unmixed with haughtiness. Will snub me,
in fact. All this for thy sake, O Pasha of the Snapt
Axle-tree! . . . How oddly things fall out! Ten minutes

ago I was called down to the parlor, — you know the kind of parlors in farmhouses on the coast, a sort of amphibious parlor, with seashells on the mantelpiece and spruce branches in the chimney-place, — where I found my father and Mr. Daw doing the antique polite to each other. He had come to pay his respects to his new neighbors. Mr. Daw is a tall, slim, gentleman of about fifty-five, with a florid face and snow-white mustache and side-whiskers. Looks like Mr. Dombey, or as Mr. Dombey would have looked if he had served a few years in the British Army. Mr. Daw was a colonel in the late war, commanding the regiment in which his son was a lieutenant. Plucky old boy, backbone of New Hampshire granite. Before taking his leave, the colonel delivered himself of an invitation as if he were issuing a general order. Miss Daw has a few friends coming, at 4 P.M., to play croquet on the lawn (parade-ground) and have tea (cold rations) on the piazza. Will we honor them with our company? (or be sent to the guard-house.) My father declines on the plea of ill-health. My father's son bows with as much suavity as he knows, and accepts.

In my next I shall have something to tell you. I shall have seen the little beauty face to face. I have a presentiment, Jack, that this Daw is a *rara avis!* Keep up your spirits, my boy, until I write you another letter, — and send me along word how's your leg.

V

EDWARD DELANEY TO JOHN FLEMMING

August 13, —.

The party, my dear Jack, was as dreary as possible. A lieutenant of the navy, the rector of the Episcopal

Church at Stillwater, and a society swell from Nahant. The lieutenant looked as if he had swallowed a couple of his buttons, and found the bullion rather indigestible; the rector was a pensive youth, of the daffydowndilly sort; and the swell from Nahant was a very weak tidal wave indeed. The women were much better, as they always are; the two Miss Kingsburys of Philadelphia, staying at the Seashell House, two bright and engaging girls. But Marjorie Daw!

The company broke up soon after tea, and I remained to smoke a cigar with the colonel on the piazza. It was like seeing a picture to see Miss Marjorie hovering around the old soldier, and doing a hundred gracious little things for him. She brought the cigars and lighted the tapers with her own delicate fingers, in the most enchanting fashion. As we sat there, she came and went in the summer twilight, and seemed, with her white dress and pale-gold hair, like some lovely phantom that had sprung into existence out of the smoke-wreaths. If she had melted into air, like the statue of Galatea in the play, I should have been more sorry than surprised.

It was easy to perceive that the old colonel worshiped her, and she him. I think the relation between an elderly father and a daughter just blooming into womanhood the most beautiful possible. There is in it a subtile sentiment that cannot exist in the case of mother and daughter, or that of son and mother. But this is getting into deep water.

I sat with the Daws until half-past ten, and saw the moon rise on the sea. The ocean, that had stretched motionless and black against the horizon, was changed by magic into a broken field of glittering ice, interspersed with marvelous silvery fjords. In the far distance the Isles of Shoals loomed up like a group of huge bergs drifting down on us. The Polar Regions in a June thaw! It was exceedingly fine. What did we talk about? We talked about the weather — and *you!* The weather has been disagreeable for several days past, — and so have you. I glided from one topic to the other very naturally. I told my friends of your accident; how it had frustrated all our summer plans, and what our plans were. I played quite a spirited solo on the fibula. Then I described you; or, rather, I did n't. I spoke of your amiability, of your patience under this severe affliction; of your touching gratitude when Dillon brings you little presents of fruit; of your tenderness to your sister Fanny, whom you would not allow to stay in town to nurse you, and how you heroically sent her back to Newport, preferring to remain alone with Mary, the cook, and your man Watkins, to whom, by the way, you were devotedly attached. If you had been there, Jack, you would n't have known yourself. I should have excelled as a criminal lawyer, if I had not turned my attention to a different branch of jurisprudence.

Miss Marjorie asked all manner of leading questions concerning you. It did not occur to me then, but it struck me forcibly afterwards, that she evinced a singular interest in the conversation. When I got back to my room, I recalled how eagerly she leaned forward, with her full, snowy throat in strong moonlight, listening to what I said. Positively, I think I made her like you!

Miss Daw is a girl whom you would like immensely, I can tell you that. A beauty without affectation, a high and tender nature, — if one can read the soul in the face. And the old colonel is a noble character, too.

I am glad the Daws are such pleasant people. The Pines is an isolated spot, and my resources are few. I fear I should have found life here somewhat monot-

onous before long, with no other society than that of
my excellent sire. It is true, I might have made a target
of the defenseless invalid; but I have n't a taste for
artillery, *moi*.

VI

JOHN FLEMMING TO EDWARD DELANEY

August 17, —.

For a man who has n't a taste for artillery, it occurs
to me, my friend, you are keeping up a pretty lively
fire on my inner works. But go on. Cynicism is a small
brass field-piece that eventually bursts and kills the
artilleryman.

You may abuse me as much as you like, and I 'll not
complain; for I don't know what I should do without
your letters. They are curing me. I have n't hurled anything at Watkins since last Sunday, partly because I
have grown more amiable under your teaching, and partly
because Watkins captured my ammunition one night,
and carried it off to the library. He is rapidly losing the
habit he had acquired of dodging whenever I rub my ear,
or make any slight motion with my right arm. He is
still suggestive of the wine-cellar, however. You may
break, you may shatter Watkins, if you will, but the
scent of the Roederer will hang round him still.

Ned, that Miss Daw must be a charming person. I
should certainly like her. I like her already. When you
spoke in your first letter of seeing a young girl swinging in a hammock under your chamber window, I was
somehow strangely drawn to her. I cannot account
for it in the least. What you have subsequently written
of Miss Daw has strengthened the impression. You
seem to be describing a woman I have known in some
previous state of existence, or dreamed of in this. Upon

my word, if you were to send me her photograph, I believe I should recognize her at a glance. Her manner, that listening attitude, her traits of character, as you indicate them, the light hair and the dark eyes, — they are all familiar things to me. Asked a lot of questions, did she? Curious about me? That is strange.

You would laugh in your sleeve, you wretched old cynic, if you knew how I lie awake nights, with my gas turned down to a star, thinking of The Pines and the house across the road. How cool it must be down there! I long for the salt smell in the air. I picture the colonel smoking his cheroot on the piazza. I send you and Miss Daw off on afternoon rambles along the beach. Sometimes I let you stroll with her under the elms in the moonlight, for you are great friends by this time, I take it, and see each other every day. I know your ways and your manners! Then I fall into a truculent mood, and would like to destroy somebody. Have you noticed anything in the shape of a lover hanging around the colonial Lares and Penates? Does that lieutenant of the horsemarines or that young Stillwater parson visit the house much? Not that I am pining for news of them, but any gossip of the kind would be in order. I wonder, Ned, you don't fall in love with Miss Daw. I am ripe to do it myself. Speaking of photographs, could n't you manage to slip one of her *cartes-de-visite* from her album, — she must have an album, you know, — and send it to me? I will return it before it could be missed. That's a good fellow! Did the mare arrive safe and sound? It will be a capital animal this autumn for Central Park.

O — my leg? I forgot about my leg. It's better.

VII

EDWARD DELANEY TO JOHN FLEMMING

August 20, —.

You are correct in your surmises. I am on the most friendly terms with our neighbors. The colonel and my father smoke their afternoon cigar together in our sitting-room or on the piazza opposite, and I pass an hour or two of the day or the evening with the daughter. I am more and more struck by the beauty, modesty, and intelligence of Miss Daw.

You ask me why I do not fall in love with her. I will be frank, Jack: I have thought of that. She is young, rich, accomplished, uniting in herself more attractions, mental and personal, than I can recall in any girl of my acquaintance; but she lacks the something that would be necessary to inspire in me that kind of interest. Possessing this unknown quantity, a woman neither beautiful nor wealthy nor very young could bring me to her feet. But not Miss Daw. If we were shipwrecked together on an uninhabited island, — let me suggest a tropical island, for it costs no more to be picturesque, — I would build her a bamboo hut, I would fetch her bread-fruit and cocoanuts, I would fry yams for her, I would lure the ingenuous turtle and make her nourishing soups, but I would n't make love to her, — not under eighteen months. I would like to have her for a sister, that I might shield her and counsel her, and spend half my income on thread-laces and camel's-hair shawls. (We are off the island now.) If such were not my feeling, there would still be an obstacle to my loving Miss Daw. A greater misfortune could scarcely befall me than to love her. Flemming, I am about to make a revelation that will astonish you. I may be all wrong in my premises and consequently in my conclusions; but you shall judge.

That night when I returned to my room after the croquet party at the Daws', and was thinking over the trivial events of the evening, I was suddenly impressed by the air of eager attention with which Miss Daw had followed my account of your accident. I think I mentioned this to you. Well, the next morning, as I went to mail my letter, I overtook Miss Daw on the road to Rye, where the post-office is, and accompanied her thither and back, an hour's walk. The conversation again turned on you, and again I remarked that inexplicable look of interest which had lighted up her face the previous evening. Since then, I have seen Miss Daw perhaps ten times, perhaps oftener, and on each occasion I found that when I was not speaking of you, or your sister, or some person or place associated with you, I was not holding her attention. She would be absent-minded, her eyes would wander away from me to the sea, or to some distant object in the landscape; her fingers would play with the leaves of a book in a way that convinced me she was not listening. At these moments if I abruptly changed the theme, — I did it several times as an experiment, — and dropped some remark about my friend Flemming, then the somber blue eyes would come back to me instantly.

Now, is not this the oddest thing in the world? No, not the oddest. The effect which you tell me was produced on you by my casual mention of an unknown girl swinging in a hammock is certainly as strange. You can conjecture how that passage in your letter of Friday startled me. Is it possible, then, that two people who have never met, and who are hundreds of miles apart, can

exert a magnetic influence on each other? I have read
of such psychological phenomena, but never credited
them. I leave the solution of the problem to you. As for
myself, all other things being favorable, it would be impossible for me to fall in love with a woman who listens
to me only when I am talking of my friend!

I am not aware that any one is paying marked attention to my fair neighbor. The lieutenant of the navy
— he is stationed at Rivermouth — sometimes drops in
of an evening, and sometimes the rector from Stillwater;
the lieutenant the oftener. He was there last night. I
would not be surprised if he had an eye to the heiress;
but he is not formidable. Mistress Daw carries a neat
little spear of irony, and the honest lieutenant seems to
have a particular facility for impaling himself on the
point of it. He is not dangerous, I should say; though I
have known a woman to satirize a man for years, and
marry him after all. Decidedly, the lowly rector is
not dangerous; yet, again, who has not seen Cloth of
Frieze victorious in the lists where Cloth of Gold went
down?

As to the photograph. There is an exquisite ivorytype of Marjorie, in passe-partout, on the drawing-
room mantelpiece. It would be missed at once, if taken.
I would do anything reasonable for you, Jack; but I've
no burning desire to be hauled up before the local justice
of the peace, on a charge of petty larceny.

P.S. — Enclosed is a spray of mignonette, which I advise you to treat tenderly. Yes, we talked of you again
last night, as usual. It is becoming a little dreary for
me.

VIII

EDWARD DELANEY TO JOHN FLEMMING

August 22, —.

Your letter in reply to my last has occupied my thoughts all the morning. I do not know what to think. Do you mean to say that you are seriously half in love with a woman whom you have never seen, — with a shadow, a chimera? for what else can Miss Daw be to you? I do not understand it at all. I understand neither you nor her. You are a couple of ethereal beings moving in finer air than I can breathe with my commonplace lungs. Such delicacy of sentiment is something I admire without comprehending. I am bewildered. I am of the earth earthy, and I find myself in the incongruous position of having to do with mere souls, with natures so finely tempered that I run some risk of shattering them in my awkwardness. I am as Caliban among the spirits!

Reflecting on your letter, I am not sure it is wise in me to continue this correspondence. But no, Jack; I do wrong to doubt the good sense that forms the basis of your character. You are deeply interested in Miss Daw; you feel that she is a person whom you may perhaps greatly admire when you know her: at the same time you bear in mind that the chances are ten to five that, when you do come to know her, she will fall far short of your ideal, and you will not care for her in the least. Look at it in this sensible light, and I will hold back nothing from you.

Yesterday afternoon my father and myself rode over to Rivermouth with the Daws. A heavy rain in the morning had cooled the atmosphere and laid the dust.

To Rivermouth is a drive of eight miles, along a winding
road lined all the way with wild barberry-bushes. I
never saw anything more brilliant than these bushes,
the green of the foliage and the pink of the coral berries
intensified by the rain. The colonel drove, with my father
in front, Miss Daw and I on the back seat. I resolved
that for the first five miles your name should not pass my
lips. I was amused by the artful attempts she made, at
the start, to break through my reticence. Then a silence
fell upon her; and then she became suddenly gay. That
keenness which I enjoyed so much when it was exercised on the lieutenant was not so satisfactory directed
against myself. Miss Daw has great sweetness of disposition, but she can be disagreeable. She is like the
young lady in the rhyme, with the curl on her forehead,—

> "When she is good,
> She is very, very good,
> And when she is bad, she is horrid!"

I kept to my resolution, however; but on the return home
I relented, and talked of your mare! Miss Daw is going
to try a side-saddle on Margot some morning. The
animal is a trifle too light for my weight. By the by,
I nearly forgot to say Miss Daw sat for a picture yesterday to a Rivermouth artist. If the negative turns
out well, I am to have a copy. So our ends will be accomplished without crime. I wish, though, I could send you
the ivorytype in the drawing-room; it is cleverly colored,
and would give you an idea of her hair and eyes, which
of course the other will not.

No, Jack, the spray of mignonette did not come from
me. A man of twenty-eight does n't enclose flowers in
his letters — to another man. But don't attach too much
significance to the circumstance. She gives sprays of
mignonette to the rector, sprays to the lieutenant. She

has even given a rose from her bosom to your slave. It is her jocund nature to scatter flowers, like Spring.

If my letters sometimes read disjointedly, you must understand that I never finish one at a sitting, but write at intervals, when the mood is on me.

The mood is not on me now.

IX

EDWARD DELANEY TO JOHN FLEMMING

August 23, —.

I have just returned from the strangest interview with Marjorie. She has all but confessed to me her interest in you. But with what modesty and dignity! Her words elude my pen as I attempt to put them on paper; and, indeed, it was not so much what she said as her manner; and that I cannot reproduce. Perhaps it was of a piece with the strangeness of this whole business, that she should tacitly acknowledge to a third party the love she feels for a man she has never beheld! But I have lost, through your aid, the faculty of being surprised. I accept things as people do in dreams. Now that I am again in my room, it all appears like an illusion, — the black masses of Rembrandtish shadow under the trees, the fire-flies whirling in Pyrrhic dances among the shrubbery, the sea over there, Marjorie sitting on the hammock!

It is past midnight, and I am too sleepy to write more.

Thursday Morning.

My father has suddenly taken it into his head to spend a few days at the Shoals. In the mean while you will not hear from me. I see Marjorie walking in the garden with the colonel. I wish I could speak to her

alone, but shall probably not have an opportunity before we leave.

X

EDWARD DELANEY TO JOHN FLEMMING

August 28, —.

You were passing into your second childhood, were
you? Your intellect was so reduced that my epistolary
gifts seemed quite considerable to you, did they? I rise
superior to the sarcasm in your favor of the 11th instant, when I notice that five days' silence on my part
is sufficient to throw you into the depths of despondency.

We returned only this morning from Appledore,
that enchanted island, — at four dollars per day. I
find on my desk three letters from you! Evidently there
is no lingering doubt in *your* mind as to the pleasure I
derive from your correspondence. These letters are
undated, but in what I take to be the latest are two passages that require my consideration. You will pardon
my candor, dear Flemming, but the conviction forces
itself upon me that as your leg grows stronger your
head becomes weaker. You ask my advice on a certain
point. I will give it. In my opinion you could do nothing
more unwise than to address a note to Miss Daw,
thanking her for the flower. It would, I am sure, offend
her delicacy beyond pardon. She knows you only
through me; you are to her an abstraction, a figure in a
dream, — a dream from which the faintest shock would
awaken her. Of course, if you enclose a note to me and
insist on its delivery, I shall deliver it; but I advise you
not to do so.

You say you are able, with the aid of a cane, to walk
about your chamber, and that you purpose to come to

The Pines the instant Dillon thinks you strong enough
to stand the journey. Again I advise you not to. Do you
not see that, every hour you remain away, Marjorie's
glamour deepens, and your influence over her increases?
You will ruin everything by precipitancy. Wait until
you are entirely recovered; in any case, do not come
without giving me warning. I fear the effect of your
abrupt advent here — under the circumstances.

Miss Daw was evidently glad to see us back again,
and gave me both hands in the frankest way. She
stopped at the door a moment, this afternoon, in the
carriage; she had been over to Rivermouth for her pictures. Unluckily the photographer had spilt some acid
on the plate, and she was obliged to give him another
sitting. I have an intuition that something is troubling
Marjorie. She had an abstracted air not usual with her.
However, it may be only my fancy. . . . I end this,
leaving several things unsaid, to accompany my father
on one of those long walks which are now his chief medicine, — and mine!

XI

EDWARD DELANEY TO JOHN FLEMMING

August 29, —.

I write in great haste to tell you what has taken place
here since my letter of last night. I am in the utmost
perplexity. Only one thing is plain, — *you* must not
dream of coming to The Pines. Marjorie has told her
father everything! I saw her for a few minutes, an hour
ago, in the garden; and, as near as I could gather from
her confused statement, the facts are these: Lieutenant
Bradly — that's the naval officer stationed at Rivermouth — has been paying court to Miss Daw for some

time past, but not so much to her liking as to that of the colonel, who it seems is an old friend of the young gentleman's father. Yesterday (I knew she was in some trouble when she drove up to our gate) the colonel spoke to Marjorie of Bradly, — urged his suit, I infer. Marjorie expressed her dislike for the lieutenant with characteristic frankness, and finally confessed to her father — well, I really do not know what she confessed. It must have been the vaguest of confessions, and must have sufficiently puzzled the colonel. At any rate, it exasperated him. I suppose I am implicated in the matter, and that the colonel feels bitterly towards me. I do not see why: I have carried no messages between you and Miss Daw; I have behaved with the greatest discretion. I can find no flaw anywhere in my proceeding. I do not see that anybody has done anything, — except the colonel himself.

It is probable, nevertheless, that the friendly relations between the two houses will be broken off. "A plague o' both your houses," say you. I will keep you informed, as well as I can, of what occurs over the way. We shall remain here until the second week in September. Stay where you are, or, at all events, do not dream of joining me. . . . Colonel Daw is sitting on the piazza looking rather wicked. I have not seen Marjorie since I parted with her in the garden.

XII

Edward Delaney to Thomas Dillon, M.D., Madison Square, New York

August 30, —.

My dear Doctor: If you have any influence over Flemming, I beg of you to exert it to prevent his coming to this place at present. There are circumstances, which I will explain to you before long, that make it of the first importance that he should not come into this neighborhood. His appearance here, I speak advisedly, would be disastrous to him. In urging him to remain in New York, or to go to some inland resort, you will be doing him and me a real service. Of course you will not mention my name in this connection. You know me well enough, my dear doctor, to be assured that, in begging your secret coöperation, I have reasons that will meet your entire approval when they are made plain to you. We shall return to town on the 15th of next month, and my first duty will be to present myself at your hospitable door and satisfy your curiosity, if I have excited it. My father, I am glad to state, has so greatly improved that he can no longer be regarded as an invalid. With great esteem, I am, etc., etc.

XIII

EDWARD DELANEY TO JOHN FLEMMING

August 31, —.

Your letter, announcing your mad determination to come here, has just reached me. I beseech you to reflect a moment. The step would be fatal to your interests and hers. You would furnish just cause for irritation to R. W. D.; and, though he loves Marjorie tenderly, he is capable of going to any lengths if opposed. You would not like, I am convinced, to be the means of causing him to treat *her* with severity. That would be the result of your presence at The Pines at this juncture. I am annoyed to be obliged to point out these things to you. We are on very delicate ground, Jack; the situation is critical, and the slightest mistake in a move would cost us the game. If you consider it worth the winning, be patient. Trust a little to my sagacity. Wait and see what happens. Moreover, I understand from Dillon that you are in no condition to take so long a journey. He thinks the air of the coast would be the worst thing possible for you; that you ought to go inland, if anywhere. Be advised by me. Be advised by Dillon.

XIV

TELEGRAMS

September 1, —.

1. — To EDWARD DELANEY

Letter received. Dillon be hanged. I think I ought to be on the ground.

J. F.

2. — To JOHN FLEMMING

Stay where you are. You would only complicate matters. Do not move until you hear from me.

E. D.

3. — To EDWARD DELANEY

My being at The Pines could be kept secret. I must see her.

J. F.

4. — To JOHN FLEMMING

Do not think of it. It would be useless. R. W. D. has locked M. in her room. You would not be able to effect an interview.

E.D.

5. — To EDWARD DELANEY

Locked her in her room. Good God. That settles the question. I shall leave by the twelve-fifteen express.

J. F.

XV

The Arrival

On the 2d of September, 187–, as the down express
due at 3.40 left the station at Hampton, a young man,
leaning on the shoulder of a servant, whom he addressed
as Watkins, stepped from the platform into a hack,
and requested to be driven to "The Pines." On arriving
at the gate of a modest farmhouse, a few miles from the
station, the young man descended with difficulty from
the carriage, and, casting a hasty glance across the
road, seemed much impressed by some peculiarity in the
landscape. Again leaning on the shoulder of the person
Watkins, he walked to the door of the farmhouse and
inquired for Mr. Edward Delaney. He was informed
by the aged man who answered his knock, that Mr.
Edward Delaney had gone to Boston the day before, but
that Mr. Jonas Delaney was within. This information
did not appear satisfactory to the stranger, who inquired
if Mr. Edward Delaney had left any meassage for Mr.
John Flemming. There *was* a letter for Mr. Flemming,
if he were that person. After a brief absence the aged
man reappeared with a letter.

XVI

Edward Delaney to John Flemming

September 1, —.

I am horror-stricken at what I have done! When I
began this correspondence I had no other purpose than
to relieve the tedium of your sick-chamber. Dillon
told me to cheer you up. I tried to. I thought you
entered into the spirit of the thing. I had no idea,

until within a few days, that you were taking matters *au sérieux*.

What can I say? I am in sackcloth and ashes. I am a pariah, a dog of an outcast. I tried to make a little romance to interest you, something soothing and idyllic, and, by Jove! I have done it only too well! My father does n't know a word of this, so don't jar the old gentleman any more than you can help. I fly from the wrath to come — when you arrive! For O dear Jack, there is n't any colonial mansion on the other side of the road, there is n't any piazza, there is n't any hammock, — there is n't any Marjorie Daw!

THE NECKLACE[1]

(*La Parure*)

BY GUY DE MAUPASSANT

The Necklace is presented as an additional example of the same type of narrative structure as that illustrated by *Marjorie Daw*, — the "hoax plot" form of the "method of story." The essential distinction between the two narratives lies in the difference of tone. *Marjorie Daw* is playfully humorous; it provokes no deeper emotion than amusement, sheer enjoyment of a complicated comic situation. *The Necklace*, however, is far more serious, even approaching the tragic, in the marring of Mathilde Loisel's young life.

SHE was one of those pretty, charming girls who are born, as if by some blunder of fate, into a family of people compelled to work for a living. She had no dowry, no expectations, no means of securing social recognition, of being appreciated or loved, or of becoming the wife of a rich, distinguished husband; and she married a subordinate clerk in the office of the Minister of Public Instruction.

She dressed simply, for she could not afford expensive gowns; but she was unhappy, as if she were not in her proper station: for women have no caste or rank, — their beauty, their grace, their charm take the place of birth and family. Their native refinement, their instinctive elegance, their nimble wit constitute their sole aristocracy and make the daughters of the people the equals of the noblest-born.

Feeling that she was entitled to every delicacy, every luxury, she suffered endless torture. She hated the

[1] Translated for this work by the Editor.

poverty of her lodgings, the blankness of the walls, the worn-out chairs, the ugly upholstery. All these things, which another woman of her station would not have noticed, tortured her, filled her with discontent. The very sight of the little Breton peasant girl who helped her in her humble housework aroused painful regrets and disappointed dreams. She had visions of silent drawing-rooms, hung with Oriental tapestries, lighted by lofty bronze candelabra; of liveried valets dozing in large armchairs, drowsy with the heavy heat of the hot-air stoves. She dreamed of grand salons furnished with antique silks, of delicate cabinets containing curiosities of inestimable value, of coquettish little rooms fragrant with perfume, arranged for five-o'-clock chats with one's most intimate friends, with men well known and greatly sought after, men whose acquaintance all the women long for and whose notice they all desire.

When she sat down to dinner, facing her husband at the round table covered with a cloth three days old, and he uncovered the soup-tureen exclaiming delightedly, "Ah, the good stew! I don't know anything better than that!" she dreamed of magnificent banquets, of shining silver, of tapestries enlivening the walls with famous characters of old and with strange birds amid fairy forests; she dreamed of exquisite dishes served on wonderful plates, of whispered gallantries received with mysterious smiles while eating the pink flesh of a trout or the wing of a quail.

She had no gowns, no jewels, — nothing. And these were the only things that she cared for; she felt that she was made for such things as these. She was anxious to please, to be envied, to be captivating and popular.

She had a wealthy friend, one whom she used to know at the convent; but she was no longer willing to visit her, for she suffered so much when she returned home. And for whole days she used to weep with regret, anger, despair, and distress.

One evening her husband came home with a triumphant air, holding in his hand a large envelope.

"There!" said he; "there is something for you."

She hastily tore off the wrapper, and drew forth a printed card bearing these words: —

THE MINISTER OF PUBLIC INSTRUCTION AND MADAME
GEORGES RAMPONNEAU
ASK THE HONOR OF
MONSIEUR AND MADAME LOISEL'S
PRESENCE AT THE PALACE OF THE MINISTER,
MONDAY, JANUARY EIGHTEENTH.

Instead of being delighted, as her husband had hoped, she spitefully threw the invitation on the table, murmuring, "What do you expect me to do with that?"

"But, my darling, I thought that you would be pleased. You never go out, and this is a grand occasion. I had no end of trouble in getting that card. Every one is after them: the affair is very select, and not many invitations are given to the clerks. You will see the whole official world there."

She glanced at him with an irritated expression, and impatiently said, "What do you expect me to wear if I go?"

He had not thought of that; he stammered out, "Why, the dress that you wear to the theater. That seems to me a very good one . . ."

Seeing that his wife was weeping, he paused, amazed, in consternation. Two great tears were slowly making their way from the corners of her eyes down to the corners of her mouth.

"What's the matter with you?" he stuttered. "What ails you?"

But with an effort she had choked down her grief, and she replied in a calm voice, wiping the tears from her cheeks, "Nothing. Only I have n't any gown, and consequently I can't go to this ball. Give your card to one of your colleagues whose wife has more clothes than I."

He was in despair.

"Come, Mathilde," he replied. "How much would the right sort of gown cost? — one that you could use again on other occasions; something quite simple?"

She reflected a few seconds, figuring the expense, and at the same time wondering what sum she might venture to name without drawing a prompt refusal and a frightened exclamation from the thrifty clerk.

Finally she replied hesitatingly: "I don't know exactly, but it seems to me that with four hundred francs I might manage it."

He paled a little, for he was laying aside that very sum to buy a gun and join a hunting-party the next summer on the plain of Nanterre, together with some friends, who were going to shoot larks some Sunday.

However, he replied: "Very well. I will give you four hundred francs. But try to get a pretty dress."

The day of the ball drew near, and Madame Loisel seemed sad, nervous, depressed. However, her dress was ready.

One evening her husband said to her: "What ails you? Come, you have acted very strangely for three days."

"I am worried," she replied, "because I have no

jewelry, not a single stone, nothing to put on. I shall look poverty-struck. I would almost rather not go."

"Put on natural flowers," he replied. "That's quite the thing at this season. For ten francs you can get two or three magnificent roses."

But she was by no means convinced.

"No — nothing is more humiliating than to look poor among a lot of rich women."

"What a fool you are!" her husband exclaimed. "Go find your friend Madame Forestier, and ask her to lend you some jewels. You are thick enough with her for that."

She uttered a cry of delight: "True! I never thought of that."

The next day she called on her friend and told her of her trouble.

Madame Forestier went to a wardrobe with a glass door, took a large jewel-case from it, brought it out, and opened it; and said to Madame Loisel: "Choose, my dear."

She saw first of all some bracelets, then a pearl necklace, then a Venetian cross, gold and stones of wonderful workmanship. She tried on the jewels before the glass, and hesitated, unable to make up her mind to leave them, to give them back.

"You have n't anything else?"

"Why, yes. Look. I don't know what pleases you."

Suddenly she discovered in a black satin case a superb diamond necklace; and her heart began to beat with immoderate longing. Her hands trembled as she took it. She put it about her neck, over her high-necked dress, and stood in ecstasy before her reflection in the mirror.

Then, hesitating and full of suspense, she asked: "Can you lend me that, only that?"

"Why, yes; certainly."

She threw herself upon her friend's neck, kissed her passionately, and hurried away with her treasure.

The day of the ball arrived. Madame Loisel scored a triumph. She was prettier than any other woman, elegant, gracious, smiling, delirious with delight. All the men stared at her, asked who she was, sought an introduction. All the Cabinet attachés wanted to waltz with her. The Minister himself noticed her.

She danced with intoxication, with passionate enthusiasm, carried away with delight, with no thought of anything else, but transported with the triumph of her beauty, the glory of her success; as it were, in a cloud of happiness at all this homage, this admiration, these aroused desires, this conquest so complete and so sweet to a woman's heart.

About four o'clock in the morning she went away. Her husband had been asleep since midnight, alone in a little deserted anteroom together with three other men whose wives were enjoying themselves.

He threw over her shoulders the wraps that he had brought for the occasion, modest, ordinary, everyday wraps, whose commonplace character contrasted sharply with the elegance of the ball-dress. She realized this and wished to escape being observed by the other women who were enveloping themselves in rich furs.

Loisel checked her: "Stop! You will catch cold outside. I will call a cab."

But she did not listen to him, and rapidly ran down the staircase. When they reached the street, they found no carriage; and they began to look for one, calling out to the cabmen whom they saw passing at a distance.

In desperation and shivering with the cold, they went down in the direction of the Seine. At last on the quay they came across one of those antiquated nocturnal coupés which one sees in Paris only after dark, as if they were ashamed of their poverty by day.

It took them to their own door in the Rue des Martyrs, and they wearily ascended the stairs. For her everything was at an end. He, on the other hand, was thinking that at ten o'clock he must be at the Ministry.

She removed the wraps from her shoulders before the glass, that she might once more see herself in all her glory. But suddenly she uttered an exclamation. The necklace was no longer on her neck!

Her husband, already half-undressed, demanded: "What in the world is the matter with you now?"

She turned toward him, at her wits' end: "I . . . I . . . I have n't Madame Forestier's necklace!"

He jumped up in consternation: "What! . . . How! . . . It's not possible!"

And they searched the folds of the dress, of the cloak, in the pockets, everywhere. They did not find a trace of it.

"You are sure you had it when you left the ball?" asked he.

"Yes, I felt it in the vestibule of the palace."

"But if you lost it on the street we should have heard it drop. It must be in the cab."

"Yes. That's it probably. Did you take the number?"

"No. And you, did n't you notice it?"

"No."

They looked at each other in dismay. Finally Loisel put on his clothes.

"I will go on foot," said he, "over the entire ground that we have covered, and see if I can't find it."

And he went out. She remained in her ball-dress, without strength to go to bed, seated helpless on a chair, without a fire, without power to think.

Her husband came back about seven o'clock. He had found nothing.

He went to the headquarters of the police, to the newspapers, to promise a reward; he went to the offices of the cab companies, — in fact, he went to every place where he felt a suspicion of hope.

She waited all day, in the same state of prostration at this terrible catastrophe.

Loisel came back in the evening, his face hollow and pale; he had discovered nothing.

"You must write to your friend," said he, "that you have broken the clasp of her necklace, and that you are having it repaired. That will give us time to turn around."

She wrote at his dictation.

And the end of a week they had lost all hope.

And Loisel, who had aged five years, said: "We must consider how we can replace this necklace."

The next day they took the case which had contained it, and went to the jeweler whose name they found inside. He consulted his books.

"It was not I, madame, who sold this necklace: I must have furnished only the case."

Then they went from jeweler to jeweler, looking for a necklace like the other, recalling its appearance as best they could, both of them sick with despair and anguish.

In a shop of the Palais Royale they found a diamond necklace which seemed just what they were looking for. The price was forty thousand francs. They could have it for thirty-six thousand.

They asked the jeweler not to sell it for three days. And they bargained with him that he would take it back for thirty-four thousand francs if the first one were found before the end of February.

Loisel possessed eighteen thousand francs which his father had left him. He would borrow the rest.

This he did, asking one thousand francs of one, five hundred of another, five louis here, three there. He gave notes, he undertook ruinous obligations, he entered into relations with the usurers, with the whole tribe of money-lenders. He compromised all the rest of his life, he risked his signature without even knowing if he should be able to honor it, and, distressed with fears for the future, by the bleak misery that was assailing him, by the prospect of all the physical privation and the mental torture that lay before him, he went to purchase the new necklace, and he laid down on the counter of the merchant thirty-six thousand francs.

When Madame Loisel brought back the necklace to Madame Forestier, the latter said coldly: "You ought to have returned it to me sooner, for I might have needed it."

She did not open the case, as her friend had feared she might do. If she had noticed the substitution what would she have thought? What would she have said? Would she not have taken her for a thief?

Madame Loisel came to know the horrible life of the poor. She undertook her part, however, heroically, without hesitation. The frightful debt had to be paid. She would pay it. They discharged their servant; they changed their lodgings; they rented a garret up under the roof.

She became acquainted with heavy housework, the

hateful cares of the kitchen. She washed the dishes, breaking her pink nails on greasy pots and the bottoms of pans. She washed the dirty linen, the shirts and the dish-cloths, and she hung them on a line to dry. She carried the slops down to the street every morning, and brought up the water, pausing at each landing to get her breath. And, dressed like a woman of the people, she went to the fruit-dealer, the grocer, the butcher, her basket on her arm, driving bargains, subjected to abuse, defending her miserable money sou by sou.

Every month notes had to be met, others renewed, extension of time secured.

Her husband worked evenings making fair copies of a tradesman's accounts, and often at night he copied manuscript at five sous a page.

And this life lasted ten years.

At the end of ten years they had paid up everything, everything, including usurers' rates and compound interest.

Madame Loisel looked old now. She had become a strong, hard, rough woman of the poor. Her hair in disorder, her skirts askew, her hands red, she spoke in strident tones. She scrubbed the floors with floods of water. But sometimes when her husband was at the office she would sit by the window and dream of that evening long ago, of the ball where she had been so beautiful and so popular.

What would have happened if she had not lost that necklace? Who knows? Who knows? How strange, how full of changes is life! How little can make or mar us!

One Sunday when she had gone for a walk in the Champs-Élysees to seek relief after the toil of the week, she suddenly observed a woman leading a child. It was Madame Forestier, still young, still beautiful and attractive.

Madame Loisel was stirred with agitation. Should she recognize her? Yes, surely. And now that she had paid her debts, she would tell her everything. Why not?

She drew near.

"How do you do, Jeanne?"

Astonished to be thus familiarly accosted by this common person, the other did not recognize her.

She stammered: "Why . . . Madame . . . I do not know . . . You must be mistaken."

"No, I am Madame Loisel."

Her friend cried out: "Oh . . . my poor Mathilde, how changed you are!"

"Yes, since I have seen you I have had many hard days, and many troubles . . . and all on account of you!"

"Of me! . . . How is that?"

"You remember the diamond necklace that you lent me for the Ministerial ball?"

"Yes. Well?"

"Well, I lost it."

"How can that be? You brought it back to me."

"I brought you back another just like it. And we have been ten years paying for it. This was not easy for us, you know: we had nothing. . . . At last it's finished and I am terribly glad."

Madame Forestier had stopped.

"You say that you bought a diamond necklace to replace mine?"

"Yes. You never noticed it, then? They were very much alike."

And she smiled with a joy that was at once proud and naïve.

Madame Forestier, deeply stirred, seized her two hands.

"Oh, my poor Mathilde! Why, mine was paste. It was worth at the very most five hundred francs!"

THE MAN WITH THE BLUE EYES [1]

(*L'homme aux yeux pâles*)

BY JEAN RICHEPIN

THIS story presents a very peculiar phase of plot structure; it belongs to the type of hoax-plots, and yet it does not pursue the conventional type of *The Necklace* and of *Marjorie Daw*, which lead the reader along an interesting line of action and then confound him with a climax at complete odds with what he has been led to expect. This narrative, on the contrary, is like those rivers in the desert, of which travelers tell us, that suddenly disappear into the sand and are seen no more. The narrative details run their course, the reader anticipates a striking climax, and — there is none. As the narrator of the tale himself says, "There is no conclusion"; and this failure to reach a climactic point constitutes, oddly enough, the very point itself of the narrative.

MONSIEUR PIERRE AGÉNOR DE VARGNES, the examining magistrate, was the exact opposite of a practical joker. He was dignity, staidness, correctness personified. As a sedate man, he was quite incapable of being guilty, even in his dreams, of anything resembling a practical joke, however remotely. I know nobody to whom he could be compared, unless it be the present President of the French Republic. I think it is useless to carry the analogy any further, and having said thus much, it will be easily understood that a cold shiver passed through me when I heard the following.

At about eight o'clock one morning last winter, as he

[1] Included among tales by Guy de Maupassant in the English translation issued by the St. Dunstan Guild. Printed by permission of the St. Dunstan Guild, publishers of Maupassant's *Works* in English.

was leaving the house to go to the Palais de Justice,
his footman handed him a card, on which was printed: —

DOCTOR JAMES FERDINAND
Member of the Academy of Medicine,
Port-au-Prince
Chevalier of the Legion of Honor

At the bottom of the card, there was written in pencil:
"From Lady Frogère."

Monsieur de Vargnes knew the lady very well. She
was a very agreeable Creole from Haiti, whom he had
met in many drawing-rooms, and, on the other hand,
though the doctor's name did not awaken any recollec-
tions in him, his quality and titles alone demanded the
courtesy of an interview, however short it might be.
Therefore, although he was in a hurry to get out, Monsieur de Vargnes told the footman to show in his early
visitor, but to tell him beforehand that his master was
much pressed for time, as he had to go to the law courts.

When the doctor came in, in spite of his usual imper-
turbability, the magistrate could not restrain a movement of surprise, for the doctor presented the strange
anomaly of being a Negro of the purest, blackest type,
with the eyes of a white man — of a man from the North
— pale, cold, clear, blue eyes. His surprise increased,
when, after a few words of excuse for an untimely visit,
the doctor added, with an enigmatical smile: —

"My eyes surprise you, do they not? I was sure that
they would, and, to tell you the truth, I came here in
order that you might look at them well, and never forget them."

His smile, and his words even more than his smile,
seemed to be those of a madman. He spoke very softly,
with that childish, lisping voice which is peculiar to

Negroes, and his mysterious, almost menacing words consequently sounded all the more as if they were uttered at random by a man bereft of reason. But the doctor's looks, the looks of those pale, cold, clear, blue eyes, were certainly not those of a madman. They clearly expressed menace, yes, menace, as well as irony, and above all, implacable ferocity, and their glance was like a flash of lightning, which one could never forget.

"I have seen," Monsieur de Vargnes used to say, when speaking about it, "the looks of many murderers, but in none of them have I ever observed such a depth of crime, and of impudent security in crime."

And this impression was so strong that Monsiuer de Vargnes thought he was the victim of some hallucination, especially as when he spoke about his eyes, the doctor continued with a smile, and in his most childish accents: —

"Of course, monsieur, you cannot understand what I am saying to you, and I must beg your pardon for it. To-morrow you will receive a letter which will explain it all to you, but, first of all, it was necessary that I should let you have a good, a careful look at my eyes, my eyes, which are myself, my only and true self, as you will see."

With these words, and with a polite bow, the doctor went out, leaving Monsieur de Vargnes extremely surprised, and a prey to doubt. He said to himself: "Is he merely a madman? The fierce expression and the criminal depth of his looks are perhaps caused merely by the extraordinary contrast between his fierce looks and his pale eyes."

And absorbed in these thoughts, Monsieur de Vargnes unfortunately allowed several minutes to elapse. Then he thought to himself suddenly: —

"No, I am not the sport of any hallucination, and this is no case of an optical phenomenon. This man is evidently some terrible criminal, and I have altogether failed in my duty in not arresting him myself at once, illegally, even at the risk of my life."

The judge ran downstairs in pursuit of the doctor, but it was too late; he had disappeared. In the afternoon, he called on Madame de Frogère, to ask her whether she could tell him anything about the matter. She, however, did not know the Negro doctor in the least, and was even able to assure him that he was a fictitious personage, for, as she was well acquainted with the upper classes in Haiti, she knew that the Academy of Medicine at Port-au-Prince had no doctor of that name among its members. As Monsieur de Vargnes persisted, and gave descriptions of the doctor, especially mentioning his extraordinary eyes, Madame de Frogère began to laugh, and said: —

"You have certainly had to do with a hoaxer, my dear monsieur. The eyes which you have described are certainly those of a white man, and the individual must have been painted."

On thinking it over, Monsieur de Vargnes remembered that the doctor had nothing of the Negro about him but his black skin, his woolly hair and beard, and his way of speaking, which was easily imitated. He had not the characteristic, undulating walk. Perhaps, after all, he was only a practical joker, and during the whole day, Monsieur de Vargnes took refuge in that view, which rather wounded his dignity as a man of consequence, but appeased his scruples as a magistrate.

The next day, he received the promised letter, which was written, as well as addressed, in characters cut out of the newspapers. It was as follows: —

Monsieur:

"Dr. James Ferdinand does not exist, but the man whose eyes you saw does, and you will certainly recognize his eyes. This man has committed two crimes, for which he does not feel any remorse, but, as he is a psychologist, he is afraid of some day yielding to the irresistible temptation of confessing his crimes. You know better than any one (and that is your most powerful aid), with what imperious force criminals, especially intellectual ones, feel this temptation. That great poet, Edgar Allan Poe, has written masterpieces on this subject, which express the truth exactly, but he has omitted to mention the last phenomenon, which I will tell you. Yes, I, a criminal, feel a terrible wish for somebody to know of my crimes, and when this requirement is satisfied, when my secret has been revealed to a confidant, I shall be tranquil for the future, and be freed from this demon of perversity, which only tempts us once. Well! Now that is accomplished. You shall have my secret: from the day that you recognize me by my eyes you will try to find out what I am guilty of, and how I was guilty, and you will discover it, being a master of your profession, which, by-the-by, has procured you the honor of having been chosen by me to bear the weight of this secret, which now is shared by us, and by us two alone. I say, advisedly, *by us two alone*. You could not, as a matter of fact, prove the reality of this secret to any one, unless I were to confess it, and I defy you to obtain my public confession, as I have confessed it to you, *and without danger to myself*."

Three months later, Monsieur de Vargnes met Monsieur X—— at an evening party, and at first sight, and without the slightest hesitation, he recognized in him those very pale, very cold, and very clear blue eyes, eyes which it was impossible to forget.

The man himself remained perfectly impassive, so that Monsieur de Vargnes was forced to say to himself: —

"Probably I am the sport of an hallucination at this moment, or else there are two pairs of eyes that are perfectly similar, in the world. And what eyes! Can it be possible?"

The magistrate instituted inquiries into his life, and he discovered this, which removed all his doubts.

Five years previously Monsieur X—— had been a very poor, but very brilliant medical student, who, although he never took his doctor's degree, had already made himself remarkable by his microbiological researches.

A young and very rich widow had fallen in love with him and married him. She had one child by her first marriage, and in the space of six months first the child and then the mother died of typhoid fever. Thus Monsieur X—— had inherited a large fortune, in due form, and without any possible dispute. Everybody said that he had attended to the two patients with the utmost devotion. Now, were these two deaths the two crimes mentioned in his letter?

But then, Monsieur X—— must have poisoned his two victims with the microbes of typhoid fever, which he had skillfully cultivated in them, so as to make the disease incurable, even by the most devoted care and attention. Why not?

"Do you really believe it?" I asked Monsieur de Vargnes.

"Absolutely," he replied. "And the most terrible thing about it is that the villain is right when he defies me to force him to confess his crime publicly, for I see no means of obtaining a confession, none whatever. For a moment I thought of magnetism, but who could magnetize that man with those pale, cold, bright eyes? With such eyes, he would force the magnetizer to denounce himself as the culprit."

And then he said, with a deep sigh: —

"Ah! Formerly there was something good about justice!"

When he saw my inquiring looks, he added in a firm and perfectly convinced voice: —

"Formerly, justice had torture at its command."

"Upon my word," I replied, with all an author's unconscious and simple egotism, "it is quite certain that without the torture, this strange tale will have no conclusion, and that is very unfortunate, so far as regards the story I intended to make out of it."

GENERAL

LA GRANDE BRETÈCHE [1]

BY HONORÉ DE BALZAC

La Grande Bretèche illustrates all the structural elements
that constitute complete narrative: setting, character, plot,
and dialogue. But it is especially interesting as a study in
"point of view."

"The narrative is, in the broad, an example of the first-
person type of approach but this passes through many successive phases. At first it is largely a matter of setting. La Grande
Bretèche is described as visible to the beholder — as yet quite
impersonal — from the top of the neighboring mountain,
from which he can look down upon the inclosure and observe
the estate at large. Then the point of view changes to a closer
inspection of the street side, through one of the numerous
holes made in the old gate by the children of the neighborhood. Almost immediately, however, vagueness and imper-
sonality are cast aside, and, in his own person, Monsieur
Horace, the narrator, takes the stage, and by night, "braving
scratches, makes his way into the garden that now had no
owner," and contemplates it at leisure, straying about the
grounds and indulging in orgies of imaginary adventure. But
he is soon visited at the inn by the notary, Monsieur Regnault,
who forbids further trespass on the deserted premises. At this
juncture, although the story is still related in the words of the
original narrator, the point of view becomes that of the notary,
who garrulously recounts his experiences in the château at the
deathbed of the late owner, the Countess de Merret. With
this change, the attitude of approach shifts over from one of
setting, and interest centers in action. But Regnault's horizon, while narrower in extent than what has preceded, is but
general, after all, and the narrator speedily seeks to supple-
ment the notary's story by that of some one to whom more
details are known. Such information he readily finds in his

[1] From *Scènes de la Vie Privée*. Translated for this work by the
Editor.

landlady, Mother Lepas, a peasant woman, who, from her own experiences, adds materially to the revelations of the notary regarding the mystery of the château. Thus, with her narrative, the point of view again changes, and again becomes more concentrated in scope. Finally, convinced that he can yet penetrate the secret of the whole mystery of La Grande Bretèche by means of Rosalie, the servant at the inn and formerly in the employ of the Countess, Monsieur Horace gains the girl's confidence, and she ultimately tells him of the gruesome scene in which she personally was an actor. Thus the point of view changes for the sixth time, and is now concentrated on the very core of the story, the discovery by Monsieur de Merret of his wife's lover and the consequent adventure.

"A further detail of structure characterizes Rosalie's story. While the account of the final details is hers, yet Monsieur Horace maintains the autobiographical attitude, giving her story in his own words and assuming the rôle of omniscience. For example, speaking of Monsieur de Merret, he says, "During dinner he [Monsieur] had observed that his wife was quite coquettishly dressed; on his way home from the club he had said to himself that she seemed to be recovering from her indisposition and that her convalescence was becoming to her." Later on, "Just as he turned the key of his wife's room, he thought he heard close the door of the closet that I have mentioned," etc. Again, when his wife replied that there is no one in the closet, "That 'no' pierced to Monsieur de Merret's very heart. He did not believe it," etc. And so on throughout the scene: we have details that Rosalie could not possibly have supplied, and that we can explain only on the omniscient basis, unless, perhaps, we assume that Monsieur Horace, while narrating Rosalie's experiences *in propria persona*, enlarged upon her account by supplying what seemed natural inferences from the data given by the girl."[1]

ABOUT a hundred yards outside of Vendôme, on the banks of the Loire, there stands a gloomy old mansion, crowned by a lofty roof, and so completely isolated that near it there is not even the foul-smelling tannery nor

[1] *Rhetorical Principles of Narration*, pp. 196–98.

the wretched inn that one ordinarily sees in the immediate neighborhood of all small towns. In front of this dwelling, facing the river, is a garden, where in days gone by rows of close-trimmed boxwood outlined the paths, but now they run quite wild. A few willows, their roots in the Loire, have grown as rapidly as the hedge about the inclosure, and half conceal the house. Weeds flourish on the sloping banks of the stream. The fruit trees, now neglected for ten years, bear fruit no longer, and their runners form a dense thicket. The fruit walls look like palisades. The paths, which used to be graveled, are full of purslane; as a matter of fact, all traces of the paths are gone.

Looking from the top of the mountain, to which cling the ruins of the old château of the Dukes of Vendôme, — the only place from which the eye can penetrate into this inclosure, — one would say that at some vague bygone time this corner of the world had been the pride of some gentleman devoted to roses and tulips — in a word, to fancy gardening — but particularly fond of fine fruits. An arbor or rather, the ruins of an arbor, are still visible, and under it there is even yet a table which has partially withstood the ravages of time. As you look at this old garden, you can picture the mild joy of quiet provincial life, just as you can picture the life of a respectable tradesman by reading the inscription on his tomb. To complete the melancholy but not unpleasant scene that stirs one's imagination, there is on one of the walls a sundial bearing this commonplace Christian inscription: *Ultimam cogita!*

The roof of the house is sadly dilapidated; the blinds are always down; the balconies are covered with swallows' nests; the doors are never open. Tall weeds have marked with green lines the cracks in the steps; the ironwork is covered with rust. Moon, sun, winter, summer, snow, have rotted the wood, have warped the boards, and have worn away the paint.

The gloomy silence that reigns there is broken only by the birds, the cats, the martlets, the rats, and the mice, who are free to run about, fight, and devour one another. An invisible hand has everywhere written the word "Mystery."

If, impelled by curiosity, you should go to inspect this house from the side toward the road, you would see a great gate with arched top, in which the children of the neighborhood have made innumerable holes. I learned later that, some ten years before, this gate had been condemned. Through these irregular openings you could observe the perfect harmony between the front of the garden and the front of the court. But the same disorder reigns here as well. Bunches of weeds grow about the pavements. Enormous cracks furrow the walls whose blackened crests are entwined with innumerable festoons of wall-wort. The steps are in fragments; the bell-rope is rotten; the gutters are broken. What fire from heaven has passed by here? What judgment has decreed that salt be sown upon this spot? Has some one here insulted God? Has some one proved traitor to France? These are the questions that naturally come to mind. Reptiles creep about, and there is no answer. This empty, deserted house is one great enigma, and no one knows the solution.

At one time the place was a small feudal estate, and bore the name "La Grande Bretèche." During Desplein's stay at Vendôme, where he had left me during his visit to a rich patient, the sight of this singular house became one of my keenest pleasures. Was it not more than a ruin? With a ruin one always feels actual his-

toric associations, associations that he can verify; but
this structure, still standing, though in a state of gradual
demolition by some avenging hand, had a mystery of
its own, a secret; at the very least it was freakish.

More than once at evening I approached the hedge
about the enclosure, now grown wild. I braved scratches,
I made my way into this garden that now had no owner,
this estate that could no longer be called either public
or private; for hours at a time I would remain in contemplation of its disorder. I would not have asked a single
question of any Vendôme gossip, even though I might
have gained thereby the true story of this strange place.
I composed delightful romances there; I gave myself up
to mild orgies of melancholy; and I was thrilled. If I
had found out the secret — perhaps the commonplace secret — of all this neglect, I never should have composed
the unspoken poems with which I indulged myself. To
me this retreat brought the most varied pictures of
human life, all darkened by misfortune; at one time it
had the air of a cloister without the monks; at another,
the quiet of the graveyard, without the dead, who speak
to one in their epitaphs; one day it was the house of
the leper; another, the house of the Fates; — but it
was, above all, the very impersonation of the province
itself, with all its conventionality and its simple life
from day to day. I have often wept there, but I have
never smiled. More than once I have felt an involun-
tary shudder when I have heard above my head the low
rustling of some frightened dove as it flew over me.
The ground is damp; and you must not be afraid of
lizards, snakes, and toads, which frequent the place in
the wild freedom of nature; particularly you must not
be afraid of the cold, for at certain moments you feel
a cloak of ice resting on your shoulders, like the hand
of the Commander upon the neck of Don Juan.

One evening I shuddered. The wind had twisted a rusty old weathercock, and its squeaking sounded as if the house had groaned, just as I had completed a dismal drama in which I had accounted for this monument to melancholy. I returned to my inn, a prey to depression. When I had eaten my supper, my hostess entered my room with an air of mystery, and said:

"Monsieur, here is Monsieur Regnault."

"And who is Monsieur Regnault?"

"What! Monsieur does not know Monsieur Regnault! Well, that is strange!" said she as she went out.

Then I saw entering the room a tall, spare man, dressed in black, his hat in his hand. He came in like a ram about to make a rush at a rival. He revealed a retreating brow, a small pointed head, and a pale face about the color of a glass of dirty water. One would have said that he was a gentleman-in-waiting to some Minister of State. The stranger wore an old coat, very threadbare about the seams; but he sported a diamond in the frill of his shirt and gold rings in his ears.

"Monsieur," said I to him, "whom have I the honor of addressing?"

He seated himself upon a chair before the fire, laid his hat on my table, and then, rubbing his hands, replied:

"Ah, it is very cold. Monsieur, I am Monsieur Regnault."

I bowed, saying to myself:

"*Il Bondocani!* Who is he?"

"I am," he continued, "the notary at Vendôme."

"I am charmed, monsieur," I exclaimed, "but, for reasons of my own, I am not about to make my will."

"Just a moment!" he cried, raising his hand as if to impose silence. "Allow me! I have understood that you are accustomed to stroll about the garden of La Grande Bretèche."

"Yes, monsieur."

"Just a moment!" said he, repeating his gesture; — this action seemed to give him actual pleasure; "Monsieur, I come in the name of and as executor of the late Madame the Countess de Merret to beg that you discontinue your visits. Just a moment! I am no Turk, nor do I wish to charge you with having committed any crime. Furthermore, you may very likely be ignorant of the circumstances that render it necessary for me to allow the most beautiful mansion in Vendôme to go to ruin. Yet, monsieur, you seem to be a man of education, and you must be aware that the laws forbid under heavy penalties that one trespass on inclosed premises. A hedge is as good as a wall. But the condition into which the place has fallen may serve to excuse your curiosity. I would ask nothing better than to allow you to come and go freely about the house; but, charged as I am to carry out the wishes of the former owner, I have the honor, monsieur, to request that you no longer enter the garden. Even I, monsieur, have not, since the opening of the will, put my foot in the house, which, as I have had the honor of telling you already, forms a part of the estate of Madame de Merret. We have merely assured ourselves of the number of windows and doors in order to determine the amount of the taxes, which I pay every year from the funds set aside for that purpose by Madame the Countess. Ah, my dear sir, that will of hers made a great stir in Vendôme!"

At this point the worthy man paused to blow his nose. I appreciated his loquacity, for I saw clearly enough that the administration of Madame de Merret's estate was the most important event of his life — that it constituted at once his reputation, his pride, his "Restoration." I should have to bid farewell to all my delightful dreams, to my romancing. I was not averse, therefore, to the pleasure of learning the truth from this official source.

"Monsieur," said I, "would it be in bad taste were I to ask you the reason for this strange state of affairs?"

At these words, an expression passed over the notary's face indicating the pleasure that all men feel who are given to riding hobbies. He pulled up his collar with an air of self-satisfaction, took a small snuffbox from his pocket, opened it, offered it to me, and, upon my declining, helped himself to a generous pinch. He was perfectly happy. A man without a hobby little knows what one can really get out of life. A hobby stands just on the dividing-line between passion and monomania. At that moment I understood the full meaning of Sterne's sage remark, and I realized the joy that Uncle Toby must have felt when with the assistance of Trim he was fairly mounted on his hobby-horse of battles and sieges.

"Monsieur," said Monsieur Regnault, "I was Maître Roquin's head clerk, in Paris; — an excellent office, of which you have perhaps heard? No? Yet an unfortunate bankruptcy has made it famous. Not having sufficient means to live in Paris with rents at the price that they reached in 1816, I came here and purchased the business of my predecessor. I had relatives in Vendôme, — among others, a very rich aunt, who gave me her daughter in marriage.

"Monsieur," he continued after a slight pause, "three months after I had received my license from his lordship the Keeper of the Seals, I was sent for one evening by Madame the Countess de Merret, just as I was on

the point of going to bed. (I was not yet married.) Her
maid, an excellent young woman, who to-day works in
this very inn, was at my door with Madame the Countess's carriage. Ah, just a moment! I must tell you,
monsieur, that Monsieur the Count de Merret had gone
to Paris to die, two months before I came here. He died
there in wretchedness, a slave to every form of excess;
— do you get my meaning? On the day of his departure
Madame the Countess had quitted La Grande Bretèche,
and had stripped it of everything. Some even asserted
that she had burned the furniture, the hangings, — in
fact, everything belonging to the premises at present
leased by the aforesaid . . . Stop! what am I saying?
Pardon me; I thought I was dictating a lease . . . That
she burned them," he resumed, "in the meadow at
Merret. — Have you been to Merret, monsieur? No,"
said he, answering his own question for me. "Ah, it is
a beautiful spot!

"For some months," he continued with a slight shake
of his head, "Monsieur the Count and Madame the
Countess had lived a strange sort of life; they received
no guests; Madame occupied the ground floor, and Monsieur the floor above. When Madame the Countess was
left alone, she never appeared in public except at church.
Later, at the château, she refused to see the friends who
came to visit her. She was already greatly altered at
the time of leaving La Grande Bretèche for Merret. The
dear woman — I say 'dear' because this diamond came
to me from her, although I never saw her on more than
one occasion — well, the good lady was very ill; she
had undoubtedly despaired of recovery, for she died
without consenting to call in a physician; consequently
many of our ladies have thought that she was not altogether in her right mind.

"Monsieur, my curiosity was consequently aroused when I learned that Madame de Merret desired my services. I was not the only one interested in her history: that evening, although it was late, the whole town knew that I had gone to Merret. The maid replied rather indefinitely to the questions that I asked her on our way to the house; nevertheless she said that during the day the curé of Merret had administered the last sacraments to her mistress, and that she did not seem likely to survive through the night.

"At eight o'clock I reached the château. I ascended the main staircase, and, after passing through several large apartments, lofty and dark, and as cold and damp as the devil, I reached the state bedchamber where the Countess lay. In view of the rumors that were in circulation about the lady (monsieur, I should never finish if I repeated to you all the stories that are told regarding her!), I had pictured her to myself as a coquette. But — just think of it — I had no little difficulty in distinguishing her on the great bed where she was lying. It is true, she had only one old-fashioned Argand lamp to give light in that immense chamber, decorated with ancient friezes so thickly coated with dust that merely to look at them made you sneeze. But then, you have not been to Merret! Well, monsieur, the bed is one of those ancient affairs with a high canopy, decorated with a flowered cretonne. A small night-table stood near the bed, and on it I noticed a copy of the *Imitation of Christ*, which, by the way, I purchased for my wife, as well as the lamp. There was also a large easy-chair for her woman attendant, and two ordinary chairs. There was no fire whatever. So much for the furniture; it would not have filled ten lines in an inventory.

"Ah, my dear sir, if you had seen as I did that immense

room, hung with tapestries, you would have felt that you had been transported into a veritable scene from a novel. It was as cold as ice. and, worse than that, it was funereal," he added, lifting his hand theatrically, and pausing. "On looking sharply and coming close to the bed, I finally made out Madame de Merret, thanks to the light from the lamp that fell on the pillows. Her face was as yellow as wax and was as narrow as your two hands placed together, palm to palm. Madame the Countess wore a lace cap, under which her hair was visible, beautiful but perfectly white. She was sitting upright, although with seeming difficulty. Her great black eyes, dulled by her fever doubtless, and already nearly dead, scarcely moved under the projections where one's eyebrows grow. . . here " (indicating the arch over the eyes). "Her forehead was damp; her emaciated hands looked like bones covered with soft skin; her veins and her muscles were distinctly visible. She must at one time have been very beautiful; but at that moment the sight of her aroused in me an emotion that I cannot define. Never, according to the opinion of those who laid her out for burial, had a living creature become so thin. In a word, it was a horrible sight! Disease had so wasted her that she was a mere shadow. Her lips, pale blue in color, did not seem to move as she spoke to me. Although my profession has made me familiar with such scenes as this, frequently coming as I do to the bedside of the dying to record their last wishes, I confess that the weeping families and the agonies that I have witnessed have been as nothing in comparison with the sight of this solitary and silent woman in that great château.

"There was not a sound in the room. I did not notice even the slight rising and falling of the sheets that should have attended the sick woman's breathing, and I stood perfectly quiet, gazing at her in a kind of stupor. I feel this minute as if I were still there. Finally her great eyes flickered; she tried to lift her right hand, but it fell back upon the bed, and these words came from her lips like a breath, for her voice could no longer be called a voice:

"'I have been waiting for you with great impatience.'

"Her cheeks flushed. To tell the truth, monsieur, it was an effort for her.

"'Madame,' said I.

"She motioned me to be silent. At this the old woman who waited on her arose and whispered in my ear:

"'Do not talk; Madame is not in a state to hear the slightest sound; and anything that you said might agitate her.'

"I sat down. After some moments, Madame de Merret summoned all her remaining strength in an effort to move her right arm, and thrust it with infinite difficulty beneath her bolster. She was quiet for just an instant; then she made a last effort to withdraw her hand, and, when she had taken out a sealed paper, drops of sweat fell from her forehead.

"'I entrust you with my will,' she said. 'Oh! my God! Oh!'

"That was all. She grasped a crucifix that was lying on the bed, quickly placed it to her lips, and — was dead.

"The expression of her staring eyes still makes me shudder when I think of them. She must have suffered greatly! There was a flash of joy in her dying glance, — the look remained fixed in her dead eyes.

"I carried the will away with me; and when it was opened I saw that Madame de Merret had made me her executor. Except for certain private legacies, she bequeathed her entire estate to the hospital at Vendôme. But her provisions with respect to La Grande Bretèche were as follows: She bade me leave the house for a period of fifty years from the time of her death just as it was at the moment when she died, forbidding any one whatever to enter the rooms, forbidding the slightest repairs, and even setting aside a fund for securing keepers, should it be necessary, in order to insure the complete execution of her wishes. At the expiration of that time, if the purpose of the executrix had been fulfilled, the house is to belong to my heirs — for monsieur knows that notaries cannot accept legacies; otherwise La Grande Bretèche reverts to whoever is entitled to it, but conditionally upon compliance with the terms indicated in a codicil which is attached to the will, and which is not to be opened until the expiration of the aforesaid fifty years. The will has not been contested; accordingly . . ."

At this point the tall notary, without finishing his sentence, glanced at me with a triumphant air, and I delighted him with a few complimentary remarks.

"Monsieur," said I to him in conclusion, "you have made so vivid an impression upon me that I can fairly see that dying woman, paler than the very sheets upon her bed; her gleaming eyes fill me with terror; and to-night I shall dream of her. But you must have formed some conjectures as to the bequests contained in this odd will."

"Monsieur," he replied, with a comical air of reserve, "I never allow myself to judge of the conduct of persons who have honored me with the gift of a diamond."

I soon loosened the tongue of the conscientious Vendôme notary, and he communicated to me, not with-

out long digressions, his observations regarding the wise
politicians of both sexes whose decrees constitute the
law in Vendôme. But his opinions were so inconsistent
and so diffuse that I nearly fell asleep, in spite of the
interest that I felt in the authentic history that he had
related to me. The dull and monotonous voice of the
man, accustomed as he no doubt was to listen to himself
and to make his clients and his fellow citizens listen to
him, triumphed over my curiosity. Fortunately he took
his departure.

"Ah, monsieur," said he to me on the stairs, "a good
many people would like to live forty-five years longer;
but, just a moment!" — and with a shrewd air he placed
his right forefinger on the side of his nose as if to say,
'Pay careful heed to this!' — "But to do that, to do
that," said he, "one must not be already sixty years old."

Aroused from my apathy by this shaft, which the
notary considered very witty, I closed the door; then I
sat down in my easy-chair and placed my feet on the
andirons in the fireplace. I was engaged in the delightful occupation of composing, in fancy, a romance after
the Radcliffe style, based on the judicial data furnished by Monsieur Regnault, when the knob of my
door was gently turned by a woman's hand and the door
itself opened. I saw the figure of my landlady, a merry,
good-natured creature, who had missed her calling; she
was a Fleming and ought to have been a figure in a picture by Teniers.

"Well, monsieur," said she to me, "of course Monsieur
Regnault has repeated to you his story about La Grande
Bretèche."

"Yes, Mother Lepas."

"What did he tell you?"

I recounted to her in a few words the gloomy and chilling story of Madame de Merret. At every sentence my landlady tossed her head and looked at me with an innkeeper's shrewdness, — a happy medium, as it were, between the instinct of the gendarme, the craftiness of the spy, and the cunning of the tradesman.

"My dear Madame Lepas," I added in conclusion, "you seem to know something more. Eh? If not, why did you come up to my room?"

"Oh, on the word of an honest woman, as true as my name is Lepas . . ."

"Don't swear; your eyes are big with a secret. You knew Monsieur de Merret. What sort of man was he?"

"Bless my soul! Monsieur de Merret was a fine-looking man, but you never saw the entire length of him, he was so tall! He was a dignified gentleman; he came from Picardy; and, as we say here, his head was right under his cap. He paid all his bills that he might n't have trouble with any one. He was full of spirits, do you understand? We women all found him very agreeable."

"Because he was full of spirits?" said I.

"Possibly," said she. "Take my word for it, monsieur, a man must, indeed, have had something before him, as the saying is, if he was to win Madame de Merret, who, without wishing to cast any reflections on others, was the most beautiful and the richest woman about Vendôme. She had an income of nearly twenty thousand francs a year. The whole town was at the wedding. The bride was pretty, a general favorite, a jewel of a girl. Ah, they made a fine couple at the time!"

"Was their marriage happy?"

"Alas! Yes and no, as far as one can guess; for, as you may imagine, we others did n't live hand in glove with them! Madame de Merret was a kind woman, very pretty, and, perhaps, sometimes suffered from her husband's quick temper; but, although he was rather reserved, we liked him. Bah! it was natural enough for one in his position to be so! When a man is a nobleman, you know . . ."

"Yet there must have been some catastrophe to separate Madame and Monsieur de Merret so suddenly, was n't there?"

"I did n't say that there was any catastrophe, monsieur. I don't know anything about one."

"Good! Now I am sure that you know all about it."

"Well, monsieur, I'll tell you the whole story. When I saw Monsieur Regnault go up to your room, I knew well enough that he would talk to you about Madame de Merret in connection with La Grande Bretèche. That suggested to me the idea of consulting monsieur, who seems to be a man of discretion, and incapable of betraying a poor woman like me, who has never injured any one, but who, notwithstanding, is uneasy in her conscience. Hitherto I 've not dared tell my story to the people about here; they 're all gossips, and their tongues are as sharp as needles. And finally, monsieur, I 've never had a guest before who has stayed at my house so long as you have, and to whom I could tell the story of the fifteen thousand francs."

"My dear Madame Lepas," I rejoined, interrupting her torrent of words, "if your confidence is going to compromise me, I would not have you entrust me with it for the world."

"Don't you be afraid," she interrupted. "You'll see."

My landlady's eagerness led me to believe that I was not the only one to whom she had confided the secret of which I was about to become the sole guardian, and I gave her my attention.

"Monsieur," she began, "when the Emperor sent

here certain Spanish prisoners of war, as well as some others, the Government quartered on me a young Spaniard who had been sent to Vendôme on parole. In spite of his parole, however, he used to go to the Prefect every day and report. He was a grandee of Spain; that much at the very least. He had an '*os*' and a '*dia*' in his name, something like Bogos de Férédia. I have it written in my books; you can read it if you like. Oh, he was a handsome young fellow for a Spaniard, who, they tell me, are an ugly lot. He was n't more than five feet three or four in height, but had a good figure; his hands were small, and he was very careful of them. Ah! You ought to have seen them. He had as many brushes for his hands as a woman has for her entire toilet. He had thick black hair, a bright eye, and a copper-colored complexion, but I liked it all the same. He had the finest linen I 've ever seen, and I 've had princesses in this house, and, among other notables, General Bertrand, the Duke and the Duchess d'Abrantès, Monsieur Decazes, and the King of Spain. He did n't eat much, but he had such a kind and refined manner about him that you could n't find any fault with him for it. Oh, I had a great affection for him, although he did n't speak four words a day, and it was impossible to draw him into conversation; if any one said a word to him, he made no reply. It was a whim, a fad, that they all have, so I am told. He used to read his breviary like a priest; he went to mass and to all the services regularly. Where did he sit? (We 've thought of that since.) Well, about two steps from Madame de Merret's chapel. As he took a seat there the first time he came to church no one thought that there was any design in it. Besides, he never took his nose out of his book, the poor young man! In the evening he used to walk on the mountain, among the

ruins of the château. It was the poor fellow's only
recreation; the place reminded him of his own country.
They say that Spain is full of mountains!

"After the first few days of his imprisonment, he began
to stay out late. I grew uneasy when I did n't see him
back by midnight; but we all got accustomed to this
whim of his; he would take the key of the house with
him, and we soon stopped sitting up. He lodged in a
house of ours on the Rue des Casernes. Some time afterward one of our stable boys said that one evening, as he
was going to water the horses, he thought he saw our
Spanish grandee swimming far out in the river, like a
fish. When he came back home I told him to look out
for the river-grass, and he seemed annoyed at having
been seen in the water.

"Finally, one day, monsieur, — or, rather, one morning, — we did n't find him in his room; and he did n't
come back. In hunting everywhere for him I found a
note in his table-drawer and also fifty Spanish gold-
pieces, the kind they call 'portugaises,' amounting to
about five thousand francs, and, besides that, in a little
sealed box, ten thousand francs' worth of diamonds. The
note said that in case he did n't return, he left the money
and the diamonds in trust to found masses in thanksgiving to God for his escape and his salvation.

"In those days my husband was still alive, and he
hurried out to search for him, and here is the odd thing
about the story! He brought back with him the Spaniard's clothes, which he found under a big stone near a
sort of pile along the edge of the river, on the side of the
château, nearly opposite La Grande Bretèche. My husband had gone there so early in the morning that no
one had seen him; so after we read the letter, he burned
the clothes, and, in accordance with Count Férédia's

wishes we said that he had escaped. The Subprefect set the whole police force on his track; but, bless me! they never caught him. Lepas thought that the Spaniard had drowned himself; but, for my own part, monsieur, I don't think so at all; on the other hand, I do believe that his disappearance was connected in some way with Madame de Merret, especially as Rosalie has told me that the crucifix, which her mistress was so attached to that she had it buried with her, was made of ebony and silver, and, during the first days of his stay, Monsieur Férédia owned one made of ebony and silver, which I never set eyes on again.

"Now, monsieur, isn't it true that I haven't any reason to worry about keeping the Spaniard's fifteen thousand francs, and don't they belong to me?"

"Surely," said I; "but have you never tried to question Rosalie?"

"Oh, yes, indeed, monsieur! But, would you believe it? — that girl is like a stone wall. She knows something; but it's impossible to make her tell it."

After a few moments' further conversation, my landlady left me a prey to vague and indefinite thoughts, to romantic curiosity, to a sort of religious terror such as you feel in a dark church at night when you can just make out a dim ray of light far away under the lofty arches; an indistinct figure glides about, a dress or a surplice rustles . . . and you shudder. La Grande Bretèche, with its tall weeds, its barred windows, its lonely rooms, suddenly assumed fantastic proportions in my eyes. I tried to make my way into the ghostly mansion and seek there the solution of this dark story, of this threefold tragedy. Rosalie became to me the most interesting personage in Vendôme. Upon closely observing her, I discovered indications of some internal uneasiness in spite of the robust health that irradiated her plump cheeks; in her heart were the seeds of remorse or of hope; her manner betrayed some secret, just as does that of fanatics who give themselves up to lives of prayer or that of the mother who has killed her child and never ceases to hear its last cry. Yet Rosalie's attitude was naïve and simple; her stupid smile had nothing of the criminal in it, and you would have declared her innocent merely to look at the huge neckerchief with the red and blue spots that covered her plump bust and was folded about her neck and held together by her gown of white and violet striped material.

"No," thought I; "I will not leave Vendôme without learning the whole story of La Grande Bretèche. To gain this end, I will, if absolutely necessary, become Rosalie's lover."

"Rosalie," said I one evening.

"Yes, monsieur."

"You are not married?"

She started slightly.

"Oh, I shan't want for husbands when I take a fancy to be miserable!" said she with a laugh.

She at once got the better of her nervousness, for all women, from the grand lady down to the servant at a tavern, have a self-possession that is quite natural to them.

"You are fresh enough, attractive enough, not to lack lovers! But, tell me, Rosalie, how came you to be a tavern-maid when you got through with Madame de Merret? She left you money enough, did n't she?"

"Oh, yes. But, monsieur, I have the best place in Vendôme."

This was one of those replies that judges and lawyers call "dilatory." Rosalie seemed to me to occupy in this romantic story a position like the middle square on a chessboard: she was at the very center of the interest, at the heart of the secret; to me she seemed involved in the complication itself. It was no longer a prosaic matter of gaining the girl's affection; she represented the last chapter of a romance, and accordingly, from this moment, Rosalie became the object of my undivided attention. Upon close study I discovered in her, as we do in all women whom we observe at close range, a number of excellent traits. She was neat and particular about her person; she was good-looking — that goes without saying; she had many of the attractions that we are accustomed to attribute to a woman, whatever be her social status, when she becomes the object of our notice.

Some two weeks after the notary's visit, one evening, — or, rather, one morning, for it was early, — I said to Rosalie:

"Now tell me all about Madame de Merret."

"Oh!" she exclaimed, "don't ask me to do that, Monsieur Horace!"

Her pretty face fell, her high, quick color paled, and her eyes lost their girlish brilliancy.

"Well," she said, "since you will have it, I'll tell you; but you must be sure to keep my secret!"

"All right! My dear, I will keep all your secrets on the honor of a thief, and there's nothing more trustworthy than that."

"If it's all the same to you," said she, "I prefer your own."

Thereupon she readjusted her neckerchief and settled herself into the posture of a story-teller; for an attitude of confidence and security is quite essential in telling a story. The best stories are always told at a certain hour and at table, just as we all are at this moment. No

one ever told a story well when standing or when hungry.
— But if I had to reproduce accurately Rosalie's diffuse style of expression, a volume would hardly be sufficient.

Now as her confused account of the event was midway between the garrulity of the notary and that of
Madame Lepas, just as the means of a proportion in
arithmetic lie midway between the two extremes, I must
relate it to you in a few words. Therefore I abridge.

Madame de Merret's bedchamber in La Grande Bretèche was on the ground floor. A small closet about four
feet deep, built into the wall, served her as wardrobe.
Three months before the evening, the events which I am
about to relate, Madame de Merret had been seriously
indisposed, so that her husband had left her by herself
in her own room and had taken a chamber on the floor
above for his own bedroom. By one of those chances
that no one can foresee, on the evening of which we have
already spoken, he had returned home later than usual
from the club where it was his custom to go to read the
papers and to discuss politics with his neighbors. His
wife, supposing that he had already come in, had retired,
and was asleep. But the invasion of France had been
the subject of a very animated discussion; and the game
of billiards had been very exciting, — he had lost forty
francs, an enormous sum in Vendôme, where every one
hoards money, and where the daily routine of life is
characterized by a simplicity altogether praiseworthy,
resulting, it may be, in a spirit of true content quite unknown to a Parisian.

For some time it had been Monsieur de Merret's custom to satisfy himself with asking Rosalie if his wife had
retired; and, upon the young woman's invariable answer
in the affirmative, he had straightway gone to his own

apartment with the cheerfulness begotten of habit and confidence. On this particular occasion, when he came in the whim seized him to go into Madame de Merret's room to tell her of his ill luck, and, possibly to seek consolation. During dinner he had observed that his wife was quite coquettishly dressed; on the way home from the club he had said to himself that she seemed to be recovering from her indisposition, and that her convalescence was becoming to her, — and he observed the fact as husbands observe everything, — too late.

Instead of calling Rosalie, who at that moment was busy in the kitchen watching the cook and the coachman play a difficult hand at brisque, Monsieur de Merret directed his steps toward his wife's apartment, guided by the light of his lantern which he had set down on the top of the stairs. His familiar step reëchoed through the corridor. Just as he turned the key of his wife's room, he thought that he heard close the door of the closet that I have mentioned above; but, when he entered, Madame de Merret was alone, standing in front of the fireplace. Her husband naturally assumed that Rosalie was in the closet; yet a suspicion that rang in his ears like the sound of bells filled him with distrust; he glanced at his wife, and in her eyes he detected a trace of confusion and apprehension.

"You are returning very late," she said.

Her voice, usually so innocent and gracious, seemed slightly altered. Monsieur made no reply, for at that moment Rosalie came in. This was like a thunderclap to him. He paced the room, mechanically walking from one window to another, with folded arms.

"Have you had any bad news, or do you not feel well?" asked his wife timidly, as Rosalie undressed her.

He made no reply.

"You may leave the room," said Madame de Merret to her maid. "I will arrange my curl-papers myself."

She foresaw an unpleasant scene merely from the expression of her husband's face, and she preferred to be alone with him.

When Rosalie had gone, or was supposed to have gone, — for she loitered for some few minutes in the corridor, — Monsieur de Merret walked up to his wife and, standing before her, said coldly:

"Madame, there is some one in your closet."

She looked calmly at her husband, and replied innocently:

"No, monsieur."

This "no" pierced to Monsieur de Merret's very heart. He did not believe it; and yet his wife had never appeared purer or more spiritual than at this very moment. He rose to open the closet. Madame de Merret seized his hand, looked reproachfully at him, and said in a strangely agitated voice:

"If you find no one, you understand that everything is at an end between us!"

The indescribable dignity of his wife's manner aroused in the gentleman a profound respect for her, but he suddenly conceived one of those resolutions that need but a larger stage to become immortal.

"No, Josephine," said he; "I will not go. In either case we should be separated forever. Listen! I know the purity of your heart, and I know that you live like a saint. You would not commit a mortal sin to save your life."

At these words Madame de Merret cast a haggard look at her husband.

"See! Here is your crucifix," said he. "Swear to me before God that there is no one there; I will believe you; I will never open that door."

Madame de Merret took the crucifix and said, "I swear it."

"Louder," said her husband; "and say after me: 'I swear before God that there is no one in that closet.'"

She repeated it without a sign of confusion.

"Very good," said Monsieur de Merret coldly; and then, after a moment of silence, he glanced at the ebony crucifix set with silver and added: "You have there a very pretty thing that I never saw before; it is very artistically carved."

"I found it at Duvivier's shop. When that company of prisoners passed through Vendôme last year he bought it of a Spanish ecclesiastic."

"Ah!" said Monsieur de Merret, hanging up the crucifix.

And he rang the bell.

Rosalie was not slow in answering the summons. Monsieur stepped quickly toward her, took her into the recess by the window opening upon the garden, and said in a low tone:

"I know that you and Gorenflot are going to be married, that want of money is all that prevents you from setting up housekeeping, and that you have told him you would not become his wife until he could see his way to become a master mason. . . . Well, go after him; tell him to come here with his trowel and his tools. Manage not to awaken any one else in the house. His fortune will exceed anything that you have expected, unless . . ." He frowned.

Rosalie left the room, but he called her back.

"Here! Take my pass-key," said he. Then in a voice of thunder he shouted down the corridor, "Jean!"

Jean who was both his coachman and confidential servant, dropped his hand at brisque and came up.

"Go to bed, all of you!" said his master; and, beckoning to Jean, he added in a low tone:

"When they are all asleep, — *asleep*, mind you, — let me know."

Monsieur de Merret, who, while he was issuing his orders, had not taken his eyes from his wife, quietly returned to her side by the fire, and began to tell her the details of the game of billiards and of the discussion at the club. When Rosalie returned, she found Monsieur and Madame de Merret conversing together most amicably.

The gentleman had recently had all the rooms plastered that composed his reception suite on the lower floor. Plaster is quite a rare thing in Vendôme: the cost of transportation makes it very expensive. Monsieur had ordered a large quantity of it, knowing that he should always be able to find a purchaser for whatever he did not make use of himself. This circumstance suggested to him the plan that he now proceeded to put into operation.

"Monsieur, Gorenflot is here," said Rosalie in a low voice.

"Let him enter," said the Picard gentleman aloud.

Madame de Merret turned pale when she saw the mason.

"Gorenflot," said her husband, "get some bricks from the carriage-house, and bring enough to wall up the door of that closet. You can use the plaster that is left over to cover the wall." Then, beckoning Rosalie and the workman to him, he said, "Listen, Gorenflot; you will sleep here to-night. But to-morrow morning you shall have your passports to go abroad to a city that I will name. I will give you six thousand francs for your journey. You will remain there ten years. If you don't like it in that place, you can settle somewhere else, as

long as it is in the same country. You will go by way
of Paris, where you will wait for me. There I guarantee
to give you six thousand francs more, payable upon
your return, provided that you fulfill the conditions of
our agreement. For this amount you ought to keep absolute silence about what you are going to do to-night.
As for you, Rosalie, I will give you ten thousand francs,
payable on your wedding-day, on condition of your
marrying Gorenflot; but to marry him, you must keep
your lips sealed. Otherwise no dower."

"Rosalie," called Madame de Merret, "come and arrange my hair."

Her husband quietly walked back and forth, keeping
his eye on the door, the mason, and his wife, but without
betraying any suspicion that might appear insulting.
Gorenflot was obliged to make some noise. At a moment
when the mason was throwing down some bricks and
while her husband was at the end of the room, Madame
de Merret seized the opportunity to say to Rosalie:

"A thousand francs a year to you, child, if you can
whisper Gorenflot to leave a crack at the bottom."
Then aloud she calmly said to her, "Go, help him."

Monsieur and Madame de Merret remained silent
while Gorenflot was engaged in walling up the door.
This silence was intentional on the gentleman's part:
he did not wish to offer to his wife any opportunity of
uttering words that might bear a double meaning; and
on Madame de Merret's part silence was a matter either
of prudence or of pride.

When the wall was half-finished, the crafty mason
seized a moment while Monsieur's back was turned and,
with his pick, broke one of the two glass windows in the
door. This made it clear to Madame de Merret that
Rosalie had spoken to Gorenflot.

At that instant all three of them saw the face of a man, gloomy and dark, a man with black hair, and fiery eyes.

Before her husband could turn around, the unfortunate lady had time to make a motion of the head to the stranger, signifying "Hope!"

At four o'clock, about daybreak, — for it was September, — the work was complete. The mason remained under Jean's charge, and Monsieur de Merret passed the night in his wife's room.

The next morning as he arose he said carelessly:

"Oh! I must go to the Mayor's for the passports."

He put on his hat, took three steps towards the door, turned, and took down the crucifix.

His wife trembled with joy.

"He will go to Duvivier's," thought she.

As soon as her husband was out of the house, Madame de Merret ran for Rosalie; then in a dreadful voice she cried: "The pick! The pick! To work! I saw yesterday how Gorenflot managed it. We shall have time to make a hole and fill it up again."

In the twinkling of an eye Rosalie brought a sharp-pointed sort of tool to her mistress, who with incredible vigor began to tear down the wall. She had already knocked off several bricks, when, as she stepped back to strike an even more vigorous blow, she saw Monsieur de Merret standing behind her.

She fainted.

"Place Madame upon her bed," said the gentleman icily.

Foreseeing what would occur during his absence, he had set a trap for his wife; he had simply written to the Mayor, and had sent word to Duvivier to come to the château.

When the jeweler arrived, the confusion in the room had just been repaired.

"Duvivier," said Monsieur, "did you purchase any crucifixes of the Spaniards who passed through here?"

"No, monsieur."

"Very good. I thank you," said he, with a tigerish glance at his wife.

"Jean," he added, turning to his confidential servant, "you will serve my meals in Madame de Merret's chamber. She is ill, and I shall not leave her until she has recovered her health."

The cruel man remained near his wife for twenty days. At first, when a slight noise was audible in the closet that had been walled up and Josephine would have endeavored to move him to mercy for the dying stranger, he did not allow her to speak a single word. He merely said:

"You have sworn on the cross that no one was there!"

THE BIRTHMARK[1]

BY NATHANIEL HAWTHORNE

The Birthmark offers a typical example of the short-story, as that form of narrative exists in modern literature. In this type unity is the controlling element. The aim of the short-story has been defined as the endeavor "to produce a single narrative effect with the greatest economy of means that is consistent with the utmost emphasis."[2] It is a story, to use the words of Stevenson, that "from all its sentences will echo and reëcho its own controlling thought; to this must every incident and character contribute; the style must be pitched in unison with this; and if anywhere there is a word that looks another way, the story would be better without it." Hawthorne's *Notebook* abounds with memoranda of narrative germs that are capable of development into short-stories as thus defined. Among such memoranda we find the following: "A person to be the death of his beloved in trying to raise her to more than mortal perfection." Here we have the "controlling thought," which, duly elaborated, has resulted in the following short-story.

IN the latter part of the last century there lived a man of science, an eminent proficient in every branch of natural philosophy, who not long before our story opens had made experience of a spiritual affinity more attractive than any chemical one. He had left his laboratory to the care of an assistant, cleared his fine countenance from the furnace smoke, washed the stain of acids from his fingers, and persuaded a beautiful woman to become his wife. In those days when the comparatively recent discovery of electricity and other kindred

[1] From Hawthorne's *Complete Works*. Published by Houghton Mifflin Company.

[2] Clayton Hamilton, *Materials and Methods of Fiction*.

mysteries of Nature seemed to open paths into the region of miracle, it was not unusual for the love of science to rival the love of woman in its depth and absorbing energy. The higher intellect, the imagination, the spirit, and even the heart might all find their congenial aliment in pursuits which, as some of their ardent votaries believed, would ascend from one step of powerful intelligence to another, until the philosopher should lay his hand on the secret of creative force and perhaps make new worlds for himself. We know not whether Aylmer possessed this degree of faith in man's ultimate control over Nature. He had devoted himself, however, too unreservedly to scientific studies ever to be weaned from them by any second passion. His love for his young wife might prove the stronger of the two; but it could only be by intertwining itself with his love of science, and uniting the strength of the latter to his own.

Such a union accordingly took place, and was attended with truly remarkable consequences and a deeply impressive moral. One day, very soon after their marriage, Aylmer sat gazing at his wife with a trouble in his countenance that grew stronger until he spoke.

"Georgiana," said he, "has it never occurred to you that the mark upon your cheek might be removed?"

"No, indeed," said she, smiling; but perceiving the seriousness of his manner, she blushed deeply. "To tell you the truth it has been so often called a charm that I was simple enough to imagine it might be so."

"Ah, upon another face perhaps it might," replied her husband; "but never on yours. No, dearest Georgiana, you came so nearly perfect from the hand of Nature that this slightest defect, which we hesitate whether to term a defect or a beauty, shocks me, as being the visible mark of earthly imperfection."

"Shocks you, my husband!" cried Georgiana, deeply hurt; at first reddening with momentary anger, but then bursting into tears. "Then why did you take me from my mother's side? You cannot love what shocks you!"

To explain this conversation it must be mentioned that in the center of Georgiana's left cheek there was a singular mark, deeply interwoven, as it were, with the texture and substance of her face. In the usual state of her complexion — a healthy though delicate bloom — the mark wore a tint of deeper crimson, which imperfectly defined its shape amid the surrounding rosiness. When she blushed it gradually became more indistinct, and finally vanished amid the triumphant rush of blood that bathed the whole cheek with its brilliant glow. But if any shifting motion caused her to turn pale there was the mark again, a crimson stain upon the snow, in what Aylmer sometimes deemed an almost fearful distinctness. Its shape bore not a little similarity to the human hand, though of the smallest pygmy size. Georgiana's lovers were wont to say that some fairy at her birth had laid her tiny hand upon the infant's cheek, and left this impress there in token of the magic endowments that were to give her such sway over all hearts. Many a desperate swain would have risked life for the privilege of pressing his lips to the mysterious hand. It must not be concealed, however, that the impression wrought by this fairy sign manual varied exceedingly, according to the difference of temperament in the beholders. Some fastidious persons — but they were exclusively of her own sex — affirmed that the bloody hand, as they chose to call it, quite destroyed the effect of Georgiana's beauty, and rendered her countenance even hideous. But it would be as reason-

able to say that one of those small blue stains which
sometimes occur in the purest statuary marble would
convert the Eve of Powers to a monster. Masculine
observers, if the birthmark did not heighten their admiration, contented themselves with wishing it away,
that the world might possess one living specimen of
ideal loveliness without the semblance of a flaw. After
his marriage, — for he thought little or nothing of the
matter before, — Aylmer discovered that this was the
case with himself.

Had she been less beautiful, — if Envy's self could
have found aught else to sneer at, — he might have felt
his affection heightened by the prettiness of this mimic
hand, now vaguely portrayed, now lost, now stealing
forth again and glimmering to and fro with every pulse
of emotion that throbbed within her heart; but, seeing
her otherwise so perfect, he found this one defect grow
more and more intolerable with every moment of their
united lives. It was the fatal flaw of humanity which
Nature, in one shape or another, stamps ineffaceably on
all her productions, either to imply that they are temporary and finite, or that their perfection must be
wrought by toil and pain. The crimson hand expressed
the includible gripe in which mortality clutches the
highest and purest of earthly mould, degrading them
into kindred with the lowest, and even with the very
brutes, like whom their visible frames return to dust.
In this manner, selecting it as the symbol of his wife's
liability to sin, sorrow, decay, and death, Aylmer's
somber imagination was not long in rendering the birthmark a frightful object, causing him more trouble and
horror than ever Georgiana's beauty, whether of soul
or sense, had given him delight.

At all the seasons which should have been their happiest, he invariably and without intending it, nay, in spite of a purpose to the contrary, reverted to this one disastrous topic. Trifling as it at first appeared, it so connected itself with innumerable trains of thought and modes of feeling that it became the central point of all. With the morning twilight Aylmer opened his eyes upon his wife's face and recognized the symbol of imperfection; and when they sat together at the evening hearth his eyes wandered stealthily to her cheek, and beheld, flickering with the blaze of the wood fire, the spectral hand that wrote mortality where he would fain have worshiped. Georgiana soon learned to shudder at his gaze. It needed but a glance with the peculiar expression that his face often wore to change the roses of her cheek into a deathlike paleness, amid which the crimson hand was brought strongly out, like a bas-relief of ruby on the whitest marble.

Late one night when the lights were growing dim, so as hardly to betray the stain on the poor wife's cheek, she herself for the first time, voluntarily took up the subject.

"Do you remember, my dear Aylmer," said she, with a feeble attempt at a smile, "have you any recollection of a dream last night about this odious hand?"

"None! none whatever!" replied Aylmer, starting; but then he added, in a dry, cold tone, affected for the sake of concealing the real depth of his emotion, "I might well dream of it; for before I fell asleep it had taken a pretty firm hold of my fancy."

"And you did dream of it?" continued Georgiana, hastily; for she dreaded lest a gush of tears should interrupt what she had to say. "A terrible dream! I wonder that you can forget it. Is it possible to forget this one expression? —'It is in her heart now; we must have it out!' Reflect, my husband; for by all means I would have you recall that dream."

The mind is in a sad state when Sleep, the all-involving, cannot confine her specters within the dim region of her sway, but suffers them to break forth, affrighting this actual life with secrets that perchance belong to a deeper one. Aylmer now remembered his dream. He had fancied himself with his servant Aminadab, attempting an operation for the removal of the birthmark; but the deeper went the knife, the deeper sank the hand, until at length its tiny grasp appeared to have caught hold of Georgiana's heart; whence, however, her husband was inexorably resolved to cut or wrench it away.

When the dream had shaped itself perfectly in his memory, Aylmer sat in his wife's presence with a guilty feeling. Truth often finds its way to the mind close muffled in robes of sleep, and then speaks with uncompromising directness of matters in regard to which we practice an unconscious self-deception during our waking moments. Until now he had not been aware of the tyrannizing influence acquired by one idea over his mind, and of the lengths which he might find in his heart to go for the sake of giving himself peace.

"Aylmer," resumed Georgiana, solemnly, "I know not what may be the cost to both of us to rid me of this fatal birthmark. Perhaps its removal may cause cureless deformity; or it may be the stain goes as deep as life itself. Again: do we know that there is a possibility, on any terms, of unclasping the firm grip of this little hand which was laid upon me before I came into the world?"

"Dearest Georgiana, I have spent much thought upon the subject," hastily interrupted Aylmer. "I am convinced of the perfect practicability of its removal."

"If there be the remotest possibility of it," continued Georgiana, "let the attempt be made at whatever risk. Danger is nothing to me; for life, while this hateful mark makes me the object of your horror and disgust, — life is a burden which I would fling down with joy. Either remove this dreadful hand, or take my wretched life! You have deep science. All the world bears witness of it. You have achieved great wonders. Cannot you remove this little, little mark, which I cover with the tips of two small fingers? Is this beyond your power, for the sake of your own peace, and to save your poor wife from madness?"

"Noblest, dearest, tenderest wife," cried Aylmer, rapturously, "doubt not my power. I have already given this matter the deepest thought — thought which might almost have enlightened me to create a being less perfect than yourself. Georgiana, you have led me deeper than ever into the heart of science. I feel myself fully competent to render this dear cheek as faultless as its fellow; and then, most beloved, what will be my triumph when I shall have corrected what Nature left imperfect in her fairest work! Even Pygmalion, when his sculptured woman assumed life, felt not greater ecstasy than mine will be."

"It is resolved, then," said Georgiana, faintly smiling. "And, Aylmer, spare me not, though you should find the birthmark take refuge in my heart at last."

Her husband tenderly kissed her cheek — her right cheek — not that which bore the impress of the crimson hand.

The next day Aylmer apprised his wife of a plan that he had formed whereby he might have opportunity for the intense thought and constant watchfulness which the proposed operation would require; while Georgiana, likewise, would enjoy the perfect repose essential to its success. They were to seclude themselves in the extensive apartments occupied by Aylmer as a laboratory, and where, during his toilsome youth, he had made discoveries in the elemental powers of Nature that had roused the admiration of all the learned societies in Europe. Seated calmly in this laboratory, the pale philosopher had investigated the secrets of the highest cloud region and of the profoundest mines; he had satisfied himself of the causes that kindled and kept alive the fires of the volcano; and had explained the mystery of fountains, and how it is that they gush forth, some so bright and pure, and others with such rich medicinal virtues, from the dark bosom of the earth. Here, too, at an earlier period, he had studied the wonders of the human frame, and attempted to fathom the very process by which Nature assimilates all her precious influences from earth and air, and from the spiritual world, to create and foster man, her masterpiece. The latter pursuit, however, Aylmer had long laid aside in unwilling recognition of the truth — against which all seekers sooner or later stumble — that our great creative Mother, while she amuses us with apparently working in the broadest sunshine, is yet severely careful to keep her own secrets, and, in spite of her pretended openness, shows us nothing but results. She permits us, indeed, to mar, but seldom to mend, and, like a jealous patentee, on no account to make. Now, however, Aylmer resumed these half-forgotten investigations; not, of course, with such hopes or wishes as first suggested them; but because they involved much physiological truth and lay in the path of his proposed scheme for the treatment of Georgiana.

As he led her over the threshold of the laboratory,

Georgiana was cold and tremulous. Aylmer looked cheerfully into her face, with intent to reassure her, but was so startled with the intense glow of the birthmark upon the whiteness of her cheek that he could not restrain a strong convulsive shudder. His wife fainted.

"Aminadab! Aminadab!" shouted Aylmer, stamping violently on the floor.

Forthwith there issued from an inner apartment a man of low stature, but bulky frame, with shaggy hair hanging about his visage, which was grimed with the vapors of the furnace. This personage had been Aylmer's underworker during his whole scientific career, and was admirably fitted for that office by his great mechanical readiness, and the skill with which, while incapable of comprehending a single principle, he executed all the details of his master's experiments. With his vast strength, his shaggy hair, his smoky aspect, and the indescribable earthiness that incrusted him, he seemed to represent man's physical nature; while Aylmer's slender figure, and pale, intellectual face, were no less apt a type of the spiritual element.

"Throw open the door of the boudoir, Aminadab," said Aylmer, "and burn a pastil."

"Yes, master," answered Aminadab, looking intently at the lifeless form of Georgiana; and then he muttered to himself, "If she were my wife, I'd never part with that birthmark."

When Georgiana recovered consciousness she found herself breathing an atmosphere of penetrating fragrance, the gentle potency of which had recalled her from her deathlike faintness. The scene around her looked like enchantment. Aylmer had converted those smoky, dingy, somber rooms, where he had spent his brightest years in recondite pursuits, into a series of

beautiful apartments not unfit to be the secluded abode
of a lovely woman. The walls were hung with gorgeous curtains, which imparted the combination of
grandeur and grace that no other species of adorn-
ment can achieve; and as they fell from the ceiling to
the floor, their rich and ponderous folds, concealing all
angles and straight lines, appeared to shut in the scene
from infinite space. For aught Georgiana knew, it
might be a pavilion among the clouds. And Aylmer,
excluding the sunshine, which would have interfered
with his chemical processes, had supplied its place with
perfumed lamps, emitting flames of various hue, but
all uniting in a soft, impurpled radiance. He now knelt
by his wife's side, watching her earnestly, but without
alarm; for he was confident in his science, and felt that
he could draw a magic circle round her within which
no evil might intrude.

"Where am I? Ah, I remember," said Georgiana,
faintly; and she placed her hand over her cheek to
hide the terrible mark from her husband's eyes.

"Fear not, dearest!" exclaimed he. "Do not shrink
from me! Believe me, Georgiana, I even rejoice in this
single imperfection, since it will be such a rapture to
remove it."

"Oh, spare me!" sadly replied his wife. "Pray do
not look at it again. I never can forget that convulsive
shudder."

In order to soothe Georgiana, and, as it were, to release her mind from the burden of actual things, Aylmer now put in practice some of the light and playful
secrets which science had taught him among its profounder lore. Airy figures, absolutely bodiless ideas,
and forms of unsubstantial beauty came and danced
before her, imprinting their momentary footsteps on

beams of light. Though she had some indistinct idea of the method of these optical phenomena, still the illusion was almost perfect enough to warrant the belief that her husband possessed sway over the spiritual world. Then again, when she felt a wish to look forth from her seclusion, immediately, as if her thoughts were answered, the procession of external existence flitted across a screen. The scenery and the figures of actual life were perfectly represented, but with that bewitching, yet indescribable difference which always makes a picture, an image, or a shadow so much more attractive than the original. When wearied of this, Aylmer bade her cast her eyes upon a vessel containing a quantity of earth. She did so, with little interest at first; but was soon startled to perceive the germ of a plant shooting upward from the soil. Then came the slender stalk; the leaves gradually unfolded themselves; and amid them was a perfect and lovely flower.

"It is magical!" cried Georgiana. "I dare not touch it."

"Nay, pluck it," answered Aylmer, — "pluck it, and inhale its brief perfume while you may. The flower will wither in a few moments and leave nothing save its brown seed vessels; but thence may be perpetuated a race as ephemeral as itself."

But Georgiana had no sooner touched the flower than the whole plant suffered a blight, its leaves turning coal-black as if by the agency of fire.

"There was too powerful a stimulus," said Aylmer, thoughtfully.

To make up for this abortive experiment, he proposed to take her portrait by a scientific process of his own invention. It was to be effected by rays of light striking upon a polished plate of metal. Georgiana assented; but, on looking at the result, was affrighted to find the features of the portrait blurred and indefinable; while the minute figure of a hand appeared where the cheek should have been. Aylmer snatched the metallic plate and threw it into a jar of corrosive acid.

Soon, however, he forgot these mortifying failures. In the intervals of study and chemical experiment he came to her flushed and exhausted, but seemed invigorated by her presence, and spoke in glowing language of the resources of his art. He gave a history of the long dynasty of the alchemists, who spent so many ages in quest of the universal solvent by which the golden principle might be elicited from all things vile and base. Aylmer appeared to believe that, by the plainest scientific logic, it was altogether within the limits of possibility to discover this long-sought medium; "but," he added, "a philosopher who should go deep enough to acquire the power would attain too lofty a wisdom to stoop to the exercise of it." Not less singular were his opinions in regard to the elixir vitæ. He more than intimated that it was at his option to concoct a liquid that should prolong life for years, perhaps interminably; but that it would produce a discord in Nature which all the world, and chiefly the quaffer of the immortal nostrum, would find cause to curse.

"Aylmer, are you in earnest?" asked Georgiana, looking at him with amazement and fear. "It is terrible to possess such power, or even to dream of possessing it."

"Oh, do not tremble, my love," said her husband. "I would not wrong either you or myself by working such inharmonious effects upon our lives; but I would have you consider how trifling, in comparison, is the skill requisite to remove this little hand."

At the mention of the birthmark, Georgiana, as usual, shrank as if a red-hot iron had touched her cheek.

Again Aylmer applied himself to his labors. She could hear his voice in the distant furnace-room giving directions to Aminadab, whose harsh, uncouth, misshapen tones were audible in response, more like the grunt or growl of a brute than human speech. After hours of absence, Aylmer reappeared and proposed that she should now examine his cabinet of chemical products and natural treasures of the earth. Among the former he showed her a small vial, in which, he remarked, was contained a gentle yet most powerful fragrance, capable of impregnating all the breezes that blow across a kingdom. They were of inestimable value, the contents of that little vial; and, as he said so, he threw some of the perfume into the air and filled the room with piercing and invigorating delight.

"And what is this?" asked Georgiana, pointing to a small crystal globe containing a gold-colored liquid. "It is so beautiful to the eye that I could imagine it the elixir of life."

"In one sense it is," replied Aylmer; "or, rather, the elixir of immortality. It is the most precious poison that ever was concocted in this world. By its aid I could apportion the lifetime of any mortal at whom you might point your finger. The strength of the dose would determine whether he were to linger out years, or drop dead in the midst of a breath. No king on his guarded throne could keep his life if I, in my private station, should deem that the welfare of millions justified me in depriving him of it."

"Why do you keep such a terrific drug?" inquired Georgiana in horror.

"Do not mistrust me, dearest," said her husband, smiling; "its virtuous potency is yet greater than its harmful one. But see! here is a powerful cosmetic. With a few drops of this in a vase of water, freckles may be washed away as easily as the hands are cleansed. A stronger infusion would take the blood out of the cheek, and leave the rosiest beauty a pale ghost."

"Is it with this lotion that you intend to bathe my cheek?" asked Georgiana, anxiously.

"Oh, no," hastily replied her husband; "this is merely superficial. Your case demands a remedy that shall go deeper."

In his interviews with Georgiana, Aylmer generally made minute inquiries as to her sensations and whether the confinement of the rooms and the temperature of the atmosphere agreed with her. These questions had such a particular drift that Georgiana began to conjecture that she was already subjected to certain physical influences, either breathed in with the fragrant air or taken with her food. She fancied likewise, but it might be altogether fancy, that there was a stirring up of her system — a strange, indefinite sensation creeping through her veins, and tingling, half painfully, half pleasurably, at her heart. Still, whenever she dared to look into the mirror, there she beheld herself pale as a white rose and with the crimson birthmark stamped upon her cheek. Not even Aylmer now hated it so much as she.

To dispel the tedium of the hours which her husband found it necessary to devote to the processes of combination and analysis, Georgiana turned over the volumes of his scientific library. In many dark old tomes she met with chapters full of romance and poetry. They were the works of the philosophers of the Middle

Ages, such as Albertus Magnus, Cornelius Agrippa, Paracelsus, and the famous friar who created the prophetic Brazen Head. All these antique naturalists stood in advance of their centuries, yet were imbued with some of their credulity, and therefore were believed, and perhaps imagined themselves to have acquired from the investigation of Nature a power above Nature, and from physics a sway over the spiritual world. Hardly less curious and imaginative were the early volumes of the Transactions of the Royal Society, in which the members, knowing little of the limits of natural possibility, were continually recording wonders or proposing methods whereby wonders might be wrought.

But to Georgiana the most engrossing volume was a large folio from her husband's own hand, in which he had recorded every experiment of his scientific career, its original aim, the methods adopted for its development, and its final success or failure, with the circumstances to which either event was attributable. The book, in truth, was both the history and emblem of his ardent, ambitious, imaginative, yet practical and laborious life. He handled physical details as if there were nothing beyond them; yet spiritualized them all, and redeemed himself from materialism by his strong and eager aspiration towards the infinite. In his grasp the veriest clod of earth assumed a soul. Georgiana, as she read, reverenced Aylmer and loved him more profoundly than ever, but with a less entire dependence on his judgment than heretofore. Much as he had accomplished, she could not but observe that his most splendid successes were almost invariably failures, if compared with the ideal at which he aimed. His brightest diamonds were the merest pebbles, and felt to be so by himself, in comparison with the inestimable gems which lay hidden beyond his reach. The volume, rich with achievements that had won renown for its author, was yet as melancholy a record as ever mortal hand had penned. It was the sad confession and continual exemplification of the shortcomings of the composite man, the spirit burdened with clay and working in matter, and of the despair that assails the higher nature at finding itself so miserably thwarted by the earthly part. Perhaps every man of genius in whatever sphere might recognize the image of his own experience in Aylmer's journal.

So deeply did these reflections affect Georgiana that she laid her face upon the open volume and burst into tears. In this situation she was found by her husband.

"It is dangerous to read in a sorcerer's books," said he with a smile, though his countenance was uneasy and displeased. "Georgiana, there are pages in that volume which I can scarcely glance over and keep my senses. Take heed lest it prove as detrimental to you."

"It has made me worship you more than ever," said she.

"Ah, wait for this one success," rejoined he, "then worship me if you will. I shall deem myself hardly unworthy of it. But come, I have sought you for the luxury of your voice. Sing to me, dearest."

So she poured out the liquid music of her voice to quench the thirst of his spirit. He then took his leave with a boyish exuberance of gayety, assuring her that her seclusion should endure but a little longer, and that the result was already certain. Scarcely had he departed when Georgiana felt irresistibly impelled to follow him. She had forgotten to inform Aylmer of a

symptom which for two or three hours past had begun
to excite her attention. It was a sensation in the fatal
birthmark, not painful, but which induced a restless-
ness throughout her system. Hastening after her husband, she intruded for the first time into the laboratory.

The first thing that struck her eye was the furnace,
that hot and feverish worker, with the intense glow of
its fire, which by the quantities of soot clustered above
it seemed to have been burning for ages. There was
a distilling apparatus in full operation. Around the
room were retorts, tubes, cylinders, crucibles, and other
apparatus of chemical research. An electrical machine
stood ready for immediate use. The atmosphere felt
oppressively close, and was tainted with gaseous odors
which had been tormented forth by the processes of
science. The severe and homely simplicity of the apartment, with its naked walls and brick pavement, looked
strange, accustomed as Georgiana had become to the
fantastic elegance of her boudoir. But what chiefly,
indeed almost solely, drew her attention, was the aspect
of Aylmer himself.

He was pale as death, anxious and absorbed, and
hung over the furnace as if it depended upon his utmost watchfulness whether the liquid which it was distilling should be the draught of immortal happiness or
misery. How different from the sanguine and joyous
mien that he had assumed for Georgiana's encouragement!

"Carefully now, Aminadab; carefully, thou human
machine; carefully, thou man of clay!" muttered
Aylmer, more to himself than his assistant. "Now, if
there be a thought too much or too little, it is all over."

"Ho! ho!" mumbled Aminadab. "Look, master!
look!"

Aylmer raised his eyes hastily, and at first reddened, then grew paler than ever, on beholding Georgiana. He rushed towards her and seized her arm with a grip that left the print of his fingers upon it.

"Why do you come hither? Have you no trust in your husband?" cried he, impetuously. "Would you throw the blight of that fatal birthmark over my labors? It is not well done. Go, prying woman, go!"

"Nay, Aylmer," said Georgiana with the firmness of which she possessed no stinted endowment, "it is not you that have a right to complain. You mistrust your wife; you have concealed the anxiety with which you watch the development of this experiment. Think not so unworthily of me, my husband. Tell me all the risk we run, and fear not that I shall shrink; for my share in it is far less than your own."

"No, no, Georgiana!" said Aylmer, impatiently; "it must not be."

"I submit," replied she calmly. "And, Aylmer, I shall quaff whatever draught you bring me; but it will be on the same principle that would induce me to take a dose of poison if offered by your hand."

"My noble wife," said Aylmer, deeply moved, "I knew not the height and depth of your nature until now. Nothing shall be concealed. Know, then, that this crimson hand, superficial as it seems, has clutched its grasp into your being with a strength of which I had no previous conception. I have already administered agents powerful enough to do aught except to change your entire physical system. Only one thing remains to be tried. If that fail us we are ruined."

"Why did you hesitate to tell me this?" asked she.

"Because, Georgiana," said Aylmer, in a low voice, "there is danger."

"Danger? There is but one danger — that this horrible stigma shall be left upon my cheek!" cried Georgiana. "Remove it, remove it, whatever be the cost, or we shall both go mad!"

"Heaven knows your words are too true," said Aylmer, sadly. "And now, dearest, return to your boudoir. In a little while all will be tested."

He conducted her back and took leave of her with a solemn tenderness which spoke far more than his words how much was now at stake. After his departure Georgiana became rapt in musings. She considered the character of Aylmer, and did it completer justice than at any previous moment. Her heart exulted, while it trembled, at his honorable love — so pure and lofty that it would accept nothing less than perfection nor miserably make itself contented with an earthlier nature than he had dreamed of. She felt how much more precious was such a sentiment than that meaner kind which would have borne with the imperfection for her sake, and have been guilty of treason to holy love by degrading its perfect idea to the level of the actual; and with her whole spirit she prayed that, for a single moment, she might satisfy his highest and deepest conception. Longer than one moment she well knew it could not be; for his spirit was ever on the march, ever ascending, and each instant required something that was beyond the scope of the instant before.

The sound of her husband's footsteps aroused her. He bore a crystal goblet containing a liquor colorless as water, but bright enough to be the draught of immortality. Aylmer was pale; but it seemed rather the consequence of a highly wrought state of mind and tension of spirit than of fear or doubt.

"The concoction of the draught has been perfect," said he, in answer to Georgiana's look. "Unless all my science have deceived me, it cannot fail."

"Save on your account, my dearest Aylmer," observed his wife, "I might wish to put off this birthmark of mortality by relinquishing mortality itself in preference to any other mode. Life is but a sad possession to those who have attained precisely the degree of moral advancement at which I stand. Were I weaker and blinder it might be happiness. Were I stronger, it might be endured hopefully. But, being what I find myself, methinks I am of all mortals the most fit to die."

"You are fit for heaven without tasting death!" replied her husband. "But why do we speak of dying? The draught cannot fail. Behold its effect upon this plant."

On the window seat there stood a geranium diseased with yellow blotches, which had overspread all its leaves. Aylmer poured a small quantity of the liquid upon the soil in which it grew. In a little time, when the roots of the plant had taken up the moisture, the unsightly blotches began to be extinguished in a living verdure.

"There needed no proof," said Georgiana, quietly. "Give me the goblet. I joyfully stake all upon your word."

"Drink, then, thou lofty creature!" exclaimed Aylmer, with fervid admiration. "There is no taint of imperfection on thy spirit. Thy sensible frame, too, shall soon be all perfect."

She quaffed the liquid and returned the goblet to his hand.

"It is grateful," said she with a placid smile. "Methinks it is like water from a heavenly fountain; for it contains I know not what of unobtrusive fragrance and deliciousness. It allays a feverish thirst that had parched me for many days. Now, dearest, let me sleep. My earthly senses are closing over my spirit like the leaves around the heart of a rose at sunset."

She spoke the last words with a gentle reluctance, as if it required almost more energy than she could command to pronounce the faint and lingering syllables. Scarcely had they loitered through her lips ere she was lost in slumber. Aylmer sat by her side, watching her aspect with the emotions proper to a man the whole value of whose existence was involved in the process now to be tested. Mingled with this mood, however, was the philosophic investigation characteristic of the man of science. Not the minutest symptom escaped him. A heightened flush of the cheek, a slight irregularity of breath, a quiver of the eyelid, a hardly perceptible tremor through the frame, — such were the details which, as the moments passed, he wrote down in his folio volume. Intense thought had set its stamp upon every previous page of that volume, but the thoughts of years were all concentrated upon the last.

While thus employed, he failed not to gaze often at the fatal hand, and not without a shudder. Yet once, by a strange and unaccountable impulse, he pressed it with his lips. His spirit recoiled, however, in the very act; and Georgiana, out of the midst of her deep sleep, moved uneasily and murmured as if in remonstrance. Again Aylmer resumed his watch. Nor was it without avail. The crimson hand, which at first had been strongly visible upon the marble paleness of Georgiana's cheek, now grew more faintly outlined. She remained not less pale than ever; but the birthmark, with every breath that came and went, lost somewhat of its former distinctness. Its presence had been awful; its departure was more awful still. Watch the stain of the rainbow fading out of the sky, and you will know how that mysterious symbol passed away.

"By Heaven! it is well-nigh gone!" said Aylmer to himself, in almost irrepressible ecstasy. "I can scarcely trace it now. Success! success! And now it is like the faintest rose color. The lightest flush of blood across her cheek would overcome it. But she is so pale!"

He drew aside the window curtain and suffered the light of natural day to fall into the room and rest upon her cheek. At the same time he heard a gross, hoarse chuckle, which he had long known as his servant Aminadab's expression of delight.

"Ah, clod! ah, earthly mass!" cried Aylmer, laughing in a sort of frenzy, "you have served me well! Matter and spirit — earth and heaven — have both done their part in this! Laugh, thing of the senses! Your have earned the right to laugh."

These exclamations broke Georgiana's sleep. She slowly unclosed her eyes and gazed into the mirror which her husband had arranged for that purpose. A faint smile flitted over her lips when she recognized how barely perceptible was now that crimson hand which had once blazed forth with such disastrous brilliancy as to scare away all their happiness. But then her eyes sought Aylmer's face with a trouble and anxiety that he could by no means account for.

"My poor Aylmer!" murmured she.

"Poor? Nay, richest, happiest, most favored!" exclaimed he. "My peerless bride, it is successful! You are perfect!"

"My poor Aylmer," she repeated, with a more than human tenderness, "you have aimed loftily; you have done nobly. Do not repent that with so high and pure a feeling, you have rejected the best the earth could offer. Aylmer, dearest Aylmer, I am dying!"

Alas! it was too true! The fatal hand had grappled with the mystery of life, and was the bond by which an angelic spirit kept itself in union with a mortal frame. As the last crimson tint of the birthmark — that sole token of human imperfection — faded from her cheek, the parting breath of the now perfect woman passed into the atmosphere, and her soul, lingering a moment near her husband, took its heavenward flight. Then a hoarse, chuckling laugh was heard again! Thus ever does the gross fatality of earth exult in its invariable triumph over the immortal essence which, in this dim sphere of half development, demands the completeness of a higher state. Yet, had Aylmer reached a profounder wisdom, he need not thus have flung away the happiness which would have woven his mortal life of the self-same texture with the celestial. The momentary circumstance was too strong for him; he failed to look beyond the shadowy scope of time, and, living once for all in eternity, to find the perfect future in the present.

ON THE STAIRS [1]

BY ARTHUR MORRISON

ASIDE from the unity of tone that characterizes this story in the noteworthy harmony between the shabby background of a "near-slum" and the unpleasant personality of the principal actors, the narrative possesses special interest as a study in plot structure. The peculiarity of the plot lies in the fact that the real motive of the action is kept out of sight, and is evidenced only through the externals that are attendant thereon. The story is essentially psychologic, and the true interest lies in penetrating the outward actions and reaching through them to the motives that lie beyond. Few details can be neglected: the five shillings contributed by Dr. Mansell, and the equal amount secured from his inexperienced understudy; the failure of Mrs. Curtis to obtain the wine that offered "the only way" to the possible recovery of the sick man; the whole problem of mutes and "plooms"; — these and a dozen other little touches outline the details of the sub-narrative and constitute a really subtile study of one of the weaknesses of human nature. In this respect, that it is consistently drawn to a single unified pattern, that all the details of setting, of character, and of plot center about one common nucleus idea, On the Stairs — like The Birthmark — presents a noteworthy example of the short-story in its typical form.

THE house had been "genteel." When trade was prospering in the East End, and the ship-fitter or block-maker thought it no shame to live in the parish where his workshop lay, such a master had lived here. Now, it was a tall, solid, well-bricked, ugly house, grimy and paintless in the joinery, cracked and patched in the windows: where the front door stood open all day long; and the womankind sat on the steps, talking

[1] From *Tales of Mean Streets*. Printed by permission of Little, Brown & Co.

of sickness and death and the cost of things; and treacherous holes lurked in the carpet of road-soil on the stairs and in the passage. For when eight families live in a house, nobody buys a doormat, and the street was one of those streets that are always muddy. It smelt, too, of many things, none of them pleasant (one was fried fish); but for all that it was not a slum.

Three flights up, a gaunt woman with bare forearms stayed on her way to listen at a door which, opening, let out a warm, fetid waft from a close sick-room. A bent and tottering old woman stood on the threshold, holding the door behind her.

"An' is 'e no better now, Mrs. Curtis?" the gaunt woman asked, with a nod at the opening.

The old woman shook her head, and pulled the door closer. Her jaw waggled loosely in her withered chaps: "Nor won't be; till 'e's gone." Then after a certain pause, "'E's goin'," she said.

"Don't doctor give no 'ope?"

"Lor' bless ye, I don't want to ast no doctors," Mrs. Curtis replied, with something not unlike a chuckle. "I've seed too many on 'em. The boy's a-goin' fast; I can see that. An' then" — she gave the handle another tug, and whispered — "he's been called." She nodded again. "Three seprit knocks at the bed-head las' night; an' I know what *that* means!"

The gaunt woman raised her brows, and nodded. "Ah, well," she said, "we all on us comes to it some day, sooner or later. An' it's often a 'appy release."

The two looked into space beyond each other, the elder with a nod and a croak. Presently the other pursued, "'E's been a very good son, ain't 'e?"

"Ay, ay, well enough son to me," responded the old woman, a little peevishly; "an' I'll 'ave 'im put away decent, though there's on'y the Union for me after. I can do that, thank Gawd!" she added, meditatively, as chin on fist she stared into the thickening dark over the stairs.

"When I lost my pore 'usband," said the gaunt woman, with a certain brightening, "I give 'im a 'ansome funeral. 'E was a Oddfeller, an' I got twelve pound. I 'ad a oak caufin an' a open 'earse. There was a kerridge for the fam'ly an' one for 'is mates — two 'orses each, an' feathers, an' mutes; an' it went the furthest way round to the cimitry. 'Wotever 'appens, Mrs. Manders,' says the undertaker, 'you'll feel as you've treated 'im proper; nobody can't reproach you over that.' An' they could n't. 'E was a good 'usband to me, an' I buried 'im respectable."

The gaunt woman exulted. The old, old story of Manders's funeral fell upon the other one's ears with a freshened interest, and she mumbled her gums ruminantly. "Bob'll 'ave a 'ansome buryin', too," she said. "I can make it up, with the insurance money, an' this, an' that. On'y I dunno about mutes. It's a expense."

In the East End, when a woman has not enough money to buy a thing much desired, she does not say so in plain words; she says the thing is an "expense," or a "great expense." It means the same thing, but it sounds better. Mrs. Curtis had reckoned her resources, and found that mutes would be an "expense." At a cheap funeral mutes cost half-a-sovereign and their liquor. Mrs. Manders said as much.

"Yus, yus, 'arf-a-sovereign," the old woman assented. Within, the sick man feebly beat the floor with a stick. "I'm a-comin'," she cried shrilly; "yus, 'arf-a-sovereign, but it's a lot, an' I don't see 'ow I'm to do it — not at present." She reached for the door-handle again, but stopped and added, by afterthought, "Unless I don't 'ave no plooms."

"It 'ud be a pity not to 'ave plooms. I 'ad — "

There were footsteps on the stairs: then a stumble and a testy word. Mrs. Curtis peered over into the gathering dark. "Is it the doctor, sir?" she asked. It was the doctor's assistant; and Mrs. Manders tramped up to the next landing as the door of the sick-room took him in.

For five minutes the stairs were darker than ever. Then the assistant, a very young man, came out again, followed by the old woman with a candle. Mrs. Manders listened in the upper dark. "He's sinking fast," said the assistant. "He *must* have a stimulant. Dr. Mansell ordered port wine. Where is it?" Mrs. Curtis mumbled dolorously. "I tell you he *must* have it," he averred with unprofessional emphasis (his qualification was only a month old). "The man can't take solid food and his strength must be kept up somehow. Another day may make all the difference. Is it because you can't afford it?"

"It's a expense — sich a expense, doctor," the old woman pleaded. "An' wot with 'arf-pints o' milk an' — " She grew inarticulate, and mumbled dismally.

"But he must have it, Mrs. Curtis, if it's your last shilling: it's the only way. If you mean you absolutely have n't the money — " and he paused a little awkwardly. He was not a wealthy young man, — wealthy young men do not devil for East End doctors, — but he was conscious of a certain haul of sixpences at nap the night before; and, being inexperienced, he did not foresee the career of persecution whereon he was entering at his own expense and of his own motion. He produced five shillings: "If you absolutely have n't the money, why — take this, and get a bottle — good: not at a public house. But mind, *at once.* He should have had it before."

It would have interested him, as a matter of coincidence, to know that his principal had been guilty of the selfsame indiscretion — even the amount was identical — on that landing the day before. But, as Mrs. Curtis said nothing of this, he floundered down the stair and out into the wetter mud, pondering whether or not the beloved son of a Congregational minister might take full credit for a deed of charity on the proceeds of sixpenny nap. But Mrs. Curtis puffed her wrinkles, and shook her head sagaciously as she carried in her candle. From the room came a clink as of money falling into a teapot. And Mrs. Manders went about her business.

The door was shut, and the stair was a pit of blackness. Twice a lodger passed down, and up and down, and still it did not open. Men and women walked on the lower flights, and out at the door, and in again. From the street a shout or a snatch of laughter floated up the pit. On the pavement footsteps rang crisper and fewer, and from the bottom passage there were sounds of stagger and sprawl. A demented old clock buzzed divers hours at random, and was rebuked every twenty minutes by the regular tread of a policeman on his beat. Finally, somebody shut the street-door with a great bang, and the street was muffled. A key turned inside the door on the landing, but that was all. A feeble light shone for hours along the crack below, and then went out. The crazy old clock went buzzing on, but nothing left that room all night. Nothing that opened the door . . .

When next the key turned, it was to Mrs. Manders's knock, in the full morning; and soon the two women came out on the landing together, Mrs. Curtis with a shapeless clump of a bonnet. "Ah, 'e's a lovely corpse," said Mrs. Manders. "Like wax. So was my 'usband."

"I must be stirrin'," croaked the old woman, "an' go about the insurance an' the measurin' an' that. There's lots to do."

"Ah, there is. 'Oo are you goin' to 'ave, — Wilkins? I 'ad Wilkins. Better than Kedge, I think: Kedge's mutes dresses rusty, an' their trousis is frayed. If you was thinkin' of 'avin' mutes —"

"Yus, yus," — with a palsied nodding, — "I'm a-goin' to 'ave mutes: I can do it respectable, thank Gawd!"

"And the plooms?"

"Ay, yus, and the plooms too. They ain't sich a great expense, after all."